PAUL E. JOHNSON in the chapter on Religious Psychology and Health states: "The new crisis in health is psychological. The progressive control of infectious and organic diseases has improved the health of modern man. But functional disorders are on the increase, and these forms of illness arise from emotional tensions.

"The rising tide of delinquency and crime, divorce and family problems, destructive rivalry and competition, industrial strife, racial tensions, and international conflict demonstrate the social aspects of our ill health.

"There is a growing recognition that illness is not cured in a closed physical system of diet, medication, and surgery. For the whole personality is involved and must be treated as a whole if health is to be attained."

GOTTHARD BOOTH, M.D., writes in the chapter, The Voice of the Body: "Modern medicine has followed this line of thinking; it has gone all out in tracking down 'disease demons' which have one thing in common: they are all defined as something destructive which attacks the otherwise healthy body in the form of bad genes, birth injuries, faults of nutrition, germs, toxic substances, etc. Psychoanalysis has added various forms of damage which civilization, specifically religious moralism, inflicts on the 'normal instincts' which seek oral, anal, and sexual gratifications. It is not difficult to see that the underlying concept of man as 'naturally healthy' represents a Manichean dualism of good and evil as warring cosmic powers."

*Purpose of this book:*
To challenge and stir discussion.

# RELIGION *and* MEDICINE

IOWA STATE UNIVERSITY PRESS, AMES, IOWA, U.S.A.

*Iowa Studies in Religion and Medicine*



# RELIGION *and* MEDICINE

## *Essays on Meaning, Values, and Health*



DAVID BELGUM, *Editor*

Medicine--Religious aspects.



Composed and printed by
The Iowa State University Press

Stock #1342

FIRST EDITION, 1967

Library of Congress Catalog Card Number: 67-26060

## FOREWORD

---

# Of Doctors and Priests

*William B. Bean*

WILFRED TROTTER, to whom we find ourselves turning whenever we need refreshment from his masterly intellect as illuminated by his powerful style, sets the stage for our discussion of the interrelations and interweavings of medicine and religion. He said that "Thought is gradually gaining courage to explore not merely the body of man but his mind and his moral capacities, in the knowledge that these are not meaningless intrusions into an otherwise orderly world, but are partakers in him and in his history just as are his vermiform appendix and his stomach; and are elements in the complex structure of the universe as respectably established there and as racey of that soil as the oldest saurian or the newest gas."

Physicians have been notably reticent in discussing matters central to the major problems of life and death. We are alleged to be irreligious, or at least agnostic. Our ma-

---

WILLIAM B. BEAN, M.D., is Professor and Head of the Department of Internal Medicine, College of Medicine, University of Iowa, Iowa City, Iowa.

terialistic age is not rich in philosophers. Within the medical orbit philosophy now is held in low esteem while laboratory instruments, delicate paraphernalia, computers, and machines are telling us more and more about what we do not understand. But we must accept religious experience even if we look at it as another biological phenomenon and add it to our basic concept of reality, admitting that it is subjective and thus outside the laws of physics. In spite of its subjectivity and its intangible quality, religious experience for many constitutes a moving reality. As George Day remarked, "It has been said that to be filled with the spirit of Jesus Christ is an experience like falling in love, and as unreasonable and incomprehensible and as incommunicable to those of us to whom it may never have happened. If we do not have it we can only hope that in God's good time it may come our way."

Following a line of discussion that Dr. Day introduced me to, I would call your attention to psychosomatic medicine not merely as a unity of two closely intertwined elements, but look upon it rather as triangular. To the body, *soma,* and the mind, *psyche,* I add the spirit, *pneuma.* By increasing our scope in this way we grow aware of the three major intertwining elements which give unity to human life.

We are only just beginning to pay due tribute to the study of ecology. Ecology is merely relating an individual man with his unique genetic and chromosomal heritage, the one example that ever was and ever will be with the additions and subtractions that exist to his own particular and changing environment. Into an expanded concept of ecology I suggest that we put his psychological and emotional reactions as well as their significance for him. This of course is in addition to mental activity and reactions. When we have a clearer understanding of the interplay of such a multitude of factors, when we see causality in terms of the many rather than the one, and when we apply our best scientific thought to such studies we hope that we will be nearer the truth than we are now. The accuracy of the mechanistic aspects of disease, so brilliantly worked out and verified in the laboratory, has tended to displace other emphasis. Nonetheless the true medical scientist had better know all he can about the psyche and the pneuma as well as the soma. What subtle factors determine why, amongst many exposed to a particular germ, only some are infected and only some of these seriously affected? Why does it happen that not only persons with certain physical types but those with particular personality characteristics tend to escape one disease or contrarywise tend to be affected most seriously? We know a great deal about specific infecting agents and much about the body's inherent or acquired resistance. This does not explain fully the great variability we note in disease as it affects the members of a community in seasons of epidemic intensity or endemic persistence.

Likewise in therapy how often do we suspect that the person's turn for the better comes from some really simple event? A flash of insight transmitted to the patient by the physician, a sudden coming into focus of puzzling or seemingly hopeless features of daily life may give the patient new insight, new encouragement, new hope which constitutes the faith that determines improvement.

Regarding a conflict between religion and science or, as it concerns us, between religion and medicine, what is its story? What is its present state and to what extent has it been artifact rather than fact? The history of science may be summarized as the battle scientists have waged to obtain freedom to use the scientific process of exploring and finding relationships between events and experiences. The church likewise fought for recognition of the validity of religious experience. The controversy fortunately is largely dead because those who spend their lives in supporting the truth of religion see no threat in accepting the world of science. Actually the experiences which form the basis of science and those which give rise to the religious beliefs for which men have fought and died, though they are sharply different, are equivalent for scientific purposes. As Dingle, the distinguished English astronomer, said, "To hear religion described as a blind attempt to escape from the conclusions of astronomical research is to hear the blind man rising from the study of acoustics pronounce his opinion that optics is an attempt to escape from the truly dreadful jazz band across the way."

As religious experience is studied as an objective phenomenon, psychologists may relate it to states now considered unusual or abnormal. Undoubtedly those to whom religious experience is the most precious aspect of life, though they rarely have a great deal of scientific curiosity or instruction, will think this a degrading attitude and a grave threat. But here again the conflict is based on misunderstanding. Science as science has no concern for the value of any experience, merely its relations. That does not mean that intrinsic values do not vary enormously, are not enormously important, and do not concern scientists as well as others. Scientists as men must have concern for values as well as for data. The physical mechanism of vibrations emanating from the larynx of the Beatles and the Westminster Choir is the same. It is foolish to deny it, though a devout person is not likely to be cheered by this revelation.

It is the lot of the physician to try to obliterate old prejudices. Often he hangs on till near the end. Establishing a new outlook is perhaps the most difficult thing a person ever tries to do. It becomes more difficult or efforts diminish as age increases. This makes me think that there was much truth in the view that the world's best ideas and work come from the young. These were Osler's ideas though they were warped by the lay press of his time. Beliefs are so firmly entrenched that even those disclosed to be in error are never uprooted suddenly. Even the most astute scientist may harbor false notions, especially out of his own field of competence. The best enzyme chemist may be a dull fellow in international politics. In fact he is almost by definition.

A major task for our unsettled times is to form a just concept of the interrelations of religion and science. For if man can achieve a harmonious balance of mind, body, and spirit, he might be able to solve the regional, national, and worldwide problems which cry so urgently for understanding first and then solution. No matter what form of views of religion one may have, the essence of the proper relation of medicine and religion is summed up in the spirit of compassion for others epitomized in the teachings of the New Testament.

How does the spirit of man differ from the basic spirit of life? Plants struggle for existence regardless of all other plants. Some like orchids parasitize others to grow wonderfully beautiful. The concern that animals feel for the welfare of other animals, apart from their mates and offspring, has never been a strong point with them. To be properly motivated in medicine or life we must follow in spirit the New Testament challenge "Love your neighbor; Love even your enemies; Love one another." These last three words, almost as simple as you could ever find, contain the hardest injunction ever laid upon us. What do they mean? They do not mean that we should fool ourselves and assume a posture of sentimentality toward our fellows and certainly not toward our patients. But the injunction to love one another means to make your neighbors, your patients feel worthwhile. Strengthen their spirit. Give them an inner glow by making them feel good the way friends make friends feel good. The wise and kind physician does this, aided by those who minister to the religious needs of the patient. It requires close harmony in a common objective—working together. We must go back to the caves and castles of antiquity when these functions were combined in one person, the physician-priest. To the direct application of the day-by-day confrontation of these life-and-death matters this book sets forth its chapters as a guide and beacon.

# Contributors

Gordon W. Allport, Ph.D., Professor, Department of Social Relations, Harvard University, Cambridge, Mass.

James B. Ashbrook, B.D., M.A., Associate Professor of Pastoral Theology, Colgate Rochester Divinity School, Rochester, N.Y.

William B. Bean, M.D., Professor and Head, Department of Internal Medicine, College of Medicine, University of Iowa, Iowa City, Iowa.

Russell J. Becker, Ph.D., Associate Professor of Pastoral Theology, Yale Divinity School, New Haven, Conn.

David Belgum, Ph.D., Associate Professor of Pastoral Care and Counseling, School of Religion and College of Medicine, University of Iowa, Iowa City, Iowa.

Gotthard Booth, M.D., Psychiatrist in Private Practice, New York, N.Y.

John W. Drakeford, Ph.D., Professor of Psychology and Counseling, Southwestern Baptist Theological Seminary, Fort Worth, Tex.

Gunter Elsässer, M.D., Psychiatrist, Institute für analytische Psychotherapie im Rheinland, Bonn, West Germany.

Viktor E. Frankl, M.D., Ph.D., Professor of Psychiatry and Neurology, University of Vienna; Head, Neurological Department, Poliklinik Hospital, Vienna, Austria; and President of the Austrian Medical Society of Psychotherapy.

ANDRE GODIN, S.J., M.A., Professor of Religious and Pastoral Psychology, International Center for Religious Education, Brussels, Belgium.

HOWARD S. HOYMAN, ED.D., F.A.P.H.A., Professor of Health Education, University of Illinois, Urbana, Ill.

GORDON E. JACKSON, PH.D., Dean and Professor of Pastoral Theology, Pittsburgh Theological Seminary, Pittsburgh, Pa.

PAUL E. JOHNSON, PH.D., Professor Emeritus of Psychology of Religion, Boston University, Boston, Mass.

ARTHUR JORES, M.D., Psychiatrist, Medizinishen Universitäts Klinik und Poliklinik, Hamburg-Eppendorf, West Germany.

ALBERT L. MEIBURG, PH.D., Chaplain, North Carolina Baptist Hospital, Winston-Salem, N.C.

O. HOBART MOWRER, PH.D., Research Professor of Psychology, University of Illinois, Urbana, Ill.

PEDER OLSEN, Dean of the Cathedral in Tönsberg, Norway.

PAUL TILLICH, DR. PHIL., The late John Nuveen Professor of Theology, The Divinity School of the University of Chicago, Chicago, Ill.

ORVILLE S. WALTERS, M.D., Psychiatrist and Director of Student Health Service, University of Illinois, Urbana, Ill.

ALLEN WHITMAN, B.D., S.T.M., Rector of Saint George's Episcopal Church, Minneapolis, Minn.

RICHARD K. YOUNG, PH.D., Chaplain, North Carolina Baptist Hospital, Winston-Salem, N.C.

WILLIAM W. ZELLER, M.D., Director of Psychiatric Education, Institute of Living, Hartford, Conn.

# Acknowledgments

1. "The Meaning of Health" by Paul Tillich. *Perspectives in Biology and Medicine,* Vol. V, No. 1, 1961, pp. 92–100.

2. "The Axes of Concern in Personality" by David Belgum. Chapter written for this book.

3. "Religious Psychology and Health" by Paul E. Johnson. *Mental Hygiene,* Vol. XXXI, No. 4, Oct. 1947, pp. 556–66.

4. "Mental Health: A Generic Attitude" by Gordon W. Allport. *Journal of Religion and Health,* Vol. 4, No. 1, Oct. 1964, pp. 7–21.

5. "The Impact of the Hospital Situation on Our Understanding of God and Man" by James Ashbrook. *Journal of Pastoral Care,* Vol. X, Spring 1956, pp. 1–15. Published by the Council for Clinical Training, Inc.

6. "Behavioral Science, Religion, and Mental Health" by Gordon W. Allport. *Journal of Religion and Health,* Vol. 2, No. 3, Apr. 1963, pp. 187–97.

7. "The Voice of the Body" by Gotthard Booth, M.D. Introduction to a book by Aarne Siirala entitled *The Voice of Illness,* Fortress Press, Philadelphia, Pa., 1964, pp. 1–25.

8. "Religion and Psychopathology" by Orville S. Walters. *Comprehensive Psychiatry,* Vol. 5, No. 1, Feb. 1964, pp. 24–35. By permission of Grune & Stratton, Inc.

9. "The Original Sin of Mankind: An Attempt at a Psychological Interpretation." Unpublished paper by Arthur Jores.

10. "Mental Health in Christian Life" by Andre Godin. *Journal of Religion and Health,* Vol. 1, No. 1, Oct. 1961, pp. 41–54.

11. "The Quest for Meaning" by Russell J. Becker. To be published in *Journal of Existentialism.*

12. "The Significance of Meaning for Health" by Viktor E. Frankl. Preached at First Unitarian Church of San Francisco, Oct. 6, 1963. © Viktor E. Frankl.

13. "The Spiritual Dimension of Man's Health in Today's World" by H. S. Hoyman. *Journal of School Health,* Vol. 36, No. 2, Feb. 1966, pp. 52–63. Published by the American School Health Association.

14. "Patient or Penitent" from *Guilt: Where Religion and Psychology Meet,* by David Belgum. © 1963. By permission of Prentice-Hall, Inc., Englewood Cliffs, N.J.

15. "The Problem of Guilt" by Gordon E. Jackson. *Pittsburgh Perspective,* Vol. VI, No. 2, June 1955, pp. 5–22, adapted from chapter in a forthcoming book by Dr. Jackson.

16. "Sin, Illness, and Guilt" by Russell J. Becker. Published in modified form in *Christian Century,* Vol. 83, No. 33, Aug. 17, 1966, pp. 1007–9.

17. "Objective Guilt and Neurosis" by Günter Elsässer. Originally delivered as a lecture at the Congress of the General Medical Association for Psychotherapy in Freudenstadt, Apr. 26, 1956. *Psyche: Eine Zeitschrift fur Psychologische und Medizinische Menschenkunde,* Vol. 10, No. 5, 1966, pp. 348–56. Published by Ernest Klett Verlag, Stuttgart.

18. "Values in Sickness and Health" by William Zeller. Mental Health Lectures—1965, co-sponsored by the *Hartford Courant* and the Institute of Living in Hartford, Conn.

19. "Spiritual Therapy for the Peptic Ulcer Patient" from *Spiritual Therapy* by Richard K. Young and Albert L. Meiburg, copyright © Richard K. Young and Albert L. Meiburg, Harper & Brothers, New York, 1960. Reprinted with permission of Harper & Row, Publishers, Inc.

20. "Therapy of Pastoral Care," pp. 78–95 from *Pastoral Care and Psychotherapy,* 1961, by Peder Olsen, translated by Herman E. Jorgensen. By permission of Augsburg Publishing House, Minneapolis, Minn., copyright owners.

21. "Integrity Therapy," pamphlet, copyrighted by John W. Drakeford.

22. "The Neurosis, Confession, and Recovery of a Protestant Minister" from *The New Group Therapy,* by O. Hobart Mowrer. D. Van Nostrand, Inc., Princeton, N.J., Insight #15, 1964.

23. "Some Practical Values of Mowrer's Insights for Pastoral Counseling" by Allen Whitman. Chapter 5 in his Master's thesis, submitted to Northwestern Lutheran Theological Seminary, Minneapolis, Minn., 1965. Permission granted by Allen Whitman.

# Preface

TWENTY-SEVEN YEARS AGO I experienced the healing effects of therapy in the Speech Clinic while a Freshman at the University of Minnesota. Since then I have had a strong personal interest in any process that professes to help distressed and distorted persons achieve wholeness and usefulness.

The study of psychology of religion and the practice of pastoral care have unearthed complex theoretical questions about and insights into man's personality—how it works and why it fails to work. But any enlightened inquiry into the nature of man and his problems, his sickness and his health, must be eclectic. Hence this book on religion and medicine, for they have long been the twin sisters of healing.

Many other inquirers into the relationships existing between the two fields have sought the same habitat as I, a university teaching hospital which is willing to have the interdisciplinary study of religion and medicine focus in the clinical concern for the patient. I am most grateful for the cooperation between the University of Iowa's School of Religion and College of Medicine, which makes such an enterprise possible in the setting of the University Hospitals. The stimulus and encouragement of colleagues from many departments in such a research atmosphere are deeply appreciated.

This book came into being through an invitation extended to 225 physicians, hospital chaplains, psychiatrists, and pastoral theologians both in America and abroad. It is the first in a series entitled *Iowa Studies in Religion and Medicine.* The scope of the volume is a bit broader than originally intended because the request elicited more general essays than essays based on clinical research. It is hoped the second volume will have more case studies. It may be possible that in a few years a symposium could attract a number of persons to present research papers at a conference called precisely for this purpose. At any rate, the following is a direct quotation of the invitation extended to the many who manifested interest in this topic:

### Symposium on Religion and Psychosomatic Medicine

To many, psychosomatic medicine is the newest and most exciting frontier even though it has roots in ancient history. Implementation of what is already known is tragically difficult because of the problems of interdisciplinary communication. Even when the intricate diagnostic questions have been answered, adequate therapy for the psychosomatic patient is often not followed up and the patient returns with the same or another symptom. The practical matter of financial waste in such recidivism, to say nothing of the unnecessary suffering involved, makes a breakthrough in this field necessary.

Two factors receiving increasing attention as contributing to psychosomatic debility are *meaninglessness* and *guilt.* Both are negative and both contribute to the patient's feeling of worthlessness and the conviction that he is not "entitled to" good health and the other rewards of life. Psychosomatic illness, in such cases, must be treated with these central and crucial factors in mind.

Viktor Frankl stresses the "will to meaning"; Gordon W. Allport believes a "unifying philosophy of life" has great value for personal adjustment; and Carl Gustav Jung found long ago that a belief system was an essential ingredient in the recovery of many of his patients, especially in middle life.

O. Hobart Mowrer has been a controversial stimulator concerning the diagnostic and therapeutic significance of guilt, but he is by no means alone. John G. McKenzie, Thomas Szasz, and Sidney Jourard are among a growing number concerning themselves with the destructive function of guilt. In a recent publication I referred to the possibility that psychosomatic symptoms may in many cases be the "amplified and distorted voice of conscience," and the phrase seemed to catch on.

For the vast majority of patients, religion has been a primary molder of their value structure, their superego or conscience, and has also historically been the agency for dealing with guilt and its resolution. The same can be said for the belief system, faith, meaning or purpose of life—issues by which many patients live and upon which they base much of their motivation to achieve health and wholeness.

In this symposium we are eager to bring together theoretical essays but *especially empirical research* papers, which would have a bearing upon the relationship between religion and psychosomatic medicine. Concerning religion, we limit our present attention to *values* and *meaning* (in traditional terms "conscience" and "faith"), or negatively stated, guilt and meaninglessness. From the medical standpoint, we are interested in both diagnostic and therapeutic issues. We feel that both fields have much to say to each other as both focus their efforts and insights on helping the psychosomatic patient.

The following essays represent a variety of emphases, for it is a controversial field. Some experimental psychologists will declare parts of this symposium poetic nonsense. There will also be ardent religionists who will claim that there have not been precise enough theological formulations of "salvation" and that we ought not lean so heavily toward the behavioral sciences. Since the purpose of this book is to challenge and to stir discussion, the editor does not mind if the reader quarrels with the contributors, nor does he mind if the essayists conflict with each other. Out of such stuff is dialogue made.

In a few cases the editor felt some of the wording was obscure. His clarifications appear in brackets.

Acknowledgment should be made of the translations from German of the essays by Jores and Elsässer, which were done by Willy Melczer, a member of the Translators' Workshop at the University of Iowa.

Deeply appreciated is the help of Paul Rothfusz, my Research Assistant for the past two years, who was an avid co-worker from start to finish.

Appreciation is expressed to the Graduate College of the University of Iowa for its aid in supporting the publication of this book.

DAVID BELGUM

SCHOOL OF RELIGION and COLLEGE OF MEDICINE
*The University of Iowa*
*Iowa City, Iowa, 1967*

# Contents

# 1

# THE HEALTH *of the* WHOLE MAN

# 1

# The Meaning of Health

*Paul Tillich*

THE DIFFICULTY and the challenge of the meaning of health is that in order to speak of health, one must speak of all dimensions of life which are united in man. And no one can be an expert in all of them. But confronting this challenge is the destiny of the philosopher and the theologian, insofar as they should envisage the whole of life. In any case, only a limited part of the immense problem can be covered.

### A LOGICAL CONSIDERATION

The title is not "the concept of health," but "the meaning of health." Concepts are defined by subsumption to a more embracing concept; meanings are defined by being brought into configuration with other meanings. This method is in many cases more adequate and not less scientific

---

PAUL TILLICH, Dr. Phil., was at the time of his death in 1966 John Nuveen Professor of Theology, The Divinity School of the University of Chicago, Chicago, Illinois.

than the method of subsumption. In our case, it is definitely adequate for a very fundamental reason. Health is not an element in the description of man's essential nature—his *eidos* or *ide,* as Plato would say; his created nature, as theology would express it. Health is not a part of man or a function of man, as are blood circulation, metabolism, hearing, breathing. Health is a meaningful term only in confrontation with its opposite—disease. And disease contains a partial negation of the essential nature of man. Conversely, in order to understand disease, one must know the essential nature of man as well as the possible distortions of it. In contemporary language one would say that health and disease are existentialist concepts. They do not grasp something of man's essential nature; certainly they presuppose this nature and the knowledge of it; but they add a new element, the possibility and reality of its distortion. Health and disease are very good examples of existentialist concepts. Like theology, medicine always did unite essentialist and existentialist elements in its thought. Therefore, psychotherapy, especially in its psychoanalytic form, and existentialism have influenced each other profoundly in the last 50 years; and the idea of an existentialist psychotherapy is only a confirmation and systematization of an actual situation.

## THE BASIC DIALECTICS OF LIFE PROCESSES

Life processes include two basic elements: self-identity and self-alteration. A centered and balanced living whole goes beyond itself, separates itself partly from its unity, but in doing so it tries to preserve its identity and to return in its separated parts to itself. Going out from one's self and returning to one's self characterizes life under all dimensions, from the structure of the atom to the growth of the plant, to the movement of the animal, to the creativity of the mind, to the dynamics of historical groups. One can call this dialectics of life processes because it implies contrasting movements, a *yes* and a *no,* as in a searching conversation. And all dialectical thought is nothing but a mirror of such life processes.

The contrast between self-identity and self-alteration produces two dangers for every living being. The first is to lose one's self in going beyond one's self and not being able to return to one's self. This happens if special processes separate themselves from the whole and produce dispersion into too many directions, a wrong kind of growth, a loss of the uniting center. In all these cases (which are represented by particular bodily and mental diseases and personal disintegrations) the self-identity is threatened and often completely lost (change of personality and memory).

In reaction to the awareness of this danger, the opposite danger appears. Afraid to lose one's identity, one is unable to go out from one's self into self-alteration. Perhaps one has attempted it, but after having been frustrated, one retreats to a limited form of existence in which the self-identity on a reduced basis is preserved; and it is not only preserved, it is compulsively defended as in most cases of psychoneurosis.

If we ask how it can be explained that the dialectics of life processes are interrupted and how its flux is stopped, we may name three main causes: accidents, intrusions, imbalances. A consideration of these would lead deeply into the philosophy of life, and especially of medicine; we can only point to some characteristics of these causes of disease, as well as to their common cause. They are rooted in what I call the ambiguity of life and of all its processes. Ambiguity means that in every creative process of life, a destructive trend is implied; in every integrating process of life, a disintegrating trend; in every process toward the sublime, a profanizing trend. These ambiguities of life produce the concrete causes of disease. The ambiguities of encounter of being with being make destructive accidents unavoidable, be it bodily injuries or psychological traumata.

The ambiguities of assimilation of elements of the surrounding world—in food, breathing, communication—make unavoidable the destructive intrusions of strange bodies, as in bodily or mental infections; the ambiguities of growth, that is, bodily growth or the development of one's spiritual potentialities, make unavoidable the appearance of imbalances. Generally speaking, disease is a symptom of the universal ambiguity of life. Life must risk itself in order to win itself, but in the risking it may lose itself. A life which does not risk disease—even in the highest forms of the life of the spirit—is a poor life, as is shown, for instance, by the hypochondriac or the conformist.

## HEALTH, DISEASE, AND HEALING UNDER THE DIFFERENT DIMENSIONS OF LIFE

When I spoke of dimensions of life, there was implied a rejection of the phrase "levels of life." This must now be made explicit. Man should not be considered as a composite of several levels, such as body, soul, spirit, but as a multidimensional unity. I use the metaphor "dimension" in order to indicate that the different qualities of life in man are present within each other and do not lie alongside or above each other. One can expediently, but not necessarily, distinguish the physical, the chemical, the biological, the psychological, the mental, and the historical dimensions. Different distinctions as well as more particular ones are quite possible. What is important, however, is to see that they do not lie alongside, but within each other, as in the metaphor "dimension" the dimensional lines cross each other in one point.

This point, in our consideration, is man. He is multidimensional unity; all dimensions, distinguishable in experienced life, cross in him. In every dimension of life, all dimensions are potentially or actually present. In the atom only one of them is actual. In man all of them are actually present; he does not consist of levels of being, but he is a unity which unites all dimensions. This doctrine stands against the dualistic theory which sees man as composed of soul and body; or body and mind; or body, soul, and spirit, etc. Man is one, uniting within himself all dimensions of life—an insight which we partly owe to the recent developments of medicine, especially psychiatry.

As confirmation of this idea, one may refer to "psychosomatic" medicine. But although this is not incorrect, one should not forget that a hyphen between "psycho" and "somatic" represents the statement of a problem and not a solution.

The multidimensional unity of life in man calls for a multidimensional concept of health, of disease, and of healing, but in such a way that it becomes obvious that in each dimension all the others are present.

I shall follow the series of dimensions as indicated before and in each case show the meaning of health and disease and the function of healing as determined by the ideas of health and disease in what one could call a philosophy of life in medical terms.

### *Mechanical Dimension*

Under the predominance of the physical dimension, health is the adequate functioning of all the particular parts of man. Disease is the non-functioning of these parts because of the machine with reduced or artificially strengthened of incidents, infections, and imbalances. Healing, then, is the removal of the diseased parts or their mechanical replacement: surgery. The prevalence of surgery since the Renaissance is based on an image of man (classically formulated by Descartes) which views him as a well-functioning body-machine, the disabled parts of which are removed or replaced so that after successful surgery, health means the functioning force. Analogies to bodily surgery in the other dimensions can be found, for instance, in the removal of elements in the psychological makeup of a person by psychotherapeutic methods. The patient is healed but reduced in power of being. A conspicuous case in which bodily surgery and psychological reduction are united is lobotomy, the total being reduced to a rather low functioning, but in some respect being healed. And under the dimension of the spirit, there can also be found an analogy in the moral and educational repressing of vital trends which have become infected or imbalanced, and dangerous for the whole. But such healing of the person is surgery; its healing is reduction of the power of being.

### *Chemical Dimension*

There is no bodily surgery which does not consider the chemical processes in the body that is operated on. Health in this dimension is the balance of chemical substances and processes in a living organism. Here, reduction by sedatives and increase by adding stimulating substances to the organism are equally important. But it is not full healing in either case. The present drug-medicine fashion puts before us a profound problem. If it is possible to determine the self-altering as well as the self-preserving life processes in a living being from the dimension of chemism, what does this mean for the dimensions of the psychological, the spiritual, and the historical? In answering this, one must realize that even if we imagined the total determination of individuals on this basis as possible, the question would remain: What about the chemism of those who determine the chemical composition of others? Who decides? Here the dimension of health in the social-historical structure—with its presuppositions of spirit, morality, culture, and religion—appears in the health idea of the "brave new world." In this idea of human health, self-alteration is reduced to a minimum and life dries up.

### *Biological Dimension*

Disregarding these extremes, which are threats on the horizon of our life, we must consider the biological dimension in which the balance is achieved between self-alteration and self-preservation. This is done by acts in which the total organism in its relation to environment and world is the object of healing, as for instance through rest, awakening of interest, increased movement, change of food and climate, etc. This is well expressed in the word "recreation," which indicates that the created vitality was stopped either in its power of going out beyond itself or in its power of returning to itself. Either the life processes had been reduced to routine existence or they were excited by the innumerable stimuli of daily life. Here a new dimension appears. The attempt to recreate life in the biological dimension demands the inclusion of the problem of health in the dimension of self-awareness—the psychological.

### *Psychological Dimension*

Health in the dimension of self-awareness shows the dialectical structure of life processes most clearly. The processes of psychological growth demand self-alteration in every moment—in receiving reality, in mastering it, in being united with parts of it, in changing it, etc. But in all this a risk is involved, and this accounts for the reluctance to take all these encountered pieces of reality into one's centered self; thus the desire to withdraw into a limited reality becomes effective. One is afraid of going out and one defends compulsively the limited place to which one has retired. Something went wrong in the process of pushing ahead. And now a reduced health is unconsciously produced. The reduced health of the neurotic is the limited health he is able to reach —but reality makes him aware of the dangers of his limitation and so he wants to overcome the limits with the help of the analyst. If in reaching some degree of liberation, reality shows itself to him irrefutably, the question arises whether the neurotic can face reality. Often he can, sometimes he cannot; and it is left to the judgment of the healer whether he shall even try to heal if the result is so ambiguous.

We can compare the causes of psychological diseases with the causes of bodily diseases. Traumatic experiences stand in analogy to accidents (and are sometimes caused by accidents) and are the intrusion of forces which remain alongside the centered self as strange elements which are not taken into the center. Healing means helping to make somebody aware of these inhibitions of the outgoing processes and accepting the fact of limited health, because if it is accepted, its compulsory form is undercut and openness for pushing ahead becomes possible. Then, of course, the danger arises that the outgoing process may become so uninhibited that the return is stopped and self-identity is destroyed.

### *Spiritual Dimension*

Again we are in the situation that we have separated the dimension of self-awareness from the dimension of spirit ("spirit," with a small *s* designating the life in meanings and values inherent in morality, culture, and religion). In these three functions of the spirit, the problem of health receives another depth and breadth, which then, conversely, is decisive for all the preceding dimensions. Morality is the self-actualization of the person in his centered encounter with the other person. This act is the basis of life in the dimension of the spirit. It is not the subjection to a law from God or man, but it is the actualization of what we potentially are, of our created nature. Its distortion in the line of outgoing is legalistic repression of parts of our being. Its distortion in the line of self-identity as a person is the lawless explosion of all possibilities.

Here the psychotherapeutic problem becomes the moral problem of the person and his self-actualization. And healing is the power of overcoming both distortions. But the healing of the spirit is not possible by good will, because the good will is just that which needs healing. In order to be healed, the spirit must be grasped by something which transcends it, which is not strange to it, but within which is the fulfillment of its potentialities. It is called "Spirit" (with a capital *S*). Spirit is the presence of what concerns us ultimately, the ground of our being and meaning. This is the intention of religion but it is not identical with religion. For as a function of the human spirit and as a realm of human activities, religion also stands under the dialectics of all life and under its ambiguities and, because its claims are higher, is even more profound than the others. Religious health is the state of being grasped by the Spirit, namely the Divine Presence, enabling us to transcend our religion and to return to it in the same experience. Unhealthy religion is the state of being enslaved—socially or personally—by a concrete religious system, producing bigotry, fanaticism, inordinate self-destructive ecstasy, dogmatism, ritualism. But neither is it healthy if in the breakthrough out of all this one loses the identity of a personal and communal religious center.

It must be added here that the healing power of the Spiritual Presence is far removed from the magic practice of "faith-healing." There *is* such a thing, a magic force from man to man. And without doubt the magic influence of the healer on the patient or of the patient upon himself is an element in most forms of healing. (Magic: the impact of one unconscious power upon another one.) But this is not the healing power of being centered in the universal, the divine center.

Here again the question arises how the healing helper, in most cases the minister or priest, can judge (like the psychoanalyst) whether the self-restriction to a religion of limited health (accepting authority, relying on a conversion experience) should be accepted or revealed in its limitation; and the same question arises in a well-established remoteness from a concrete religion. When is conversion required for Spiritual health?

### *Historical Dimension*

When dealing with the cultural function in the light of the idea of health, we are driven to the last of the dimensions of life, the historical. The decisive question here is: To what degree is personal health possible in a society which is not a "sane society" (Erich Fromm)? "By creating a sane society" is an inadequate answer: first, because it disregards the ambiguities of historical existence which can be conquered only fragmentarily; second, because it overlooks the fact that without personal health in the leading groups, no social health is possible (the communist society). The cultural situation of a society has the same dialectics—the inhibition against pushing forward or the impossibility of returning to a guiding set of symbols. The unsolved situation in this respect is partly the result, partly the cause of the lack of health in all the other dimensions. But this goes beyond our limited subject.

## HEALING, SEPARATED AND UNITED

The road through the many dimensions, and the meaning of health within them, has shown (1) that the dialectics of life processes are the same under each dimension; (2) that in each of them the others are presupposed; (3) that there is always a fulfilling and a reducing idea of health; (4) that complete healing includes healing under all dimensions.

This raises the question of the justification of limited healing. Human finitude makes particular healing necessary. The hurt finger requires surgical or chemical help, the physically healthy neurotic requires psychotherapeutic help. There are special helpers and healing methods called for under every dimension. But this independence of particular ideas of health and healing is limited by the mutual within-each-otherness of the dimensions. This is partly untrue to the human situation and leads to a phenomenon I would call "unhealthy health." It comes about if healing under one dimension is successful but does not take into consideration the other dimensions in which health is lacking or even imperilled by the particular healing. Successful surgery may produce a psychological trauma; effective drugs may calm down an uneasy conscience and preserve a moral deficiency; the well-trained, athletic body may contain a neurotic personality; the healed patient of the analyst may be sick through a lack of an ultimate meaning of his life; the conformist's average life may be sick through inhibited self-alteration; the converted Christian may suffer under repressions which produce fanaticism and may explode in lawless forms; the sane society may be the place where the pressure of the principles of its sanity may produce psychological and biological disruptions by the desire for creative insanity.

Particular healing is unavoidable, but it has the tendency to provoke diseases in another realm.

Thus, it is important for healers always to cooperate in

every healing situation. This requirement was embodied in the ideal of the *soter,* the saviour (precisely, "the healer") who makes healthy and whole. The word has been applied to medical men, to gods of healing, to great rulers, to divine-human mediators. They all were considered to be healers. But the ideal was the *one* healer, the saviour, whose healing powers indicate the coming of the new eon. This is the background of the New Testament accounts of healing, which should not be taken as miracle stories, but as stories pointing to the universal healer.

This mythological symbol, which was applied to the man Jesus, shows the unity of the religious and the medical most clearly. And if salvation is understood in the sense of healing, there is no conflict between the religious and the medical, but the most intimate relation. Only a theology which has forgotten this relation, and sees salvation as the elevation of the individual to a heavenly place, can come into conflict with medicine. And only a medicine which denies the non-biological dimensions of life in their significance for the biological dimension (including its physical and chemical conditions) can come into conflict with theology. But an understanding of the differences as well as the mutual within-each-otherness of the dimensions can remove the conflict and create an intensive collaboration of helpers in all dimensions of health and healing.

The concept of health cannot be defined without relation to its opposite—disease. But this is not only a matter of definition. In reality, health is not health without the essential possibility and the existential reality of disease. In this sense, health is disease conquered, as eternally the positive is positive by conquering the negative. This is the deepest theological significance of medicine.

2

## The Axes of Concern in Personality

*David Belgum*

AN AXIS is a line passing through a body so that it actually or supposedly revolves upon it, as the axis of the earth. It is at the center of man's life, as at the hub of a wheel, that he is a unique person. Most attempts at describing the core of personality have to decide what is central and what is peripheral in man's life.

Fads have come and gone in analyzing man and his problems. There has been a tendency toward distortion and special pleading.

From the religious perspective there has sometimes been a spiritualizing of man to the neglect of his physical and material aspects. Such was the case of a young man who thought his wife and he had only to agree on certain doc-

DAVID BELGUM, Ph.D., is Associate Professor of Pastoral Care and Counseling, School of Religion and College of Medicine, University of Iowa, Iowa City, Iowa.

trines and religious practices and all the complexity of their marital conflict would suddenly clear up. He avoided confrontation with certain practical, physiological, sexual, and psychological problems by "elevating" the entire matter to a "mixed" marriage and religious issue. Others assume all problems can be solved by prayer and a right relation to God. This overlooks the existential situation of man *in the body,* the tangible and specific ingredients of life. Such "spiritualizing" of man's personality far exceeds Scripture, which takes a holistic view of man and makes no artificial dichotomy between body and spirit.

From the behavioral sciences has come the attempt to quantify material evidence about man, to test and measure, to organize a statistical analysis of personality. A university president shows how this works in education:

> In short, our system tends to reduce everything about a student to a few key numbers.
>
> In describing a particular student, we often say something like this: Steve Martin? Oh, yes, he was 35th in a high school class of 280, he scored 553 on the verbal and 610 on the quantitative College Board tests, his college gradepoint average was 2.85, and he scored 575 on the Graduate Record Examination. There you have the biography of Steven Martin reduced to stark essentials. No nonsense about his curiosity, his moral fiber, his dreams and aspirations, his social consciousness, his human decency, his imagination, his philosophy of life, or his aesthetic sensibilities. These things cannot readily be measured, at least not yet, and so we tend to ignore them in our description of Steve Martin, and to concentrate on the quantitative and the measurable—however incomplete they may be in describing a complex, many-faceted human being.[1]

Meanwhile medical specialists have come to rely on increasingly intricate and exact measurement technology; and indeed some of the most dramatic breakthroughs in the battle against disease and in spectacular surgery owe their success to such methods. Yet many fear that exclusive focusing on the quantitative and measurable in medicine misses the mark, because man does not live by bread alone nor even by elaborate biochemistry alone.

It is the purpose of this chapter to create a scheme for encompassing both of the above legitimate facets of the person and to bring them into a dynamic relationship.

[1] Howard R. Bowen, *The Daily Iowan,* Apr. 10, 1964, p. 2.

### AXES OF TIME AND SPACE

The axis of time runs through the center of man's existence. Like a man standing on a long, straight stretch of railroad track on the prairie, he looks over his shoulder into the past until the track disappears into the horizon. If he looks ahead, into the future, the same is true. But he stands or acts always in the present existential moment. Hence we may say that the red thread of *time* runs through his life and personality like an axis, and on it his life turns and moves on.

Returning to our theme of the measurable and the nonmeasurable aspects of life, we find them also somewhat separated on this axis. The past is more knowable, easier to pin down and to analyze. Prediction of what will happen in the future is more difficult. No wonder more energy is spent on gathering data about what has happened; it is more rewarding and yields facts and statistics we can control. True, science has come far in prediction, but farther in the physical sciences than in the realm of personality.

The present tense contains the point of tension, the occasion of choice, the moment when a person hopes to bring the benefits of past experience into his plans and actions of the future. This is the characteristic we feel to be most uniquely human, this self-awareness about the significance of the time element in one's life and the constant responsibility for choosing in the present tense.

The axis of space, on the other hand, also is a sort of continuum in man's existence, for this element tends to be more or less measurable, ranging from the tangible and physical to the intangible and so-called spiritual or less measurable, the immaterial. Again, the person seems to be in the middle with a mixture of both physical and spiritual elements or aspects that plague analysis—sometimes referred to as the "body-mind problem." Man has been variously referred to as animal or angel or a combination of both.

A case in point is an orthopedic patient in a general hospital. In middle age he finally presents himself with a nonfused fracture in his upper arm caused by an accident 17 years previously. X-ray and physical examination outline the problem with great accuracy; the exact capacity of his arm is measured. Since he gets along satisfactorily, one of the more puzzling aspects of the case is why he finally now presents himself for therapy. The picture is not complete until a chaplain discovers that there is marital discord, and that the very day of his physical examination in the orthopedic department, his wife is beginning divorce proceedings through her lawyer. Suddenly a host of emotional and social factors come into focus. Is he finally seeking treatment to correct a disfiguring condition as a last-ditch effort to please his wife and stave off the divorce; or is he taking independent action after all these years because he is at last free to spend his money as he wishes without her nagging? It is obvious that the material structure of his bones and flesh constitutes only half the case. The case must be completed at the other end of the space continuum, the immaterial and nonphysical aspects must necessarily be taken into consideration in treating the whole person.

Hence we make a plea for equal consideration of the future as well as of the past in the time axis; and as much attention to the spiritual, immaterial, and immeasurable as to the physical, material, and measurable end of the space axis of personality. We propose to outline these two axes in more detail and call this scheme a *personagraph.*

## A PERSONAGRAPH

What kinds of questions do counselees ask and what do they say about their situation? The hospital chaplain or pastoral counselor frequently hears the following:

"*Why* did it happen to me?"

"There's no *future* for me!"

"How can I break from my *past*?"

"Who am *I* to undertake such a project (or face _____)?"

It is hoped that the scheme in Figure 2.1 will provide some structure for understanding a particular individual while not requiring refined or elaborate statistical method. Yet it is comprehensive and objective enough to cover the two axes of concern voiced by the above questions and many others. The personagraph is an outline for writing descriptively and systematically about a person.

Let it be clearly understood that this self-rating scale makes no pretense at statistical precision or refinement. Its aim is simply to raise and clarify certain major issues for the purpose of pastoral counseling. Neither is this approach incompatible with other more precise instruments, for in

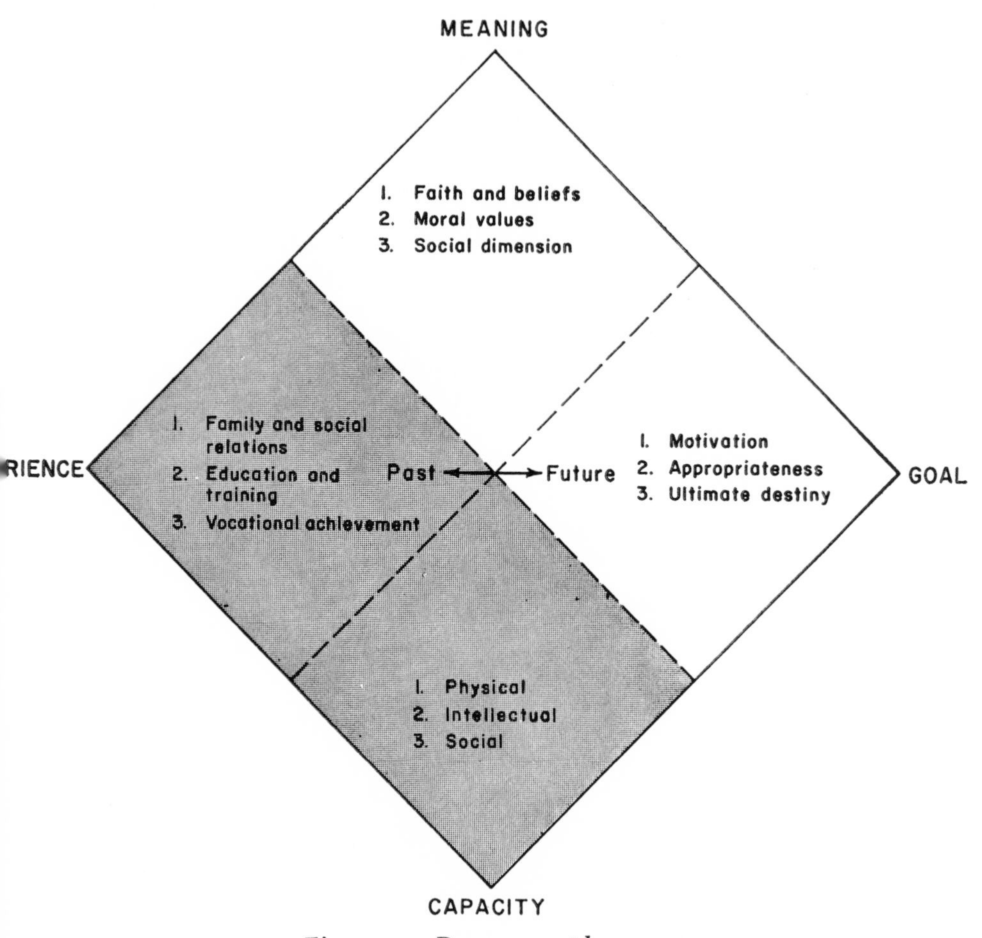


*Fig. 2.1. Personagraph.*

the discussion the client may see the real value of information which might be gleaned from psychological testing, further vocational aptitude profiles, or a medical examination. At present there are no plans to establish "norms" or make comparison with control groups. To use a term from Gordon Allport, it is *idiographic*—unique to this one individual.

### *Personagraph Outline*

A. CAPACITY serves as a foundation for the house of personality that one builds. Most diagnosis begins with the question of the person's present capacity to function. What kind of disorder is it? Has order been disrupted as in the case of a broken bone; or has order never existed as in a congenital deformity, mental retardation, or certain kinds of character disorders?

1. *Physical capacity* is thoroughly checked—the blood sugar for diabetes, the X-ray for tuberculosis, and the electroencephalogram for possible epilepsy. Metabolism and neural reflexes give clues of disorder and disease—lack of capacity; or negative findings in these areas can rule out certain maladies. Great strides have been made in the accurate measurement of physical capacity. Nuclear medicine has opened new vistas in scanning devices. Refined studies in genetics have clarified the person's awareness of his hereditary potential (and problems). Unfortunately, sometimes the investigation of the person begins and stops with this thorough measurement of physical and bodily functions.

2. *Intellectual and emotional factors* have more recently become subject to strictly disciplined measurement. Although the I.Q. is best known and has been made more accurate because of cross-cultural studies, we now feel we can give a person a statistical score on such factors as introversion-extroversion, depression, paranoia, masculinity-femininity, and many others. This is a higher level of capacity because it suggests to what extent he can use his brain and vital energies, his muscular and skeletal systems in the appropriate manner which will enhance his life instead of destroy it. Here we see his ability to reason and see relationships, to perceive significance as well as simply to have reflex sense perceptions. Some have great capacity in this area, some very little, and most of us fall somewhere in between on the big hump of the "normal curve."

3. *Social capacity* is a still broader category. It implies the channeling of the person's physical and intellectual and emotional energies and strengths into some interpersonal relationships so that he participates creatively and appropriately in civilization from the smallest family and friendship circles to the intricate fabric of manners and morals, commerce and government. Social capacity includes learned as well as inherent elements, the folkways and mores of the

individual's group which he has learned with greater or lesser pain or willingness, and whatever basic temperament seems "natural" to the person. How one arrives at his social capacity is a moot question; but the fact remains that one person seems to be able to think of others, be altruistic and civic-minded—he always sees the social consequences of his actions—whereas the next person is clearly egocentric, tactless, and basically an isolate who enjoys being left alone.

Although there seems to be a broadening direction in this progression from physical to intellectual to social capacity, the fact remains that current medical, psychiatric, and psychological approaches to the question of capacity have employed increasingly refined tests and measurements for diagnostic purposes. Before a therapist treats anyone, he wants to know "what the patient has" and "to what extent." Does the diabetic need much or little insulin? Is the patient so depressed that he needs to be hospitalized or can he be treated as an outpatient? All the factors that can be measured are considered thoroughly. The stress on the scientific method, however, makes a professional member of the health team reluctant to deal with matters which cannot be neatly measured and statistically computed for research purposes—hence the stress on the physical end of the axis.

B. EXPERIENCE is likewise subject to tangible investigation. Events that have happened can be historically verified to a certain degree. Evidence and facts can be produced after certain prescribed procedures have been followed. Lawyers, historians, detectives, social workers, etc. have developed their methods of recreating the "case." In a sense, past experience can be a tangible and measurable facet of our personagraph.

1. *Family and social relations* represent some of the most vital past experiences which a person can bring to the present moment. Freudian and developmental psychology have shown the formative significance of early mother-child and sibling relationships. These can be negative or positive.

A 13-year-old boy had already spent several years in a mental hospital labeled a "psychopathic deviate." Since earliest boyhood his father had trained him in stealing. If he succeeded in theft, he was rewarded and loved by his father; if he failed to break the law he was punished severely.

The pattern of "character disorder" was firmly entrenched. He had his whole value structure reversed: to conform to society he had to reject his father. Unless some drastic change took place, he might be fixated at this distorted adjustment. The last the author knew of him he was 18 years old and still relatively unchanged except that he had been transferred to an adult ward.

By age six the child has had many experiences with his peers outside the family. Among playmates he has been accepted or rejected. The pattern of social relationships grows for better or worse and must be taken into account for a complete description of the person as he is today. Family disorganization, lack of close emotional ties, frequent brutality and insensitivity, uncertainty about food and shelter would contribute to a negative score. Family love and security, social approval, cultural opportunities, and encouragement would raise the score. With good interview technique, home studies, and social investigation, it is possible to give a relatively accurate and meaningful rating for this facet of experience.

2. *Education and training* are more deliberate efforts at shaping the personality. The cumulative public school record indicates quite accurately how much of the person's capacity he has been able to use at various stages of his personality development. This also constitutes equipment, skills, methods, and resources available to cope with the future. Native capacities require training and focusing. In the United States the period of educational experience is very long, reaching far into mature adulthood and even beyond marriage. But the record of this experience is tangible (as in the case of Steve Martin, see above). From this record may be drawn recommendations that open and close doors, that limit or expand the life space within which the person is free to express himself. Again one could give a negative or positive rating for this kind of experience, depending upon whether the training has been constructive and appropriate, enhancing the person, or misguided and ineffective in equipping the person to meet adult responsibilities. Obviously this score would be most meaningful in comparison with the rating on capacity. It is in such a context that a term like "under-achiever" is used in vocational guidance.

3. *Vocational achievement* for the teen-ager may be

almost synonymous with his educational record; but for the person who has completed his basic training, the work record in the company's personnel file is of great importance. What has the person actually been able to do with his capacity and training? For Adler this was the touchstone of a person's sense of worth. For others it is reality testing—how he functions in the practical, work-a-day world. He earns not only his living but the respect of significant others in his life, to say nothing of his self-respect. This part of experience is also measurable in hours, units of production, time begun and finished, and value to society, whether calculated by financial worth or social status. So one's vocational achievement is either a plus or a minus experience, from very rewarding to utter failure.

So we have come half way around the diagram—the half that is relatively measurable, tangible, and suitable for statistical manipulation. Research in personality draws heavily on this half because it is easy to set up control groups and record data according to height and weight, age and sex, social class or educational level, I.Q. and grade point averages. But these two sections have dealt with only one end of each axis: the past of the time axis and the material end of the space axis. We now turn our attention to the other half of each axis: the spiritual and the future, which we here call "meaning" and "goal."

We should not oversimplify our diagram by making it appear that the elements of capacity and experience are of little or no concern to religion just because they are measurable, more tangible or "materialistic" than *meaning* and *goal.* Religion views man's physical nature and capacity from the standpoint of the doctrines of creation and providence. The created order is not minimized. Similarly what man has achieved or how he has used his talents is viewed from the perspectives of stewardship and vocation, the notion that man has a responsibility to focus and use his energies and capacities to the fullest in loving service of mankind.

C. MEANING is being rediscovered as an essential part of the mature personality and a vital factor in mental health. Hobbs finds this true in clinical practice:

Contemporary culture often produces a kind of neurosis different from that described by Freud. Contemporary neuroses are frequently characterized not so much by repression and conversion as by an awful awareness and a merciless raw anxiety . . . not lack of insight but lack of a sense of identity, of purpose, of meaning in life. Because of a dehumanization of existence, as Kierkegaard pointed out, he has a sickness unto death. Indeed, in many of the people I work with there seems to be a substantial component of realism in their neurotic condition. Nothing can make a person more anxious, or more guilty, than an unrelentingly clear appreciation of the absurd and desperate condition of man today.[2]

Senselessness, purposelessness, futility, meaninglessness, and guilt are depressing enemies of mental health. Since this is certainly harder to measure than temperature or basal metabolism rate, no wonder it is passed over lightly. Besides, who has answers for such questions? One cannot blame doctors and nurses for being perplexed by such issues, for gradually withdrawing from the dying and "hopeless" patient and focusing attention on other patients where tangible treatments are bringing concrete results.

1. *Faith and belief systems* seem necessary for everyone regardless of what form they may assume or what the intellectual content may be. We distinguish between faith and belief systems, attributing to the former a pervasive sense of trust and commitment, a basic assurance that the world and life in it are not accidental, chaotic, or meaningless. Faith implies that the world of things and life (events and persons) is trustworthy and purposeful in spite of our inability to grasp it all with our finite minds. On the other hand, belief systems spell out this faith in more detail, give names and structure to this more pervasive sense. In Christianity the Apostles' Creed is such a statement of specific beliefs. It is not our purpose here to evaluate the great number of belief systems in our world today. Rather, we ask, "In an attempt to understand a given personality, what role do we find his faith or belief systems playing? Is the person aware of and relying upon such structures, or is he plagued by a lack of purpose and meaning, rhyme or reason for his existence?"

Hobbs describes the function of meaning as the fifth of five "gains in psychotherapy":

Man constantly engages in building and repairing and extending and modifying cognitive structures that help him make personal sense of the

[2] Nicholas Hobbs, "Sources of Gain in Psychotherapy," *American Psychologist,* 17 (11):742, Nov., 1962.

world. The individual has got to have a cognitive house to live in to protect himself from the incomprehensibilities of existence as well as to provide some architecture for daily experiencing. . . . He must adopt or invent a personal cosmology. . . . The individual seeks psychotherapy (or some other source of cognitive control) when his cosmology, his personal system for imposing order in the world, breaks down to an alarming degree. With increasing anxiety, order must be restored.[3]

When we consider the stresses that Saint Paul sustained and overcame, we might well relate such strength to the kind of faith expressed in his Epistle to the Romans 8:28, 37–39.

We know that in everything God works for good with those who love him, who are called according to his purpose. . . in all these things we are more than conquerors through him who loved us. For I am sure that neither death, nor life, nor angels, nor principalities, nor things present, nor things to come, nor powers, nor height nor depth, nor anything else in all creation, will be able to separate us from the love of God in Christ Jesus our Lord.[4]

Any study of the personality of Paul would have to take into account the central place of such a faith and world view.

Fromm maintains that man develops feelings of hostility, powerlessness, and aloneness because of a loss of former securities and conviction. There is now a shallowness in man because of his new standards of science, individualism, and progress, none of which are able to provide adequate meaning or comprehensive cohesion in his life. He advocates that man find new meaning in love and work, the former looking beyond himself to others, the latter giving expression to his creative and higher nature. Jung likewise claimed that modern man is superficial and rootless because he has relinquished former faiths and belief systems which provided a meaning for his existence in continuity with previous generations.

Concerning our personagraph, we simply ask whether or not a given individual is aware of the function *meaning* plays in his life or the way he feels about the fact that his life is not undergirded by any such faith dynamic.

2. *Moral values* in contemporary society are frequently considered a private matter, but that is an illusion. Our

[3] *Ibid.*, pp. 746, 747.

[4] *The New Testament,* Revised Standard Version, New York: Thomas Nelson and Sons, 1946.

ethical standards have been learned from parents, peers, the church, the public schools, the mass media, etc. Likewise, the consequences of violating the moral order are administered by society. For our purposes it is not so much a matter of whether there are or are not certain standards. The laws of society are a given fact. What concerns us in the personagraph is what meaning this moral value structure has for the individual. Does he fret under law and resent authority, or does he see rules and regulations as constructive facilitators for social living in a complex society? How does he feel about his own conduct or occasional failure to live up to his and society's standards: guilty or indifferent? What rating would he give himself?

Looking at values from a social context point of view leads naturally into the third category under meaning.

3. *Social dimension* would imply that a person finds his life worthwhile in relation to other people—as he fits into the family, the civil rights movement, a group of co-workers in his place of business, the church, etc. Some would rate very low on this scale because their social orbit is so limited; they seldom see an event or activity apart from its significance for themselves in isolation. A low score on this scale implies egocentricity and withdrawal from society. In spite of an apparent external social activism, one picks up clues that this person's favorite form of speech is first person singular. Has this been a problem for our subject, caused him heartache, interfered with his work or family relationships, etc.? Mind you, we are interested in *his* rating himself, not *our* judgment of him.

The biblical view of social dimension is that of the covenant. Remaining faithful to previous promises and commitments was considered as essential for Israel as for God. Such social and ethical responsibility attributes great value to the individual and assumes a larger meaning for the individual person, for his tribe or people, and for history itself. Today, by contrast, we hear much about people being used, manipulated as means to an end. What stance does our subject of the personagraph take? Does he find meaning in his life as part of a larger social structure, or does he not need to go beyond himself to find sufficient meaning for his existence?

Cabot put it succinctly in his book, *What Men Live By:*

> There is no originality in my suggestion that we should focus our efforts upon work, play, love, and worship. For though we talk a great deal about efficiency, economics, hygiene, and other matters of secondary importance, at bottom we all know well enough what we need, and what the paraphernalia of civilization are really meant for. . . . I do not say that everyone *wants* only the ends which I have named. He usually wants fame, riches, wisdom, talents, personal beauty, and an easy time of it generally.[5]

These words serve to bridge our two categories of meaning and goal. Our goals are largely determined by our values and philosophy of life. We aim for what we think is "good."

Religion is interested in this relationship between meaning and goal because it is precisely at this point that idolatry in various forms has arisen. If a childless couple begins to think of possessing a child as the one, ultimate "good" or goal in their lives, they may be drawn to do almost anything to attain it including buying a baby through the black market. Idolization of any one segment of life leads to distortion of personality whether the exaggerated part is health, sex, education, intellect, patriotism, etc., any one of which is a legitimate but limited good in itself and in its proper context. Mature religion has subsumed these lesser goals and values under a universal and infinite perspective expressed in worship and faith.

D. GOAL may be said to have drawing power just as instinct or drives may be said to have pushing power. It is often said of a criminal, after full investigation of his background, environmental circumstances, and psycho-physical constitution, that certain factors or forces "drove him to do it." Such analysis relies heavily upon the two categories of *capacity* and *experience*—the past and the material in our personagraph. Who will deny that hunger, sex, and self-preservation are indeed powerful drives? But we should not neglect the power of goals to draw a person onward toward specific behavior and to shape personality itself.

1. *Motivation* comes from the Latin word meaning "to move." What moves a person toward certain goals? Or more

[5] Richard C. Cabot, *What Men Live By*, Boston: Houghton Mifflin Company, 1914, pp. xvii, xviii.

significantly, is the individual aware of his motivations? Although none of us can be fully aware of all the subtle nuances of motivation, the healthy personality has self-awareness and does not flounder along as a slave of unconscious drives and impulses. Future expectations and rewards have a great influence upon behavior. Some persons with much vital energy focus their attention upon a specific goal until it is accomplished; others with similar physical and mental capacity do not harness their powers effectively and their efforts are dissipated or misguided. William James maintained that most people use a very small percentage of their total capacity.

A 35-year-old clergyman was filling out his personagraph during an interview and suddenly stopped at this point. He had rated himself very high on the other three categories, but when we came to *goal* he said, "It suddenly occurs to me that I have never chosen a goal in my life. My parents chose my college; I drifted into marriage with my high school sweetheart more as a path of least resistance than a deliberate choice; and my father-in-law not only urged me into the ministry and picked out my seminary but also arranged for my first parish." Even his marital conflict was not settled by his decisive action; his wife just died. His motivation, his choosing of goals that could honestly be his own, the effort and decision to "launch out into the deep" (a scriptural text on which he had often preached [Luke 5:4]) —these he now saw as the crux of his problem. He had looked enough into the past and his own capacities; he needed to turn his attention to the future and become what some psychologists call "goal oriented."

2. *Appropriateness of goals* cannot be judged in ethereal detachment from the body or the facts of past experience. Here again we see the interrelatedness of the four categories. What is an appropriate goal of rehabilitation for a young man paralyzed from the neck down because of an auto accident? For the first patient, age 16, no physical therapy was recommended because he was adjudged a simple, irreversible, custodial care case for a nursing home. It was feared his mother would have too high hopes and spend the family's savings uselessly on expensive treatment. The second patient, age 20, appeared equally hopeless to begin with.

Gradually he was able to have the traction tongs removed from his head, later his collar support was withdrawn and he could lie in a semireclining position. Next he was able to talk without shutting off his tracheotomy tube. At the time of this writing he could touch his mouth with both hands and was exhilarated at the prospect of feeding himself.

Where is the line between having sufficient motivation to want to use all of one's strength toward the attainment of a worthwhile goal and the futile striving for the impossible? The latter is illustrated by a pathetic unqualified student who had been turned down by three professional schools. When asked what his future plans were if he should be turned down at the fourth school, he could only answer that he guessed he would keep trying.

The healthy personality does not rely heavily upon rationalization and other reality-avoiding defense mechanisms. The mature person chooses goals after due consideration, taking into account his capacity, his training, the welfare of his fellowmen, his own moral obligation, and the consequences of his action.

3. *Ultimate destiny* is a dimension many people ignore. We need to ask how our subject distinguishes between long-range and short-term goals. Some people have a limited perspective and feel they do well to get through till Friday, till quitting time; others hope they will live to see their children married or their house mortgage paid off. Some farsighted and creative pioneers do not hesitate to begin projects in medical research or social legislation. A man of deep religious faith finds himself in a still larger perspective as part of God's plan for history from the beginning of time. He finds expression of his destiny in the majestic liturgical words of the *Te Deum laudamus* from Matins:

> The glorious company of the Apostles praise thee.
> The goodly fellowship of the Prophets praise thee.
> The noble army of Martyrs praise thee. . . .
> Make them to be numbered with thy Saints,
> in glory everlasting.[6]

On the above note we have come full cycle from the tangible and measurable. Our personagraph has included

[6] *Service Book and Hymnal,* Minneapolis: Augsburg Publishing House, 1958, p. 133.

height and weight, temperature and X-ray readings at one end of the spectrum and the conviction that one's destiny is Eternal Life at the other extreme. Yet to give a comprehensive picture of personality we must include *meaning* and *goal* as well as *capacity* and *experience*. Anything less is narrowly selective of evidence and prejudices the final analysis from the start, hardly in keeping with the best tradition of objective description which is considered so essential in the behavioral and social sciences as well as in medicine or psychiatry.

### RESPONSIBILITY

A brief word must be said about choice or responsibility. This has most often been discussed under the battle flags of "freedom vs. determinism." This is an unfortunate dichotomy. There is no simple either/or. We may not be free to choose the environment and heredity we bring to the present moment, but we are "responsible for our response" (to quote Wayne Oates). It should be our hope to help persons to be accountable for as much—not as little—as possible. The person must accept responsibility for his capacity and past experiences as he channels them through the choice point of the present moment, guided by the meaning life has for him, toward some future direction and goal. Behavioral sciences are in a state of flux on this question as evidenced by an article in the *American Psychologist* entitled "Determinism-Freedom in Contemporary Psychology: An Ancient Problem Revisited."

> Indeed, the emergence of a science of behavior has not only eroded the foundation of early animistic and metaphysical views regarding the nature of man but it has also had a disquieting effect upon modern humanistic and, broadly speaking, liberally ethical approaches to human conduct and values. Scientific formulations, some hold, with their implicit determinism and cut-and-dried cause-and-effect relationships couched in quantitative terms, are bound to result in conceptualizations of man that will rob him of human dignity if not of his very essence.[7]

If this be true, it is essential to restore the concept of responsible choice to our understanding of personality dy-

[7] Ludwig Immergluck, "Determinism-Freedom in Contemporary Psychology: An Ancient Problem Revisited," *American Psychologist*, 19(4):270, Apr., 1964.

namics. It is equally as important for personality theory as for practical psychotherapy. A ground swell in this direction is already taking place as emphasized by such men as Thomas Szasz, O. Hobart Mowrer, Jourard, Viktor Frankl, Glasser, and others.

### PROFILE SHEET

The scoring of the personagraph is at the same time simple and highly individualistic. Its purpose is not that of statistical comparison; it is an attempt to help the individual think through a balanced analysis of his own personality. Wherein does he find his strengths and his problems? He may interpret it as he wishes since it is quite open-ended.

Let us begin with the category of capacity at the bottom of Figure 2.2. A person may view his own body as a liability or as an asset in terms of proportion, muscular strength, pleasing appearance, essential vitality, the presence of disease or its after-effects (as in polio or amputations), etc. Under number 2, intellectual capacity, we likewise do not set an absolute criterion against which the subject is to judge himself. An I.Q. of 100 has relative significance ranging from quite sufficient for the average worker to a real handicap for a man aspiring to be Dean of the College of Law. The same goes for the mental capacity for reasoning, remembering, and judgment. Social tact and finesse, the ability to adjust to one's social milieu and to meet one's social obligations, can be rated in much the same way. The simple question is, "Do I view this factor as a liability or an asset?"

Give each one of these three factors under capacity a maximum of 100 per cent and consider each mark as 10 per cent. We note in Figure 2.2 that our subject has given himself the following scores:

1. Physical—60 per cent (six marks out from the center)
2. Intellectual—50 per cent (proceeding five more marks on the scale)
3. Social—50 per cent (the third dot on the capacity scale)

Likewise the scores for experience are:

1. Family—40 per cent (an inadequate, weak, and negative description)

2. Education—70 per cent
3. Achievement—60 per cent

Meaning is rated as follows on Figure 2.2:

1. Faith—50 per cent
2. Moral values—60 per cent
3. Social dimension—40 per cent (note similar low rating on Family and social relations under experience)

Goal has the highest total rating:

1. Motivation—70 per cent

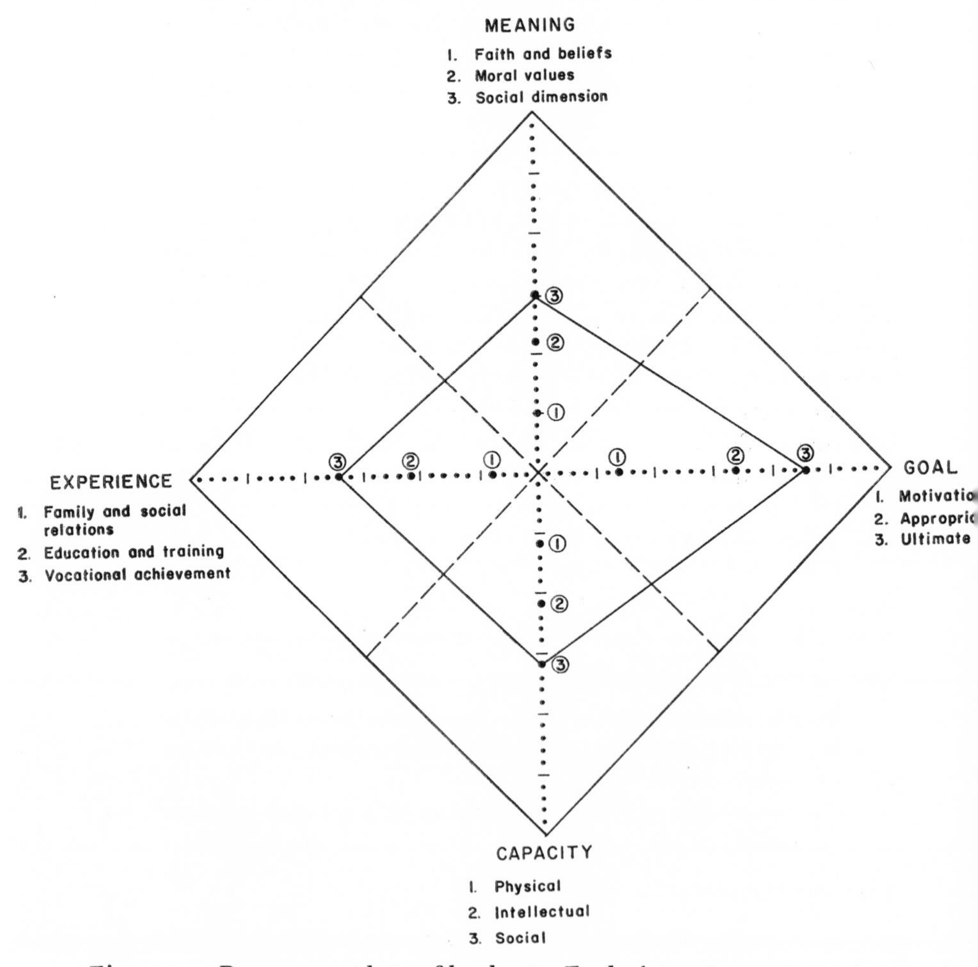


*Fig. 2.2. Personagraph profile sheet. Each dot represents 10 per cent.*

2. Appropriateness—100 per cent
3. Ultimate destiny—60 per cent

It is significant that in this counseling case the client finally saw for himself that his goals were unrealistic in comparison with his capacity. After a few sessions he was willing to take aptitude tests and to accept the insights of vocational guidance. He redirected his course from a university program to a trade school's course in the installation and repair of air conditioning equipment. Note that he rated himself 100 per cent on appropriateness of his goal to begin with. The overestimation of himself was later seen as a reaction to his father's rejection. He was able to say, after some counseling and confrontation, that he had been motivated largely by an attitude of "I'll show that old so-and-so that I can make something of myself without him!" But the hatred that he bore his father was distorting his realistic evaluation of his capacity, and his planning was inappropriate. Under the heading of moral values he was confronted with his hatred of his father, and he saw that he was suffering under this sin of hatred. (Ironically, he was an acolyte at the 9:00 A.M. Communion Service in his parish, while his parents attended the 11:00 A.M. Communion Service; they never spoke to each other and he lived away from home and supported himself though still in high school.) Much of the problem was resolved by a formal reconciliation and private confessional experience in the pastor's study at the church. It was like a new lease on life for a young man who four months before had been found walking the streets of a large city at 2:00 A.M. in a near-psychotic daze of amnesia. It seems that various factors in his personagraph had to be seen in relationship and perspective.

As lines are drawn connecting the outer limits of the subject's ratings (i.e. all the number 3's as in Fig. 2.2), one gets an impression of the living space within which he is functioning. To demonstrate that the statistical score cannot be evaluated in isolation we could mention that the young man with the "spiritual" view of his mixed marriage problem rated himself absolutely 100 per cent on everything—a perfect specimen. When he showed his wife his score in a joint interview, she screamed at him, "You Pharisee!" And maybe she was correct. It goes without saying that a person with such a score does not think he needs any help.

Obviously it is futile to treat biologically problems that arise primarily in the "meaning" area of life, just as it is impractical to forgive a person of his brain tumor. The intangible and nonmeasurable aspects of personality have their own level of discourse and treatment. They must be taken into account by therapists who believe them to be significant. Here the materialist is handicapped; he is not able to understand them because, as Paul says, "they are spiritually discerned." (I Corinthians 2:14)

We are getting a bit beyond the original purpose of this chapter when we speak about methods of dealing with what we find in the personagraph. Our purpose has been to demonstrate that to understand the individual we need to bear in mind both axes of concern in personality.

# 3

# Religious Psychology and Health

*Paul E. Johnson*

THE NEW CRISIS in health is psychological. The progressive control of infectious and organic diseases has improved the health of modern man. But functional disorders are on the increase, and these forms of illness arise from emotional tensions. A recent survey conducted by the Surgeon General's Office revealed that 50 per cent of all people in the United States who seek medical help suffer primarily from emotional difficulties.[1] Other surveys show as high as 80 per cent of all cases of illness to have psychogenic or emotional complications. The prevalence of these functional disorders has given rise to the new field of psychosomatic medicine, which is concerned with investigating the relations of mind and body in the production of illness and health.

PAUL E. JOHNSON, Ph.D., is Professor Emeritus of Psychology of Religion, Boston University, Boston, Massachusetts.

[1] Karen Horney, *Are You Considering Psychoanalysis?* New York: W. W. Norton & Company, 1946, p. 16.

These medical investigations are showing that the emotional tensions of fear, anger, guilt, frustrated desire, aversion are causing (1) gastrointestinal disturbances, such as peptic ulcer, loss or excess of appetite, indigestion, vomiting; (2) disturbances of eliminative functions, such as diarrhea, constipation, mucous colitis; (3) cardiovascular disturbances, such as high blood pressure (essential hypertension), pains, palpitations and irregular beats of the heart; (4) respiratory disturbances, such as asthma, hay fever, laryngitis, chronic cough; (5) skin disturbances; (6) convulsions; (7) headache; (8) genito-urinary disturbances, such as enuresis, sexual frigidity, and impotence; and (9) endocrine disturbances, such as thyroid disorders, diabetes, and so forth.[2]

It is evident, then, that the health crisis we face today is deep-seated in the dynamic forces of the psychic life. Mental illness has reached a new high, with patients overcrowding mental hospitals. The rising tide of delinquency and crime, divorce and family problems, destructive rivalry and competition, industrial strife, racial tensions, and international conflict demonstrate the social aspects of our ill health. It is now clear that no social tensions can be solved without reducing the emotional tensions in the personalities who constitute society. To reach the causes of these disorders—personal, interpersonal, and intergroup—we must ask why people behave as they do. We must understand the motives that lead to expression and repression, to effective social action or to crippling emotional conflicts.

The causes of ill health are many. The cures are intricate and difficult. There is a growing recognition that illness is not cured in a closed physical system of diet, medication, and surgery. For the whole personality is involved and must be treated as a whole if health is to be attained. When keys are found to unlock emotional repressions and resolve distressing mental conflicts, then health is possible in a larger sense. Who will turn the keys to emotional health?

This is no time for rivalries for prestige and glory or disputes over jurisdiction. The struggle for power and superiority is one of the epidemic viruses of our civilization. It can only intensify our aggravations and hasten our common

[2] Leon J. Saul, "Physiological Effects of Emotional Tension," in *Personality and the Behavior Disorders*, J. McV. Hunt, ed., New York: The Ronald Press, 1944, Chap. 8. See also H. F. Dunbar, *Emotions and Bodily Changes*, 3rd ed., New York: Columbia University Press, 1946.

disaster. The medicine man has magnified mystery. The healers have belonged to one esoteric cult after another: the magician, the priest, the apothecary, the physician, the surgeon, the psychiatrist. Each has his awe-inspiring ritual, his followers, and his cures. But the healing arts are too complex and too interrelated for solitary isolation. Specialists are interdependent, and the more they specialize, the more they require cooperation if they are to cover the field of human needs. The modern clinic is a salutary pattern of cooperation, each specialist correlating his work with that of others.

To provide such cooperation, there is now emerging the health team. Every up-to-date hospital and health center is conducted on this cooperative basis of many specialists working together for the health and welfare of the patient. To the medical team of specialists in diagnosis and treatment—including physicians, surgeons, nurses, X-ray and laboratory technicians, electric and diathermic therapists—will be added psychiatrists, occupational therapists, social workers, clinical psychologists, group therapists, and chaplains.

During World War II, neuropsychiatric teams were organized by the Surgeon General's Office and utilized at all levels of the army in a wide variety of overseas and interior installations, such as hospitals; neurological centers; consultation, disciplinary, and rehabilitation units; and induction, redistribution, and separation centers. These teams consisted of a psychiatrist, a clinical psychologist, and a social worker. The neuropsychiatric team has the advantage of correlating the unique training and experience of specialists. It permits each member to use his most highly developed technical skills, while supplementing and confirming the other members in the largest service to the patient.[3]

The health team cannot be a closed circle of in-facing initiates with backs to the outside world; rather, it must be an open circle ready to welcome new workers and able to expand as new areas of useful cooperation are discovered. In such expanding health teams, there will be need for the pastoral psychologist to bring the resources of religion to the aid of mental health. The pastor who is thoroughly prepared in clinical psychology will be useful as an individual coun-

[3] M. L. Hutt, W. C. Menninger, and D. E. O'Keefe, "The Neuropsychiatric Team in the United States Army," *Mental Hygiene,* 31:103–19, Jan., 1947.

selor and also as a group therapist. These pastoral services may be provided at a hospital or a church, a home or an office, or wherever persons may meet for counseling or group fellowship. In every therapeutic service the pastor works through interpersonal relations rather than abstract ideas.

## PASTORAL COUNSELING

As a counselor, the pastor interviews the emotionally distressed. Not until a person is under stress does he seek counsel, and then he wants someone who will listen patiently, respond to his feelings honestly, and understand without condemnation. Sooner or later everyone needs such a counselor, and fortunate is he who finds one he can trust. Such a counselor may be found in one's own family or in a neighbor, teacher, physician, lawyer, and so on. But psychologically trained counselors who have responsive attitudes are few in number and not often accessible. The pastor who may be accessible is apt not to qualify in psychological understanding. For this reason theological schools are now introducing more instruction in pastoral psychology, and many ministers are entering hospitals for clinical training. The pastor who is qualified to do skillful counseling will have a busy practice when people find him equipped with resources to meet personal needs.

What does the pastoral counselor add to the health team? Does he have any values not offered by other counselors?

1. To those suffering from *guilt* the pastor offers the healing of confession and forgiveness. Guilt wounds self-respect and confidence, by deep feelings of condemnation, remorse, and unworthiness. Because sin is a religious teaching, the sufferer who is under religious judgment is not relieved until he makes confession and receives forgiveness from God and a religious authority who represents him.[4] A well-respected schoolmaster has long suffered from a compulsive neurosis rooted in deep-lying guilt and fear of divine wrath. His boyhood sins were minor, and later misdeeds imaginary, yet his life was confined in agony which did not yield after years of psychiatric treatment. A wise psychiatrist, therefore, referred him to a pastoral counselor to make con-

[4] L. J. Sherrill, *Guilt and Redemption*, Richmond: John Knox Press, 1945.

fession and receive forgiveness. When he was invited to view God as a forgiving Father rather than a stern Judge, he said, "If I had only been taught that when I was younger, how much suffering it would have saved me!"

2. To those suffering from *sorrow* the pastor offers the healing of grief. After the Cocoanut Grove fire, when Boston hospitals were crowded with victims, Dr. Erich Lindemann made a psychiatric study of 97 cases of severe grief. He found a syndrome of upset nervous system, deep sighs, loss of appetite, insomnia, excessive fatigue, intense distress, preoccupation with the deceased, loss of interest in other persons, guilt, hostile feelings, and dependence. In his treatment of grief, he found it necessary to review the events of the tragedy, talk over the details of life with the loved one, encourage weeping and expression of guilt, until the bereaved was able to accept the loss. Realizing that bereaved persons come to ministers oftener than to physicians, he has taken every occasion to educate ministers as to how to counsel such persons to find outlets for their grief and win release. The pastor has the religious sacraments and "strategies of solace" to comfort and bring courage to those who face death.[5]

3. To those suffering from *anxiety* and *fear*, the pastor offers increase of faith. While religious teachings may incite anxiety because of sin and fear of divine power, yet the dominant note of religious experience is faith. "Though he slay me, yet will I trust him." (Job 13:15) For to most believers religious faith is founded on God as a Sustainer of Values, who defends and upholds the good against the evil. The evils we fear and worry about become intolerable unless we can trust in a larger good that evil does not destroy.

How is this faith transferred from the counselor to the counselee? By contagious empathy far more than by words or arguments. Verbal efforts to cheer up and reassure anxieties demand a show of optimism that either represses or accentuates the fear by deepening the contrast. But a counselor who has genuine faith cannot hide it, for it is eloquent in every breath and posture. "This morning I have actually relaxed," said a neurotic patient to the counselor, "because your face is so calm." Not what we protest or even what we

[5] J. L. Liebman, *Peace of Mind,* New York: Simon and Schuster, 1946, pp. 105–33.

profess, but what we feel has most influence on other persons. Does one have to be religious to have confidence? The answer may be "No" until we realize that psychologically religion is faith, and faith is a religious attitude, a trust in some sustainer of value. Whoever has faith feels sustained, and that feeling of faith sustains others.

4. To those who suffer from *hostility* the pastor offers the spirit of love. A woman who has been unjustly disinherited of a large estate by divorce, death, and legal chicanery comes every week to the clinic, but gains no relief from a choking cough that prevents speaking or breathing comfortably.

"Have you ever heard the phrase *choking with anger?*" she was asked.

"Yes," she replied bitterly to the counselor, "that is just my condition, but I will never forgive and I will never give up fighting to get my money."

Anger must be cured before illness can be cured.

A young mother came to the same clinic with her 3½-year-old daughter, who has vomited after meals since birth. The mother admitted that she had not wanted the baby, because during pregnancy she had quarreled with her husband, with his family, and with her own family. What with feeding difficulties and the vomiting, she had become so disgusted that she had continued to resent and reject the daughter. After counseling, the mother was able to be more affectionate to the daughter and the vomiting ceased.

Karen Horney, the psychiatrist, points to lack of affection as the major cause of neurotic and delinquent tendencies.[6] Christianity holds love highest of all values and demonstrates the power of a beloved community. Yet every individual needs to discover love for himself, and learn to love by being loved. "We love him because he first loved us." (I John 4:19) And as in faith so in love, words are not enough. The transforming power of love is a transfer of attitudes, by the contagious empathy of genuine interest in and affection toward another. This is what the psychotherapists call "relationship therapy," a deepening sense of comradeship that releases defensive repressions, as it heals hostility and isolation.

[6] Karen Horney, *The Neurotic Personality of Our Time,* New York: W. W. Norton & Company, 1937, pp. 79–80.

**GROUP THERAPY**

Group therapy was started in 1905 by Dr. Joseph H. Pratt as a class method of treating tuberculosis patients in Boston. About the same time (1908), Jacob L. Moreno in Vienna initiated psychodrama as spontaneous stage plays produced by juveniles to act out their own problems. In 1911 he formed self-help groups among prostitutes and in 1916 among displaced war refugees. Bringing these ideas to America in 1927, he started a "therapeutic theater" for mental patients, and sociometric groupings at the New York State Training School for Girls. In 1930 Dr. Pratt launched group therapy at the Boston Dispensary for psychoneurotic patients referred from the medical clinic because of painful symptoms without apparent organic cause. These classes have continued to the present time with marked success in restoring a large percentage of patients to health. Other medical centers, mental hospitals, and penal and social agencies, as well as the United States Army, have introduced group psychotherapy.[7]

At the Boston Dispensary Dr. Pratt has made effective use of the health team. This team includes the physicians of the medical clinic, the psychiatrists of the nerve clinic, social workers, and religious psychologists. The first secretary of the Thought Control Class (as the patients named it) was a social worker, Miss Edith Canterbury. The religious psychologist, until his retirement in 1946, was Winfred Rhoades. He assisted Dr. Pratt in the Thursday morning class, and for many years conducted a Monday evening class in the same way. In collaboration with Dr. Rose Hilferding, a medical psychologist, he has interviewed over 4,000 patients, adding counseling to group treatment. His lectures to the classes have appeared in numerous books that have a wide reading.

Since Mr. Rhoades's retirement, the author of this chapter has succeeded him in conducting the classes. Advanced students, candidates for the Ph.D. degree at Boston University in psychology of religion, are as welcome at the Boston Dispensary as medical students, as they assist in the group therapy and the interviewing. Other students in pastoral psychology assist in group therapy at Boston Psycho-

[7] J. W. Klapman, *Group Psychotherapy,* New York: Grune and Stratton, 1946; J. L. Moreno, ed., *Group Psychotherapy,* New York: Beacon House, 1945; and S. R. Slavson, *An Introduction to Group Therapy,* New York: The Commonwealth Fund, 1944.

pathic Hospital, in recreation, occupational therapy, and sociometric studies of interpersonal relations of patients.

What does group therapy do for mental health? It is generally recognized that neurotic and psychotic patients are disturbed in their interpersonal relationships. Their emotional distresses reflect anxiety or failure in getting along with other persons. Individual psychotherapy establishes a good relationship with the counselor. Group psychotherapy can develop better relations with many persons and thereby enlarge the patient's freedom to enjoy and activate his social adjustment. Class methods provide group instruction, but are apt to be formal unless lectures provoke active discussion among the patients. Spontaneous interpersonal action is the aim of psychodrama and sociometry, with release of repressions, reenactment of conflicts, and growth through dynamic interplay of personalities upon one another.

To be more specific, there are five unsocial tendencies that group therapy aims to correct by inviting interpersonal activity:

1. *Timidity* needs social skills, to be learned in doing things with other persons.
2. *Isolation* needs social response, to be had in conversation, play, and work with others.
3. *Egocentricity* needs social participation, to be gained in feeling the belongingness of membership in a group.
4. *Inferiority* needs social leadership, to be developed in taking responsibility for others.
5. *Aggressiveness* needs social balance, to be won by interest in and appreciation of other persons in the group.

How does religion come into such group therapy? Historically every religious leader has drawn together a circle of disciples who share deeply and walk together in a common life. Every religion has formed communities, and the closest knit communities have usually been communal religious groups. Monasteries are social organisms; religious orders are brotherhoods; churches, synagogues, temples, and mosques are centers of unifying fellowship. Great religions seek a universal community where all may dwell together as one family of earth under benevolent heaven. Dr. J. L. Moreno recognizes this therapeutic value of the religious group:

> Christianity can be looked at as the greatest and most ingenious psychotherapeutic procedure man has ever invented, compared with which medical psychotherapy has been of practically negligible effect. It can be said that the goal of Christianity was from its very beginnings the treatment of the whole of mankind and not of this or that individual and not of this or that group of people.[8]

Dr. Pratt has noted the similarity of his group-therapy class to the religious class or prayer meeting in the evangelical churches of the past century. His roll call recognizes each member as worthy of special attention; the period of relaxation is similar to a season of prayer; his reports of progress are equivalent to the testimonies of religious growth; his inspirational talks are aimed at emotional response as is the sermon or the religious talk. He encourages ministers to employ his methods of group therapy in church groups to improve the emotional health of the members. Christian Science has had a remarkable growth by using similar methods to meet health needs. But the emphasis in the Protestant churches and in the Federal Council of Churches is on the cooperation of religious therapists with medical therapists. Whether in the Emanuel movement of an earlier day; or in the church clinic as in some New York churches; or in pastoral counseling centers as at Hennepin Avenue Church in Minneapolis and the Cathedral Church of Saint Paul in Boston; or in many hospitals where chaplains work with the physicians, psychiatrists, and social workers—the aim in all these services is to form a health team to bring all possible healing resources to the patient.

### THE HEALTH RESOURCES OF RELIGION

There are some who do not welcome the religious therapist to the health team. They sincerely believe with Marx that religion is an opiate, or with Freud that it is an illusion that offers escape rather than reality. We do not intend to debate here the logical fallacies in such a position, as H. Crichton-Miller does in a recent article.[9] The relation of

[8] J. L. Moreno, *Who Shall Survive?* Washington, D.C.: Nervous and Mental Diseases Publishing Company, 1934, p. 4.

[9] H. Crichton-Miller, "The Value of an Illusion," *Mental Hygiene,* 31:38–49, Jan., 1947.

religion to health is a pragmatic question of what are the consequences. When Jung declares his experience of healing in the following terms, he is simply reporting the results as he observed them:

> Among all my patients in the second half of life—that is to say, over thirty-five—there has not been one whose problem in the last resort was not that of finding a religious outlook on life. It is safe to say that every one fell ill because he had lost that which the living religions of every age have given to their followers, and none of them has been really healed who did not regain his religious outlook.[10]

To the health worker, the use of religious therapy will likewise depend not on theoretical but on practical considerations. If religion helps make sick people well, and well people better, then religion will be worth trying. For we leave no stone unturned, and no useful health agent neglected in our desire to extend health more abundantly to all. The increasing number of chaplains in hospitals, the reference of patients by physicians, psychiatrists, and social workers to pastors are some indications that religion can play a useful role in the health program.[11] Of course much depends upon that pastor. If he is crude, dogmatic, arrogant, or foolish, he can do more harm than good. And this is likewise true of the physician or of any other health worker. The wise selection and adequate training of each health worker is the answer to this dilemma. When the pastor is well qualified by temperament, understanding, and skill, he proves to be a useful member of the health team. For he brings unique values to the healing process not otherwise present.

What are the health resources of religion? It is significant that *health* and *holy* are derived from the same root in many languages, meaning "whole." The religious goal is identical with the goal of healing—to make men whole. Religious experience is deeply embedded in the emotional life, and when truly oriented it permeates the attitudes that are conducive to health. These are some of the healthy attitudes that rise in the creative power of religious experiences: (1) the sense of personal worth; (2) trust in the ultimate victory

[10] C. G. Jung, *Modern Man in Search of a Soul,* New York: Harcourt, Brace and Company, 1933, p. 264.

[11] H. P. Schultz, *Report on the Clergy-Physician Relationship in Protestant Hospitals,* Evansville, Ind.: American Protestant Hospital Association, 1942.

of good over evil; (3) membership in a communal fellowship; (4) the support of invisible yet constant companionship; (5) confession and forgiveness; (6) the urging and guiding of growth; (7) the aspiration and dedication of worship; and (8) the discipline or way of life.[12]

When a twenty-one-year-old college girl was admitted to a mental hospital, she presented a picture of violent, undiscriminating fury with extreme combativeness and negativism. During the course of six weeks she progressed under psychotherapy and group therapy sufficiently to be discharged. Because she was oriented to religious ideas of perfection and divine guidance, she was referred to a religious psychologist at the hospital. Five interviews were held, during which she told of her childhood as the second of eight children, and her painful sense of rejection, humiliation, and loneliness because of her feelings of inferiority and isolation. On several occasions after graduation from high school, she had left home on compulsions that God was leading her and she must follow. She had always been afraid of people, but after a conversion experience, she felt much closer to people.

The release through confession, the tracing of new insights out of her confusion, the analysis of motives for her behavior, and the planning of next steps to take gave her a better perspective. She came to see the need of relating her religious experience to her social responsibilities, and to consider impulses in the light of what is the most reasonable thing to do. She recognized her need of growth, rather than of perfection, of social life rather than of seclusion, of religious deeds of unselfish kindness rather than moments of ecstasy. She became interested in making gifts for her parents, in choosing stories to read her younger sisters, and in cooking food the family at home would enjoy. When she returned home, she was preparing to let God lead her toward people rather than away from them and to take her place in religious and social groups as she had not before. She seemed to find some of the health values noted above, and a year later the hospital received a good report of her continuing progress.

How are these religious resources open to persons in quest of health and wholeness? Not by rigid dogmatisms or set forms, not by verbal reassurance or persuasion, not by moral advice or traditional authority, for all these are external and coercive pressures that have blocked the contagion of the religious spirit. Rather do we find religious influence moving by psychological energies through other channels. Among these psychological channels are: (1) empathy and

[12] Paul E. Johnson, *Psychology of Religion*, New York: Abingdon-Cokesbury Press, 1945, pp. 240–44; Seward Hiltner, "The Contribution of Religion to Mental Hygiene," *Mental Hygiene*, 24:366–77, July, 1940; and Milton E. Kirkpatrick, "Mental Hygiene and Religion," *Mental Hygiene*, 24:378–89, July, 1940.

example; (2) fellowship and sharing; (3) learning by doing together; (4) growing in unselfish service; (5) faithful practice of ideal principles; and (6) prayers of gratitude and trust to heal anxiety and guilt.

Miracles of religious healing occur whenever psychological conditions warrant them. Whether such miracles are supernatural, let theologians debate. To our empirical view, we can at least say that they are miracles of interpersonal relations. When a person radiates the religious attitudes of faith, hope, and love, he may become a therapist to those who feel the same attitudes responding in them. The action of these spiritual energies is psychological. They offer effective resources for mental health.

# 4

## Mental Health: A Generic Attitude

*Gordon W. Allport*

THE WHOLE of my argument can be summed up in three stories—all of them true.

In a provincial Austrian hospital, a man lay gravely ill—in fact, at death's door. The medical staff had told him frankly that they could not diagnose his disease, but that if they knew the diagnosis they could probably cure him. They told him further that a famous diagnostician was soon to visit the hospital and that perhaps he could spot the trouble.

Within a few days the diagnostician arrived and proceeded to make the rounds. Coming to this man's bed, he merely glanced at the patient, murmured "Moribundus," and went on.

Some years later, the patient called on the diagnostician

GORDON W. ALLPORT, Ph.D., is Professor, Department of Social Relations, Harvard University, Cambridge, Massachusetts.

and said, "I've been wanting to thank you for your diagnosis. They told me that if you could diagnose me I'd get well, and so the minute you said 'moribundus' I knew I'd recover."

According to this story, even life itself may hang upon an attitude and an expectation.

My second story: a psychiatrist friend of mine—a believer in conditioned reflex therapy—tells of an alcoholic woman patient. To remove her appetite by the conditioning method, he placed a glass of whiskey in front of her while he administered a powerful emetic. Before long she learned to vomit whenever she smelled liquor. Needless to say, her consumption of alcohol completely ceased. Up to this point in the story we would say that a specific conditioning technique was ingeniously successful. Unfortunately, this therapy was her undoing. For whenever a salesman came to the door, or even her bosom friends, smelling (as many of them did) of alcohol, she straightway threw up on her visitors.

Curing the habit mechanically all by itself did not rehabilitate her. The cure was not set in the context of her total life.

The third story, with a rather brighter outcome, concerns a very small boy, an obsessive thumb-sucker. Every known method of reward and punishment—and reward and punishment are the be-all, end-all, and cure-all of therapy based on currently fashionable learning theory—such as tying the thumb, soaking it in bitter aloes, slapping, candy-giving and candy-withholding—all were tried, but to no effect. The habit grew firmer, and by the age of six the lad was a public spectacle.

One bright day he stopped his thumb-sucking completely. When the astonished parents dared to inquire why the ingrained habit had been so abruptly broken, the child replied simply, "Big boys don't suck their thumbs."

Somehow, somewhere, this generic idea had got through to him, and the specific compulsion vanished. The lad was cured.

## THERAPIES: PARTICULARISTIC AND GENERIC

In different ways, these three stories all bear upon our problem. What is the problem? Simply this: How in the helping professions—and here I include psychiatry, the ministry, social work, applied psychology, and education—can we recover some of the common sense that we seem to have lost along the way? What has happened historically, I believe, is this: During the nineteenth century, the social and psychological and medical sciences found themselves unable to handle the whole vast complex of mental and social life. Therefore, in imitation of natural sciences, they set out to solve one small problem at a time. Events have causes, and so the logical thing is to focus upon a specific pathological event, find its cause and remove it. The successes of Jenner, Lister, and Pasteur were vastly impressive. Their example seemed well worth following in the field of mental illness.

The conviction that man's psyche is secondary to his soma became set. The brain, of course, is a physiological organ. If you change this organ through drugs, conditioning, or even hypnosis, you change a man's attitudes and actions. The image of materia medica and surgery were dominant. John Whitehorn has called it the "pseudo-surgical formulation in psychotherapy."[1]

At the present time in the treatment of mental disorder and mental retardation, it is still fashionable, indeed more fashionable than ever, to administer all sorts of miracle drugs. Pharmacotherapy is an instance of specific therapy, based on a biochemical view of mental disorder. That such treatment often has favorable effects cannot be denied. Yet an observant nurse in a nearby clinic said to me, "Giving drugs without giving love is of no lasting benefit at all. The patient still has his problems; he still is frightened and insecure; he still feels isolated, rejected, forsaken by God and man."

And speaking of drugs, the baffling problem of addiction illustrates the point. In spite of his suffering, an addict generally returns to drugs after release from prison or from hospital. Even psychotherapy, it is said, helps only from 3 to 17 per cent of the cases. "The addict 'solves' all his problems with the pill, the potion, the smoke or the needle."[2] To do so is a way of life, a way common to between 25,000 and 40,000 persons, mostly youth, in New York City alone. These unhappy persons are victims of a generic attitude that might

[1] John C. Whitehorn, "Types of Leadership Involved in Psychotherapy," *American Journal of Psychotherapy,* 16:366–78, 1962.

[2] E. M. Brown, "The Juvenile Narcotic Addict: A Profile," *The Pastoral Counselor,* 1:26–30, 1963.

be called "magical thinking." E. M. Brown characterizes this generic attitude as one that considers the concrete moment to be the only reality, subjective reality to be more important than external reality, and the person's point of view to be absolute and unconditional. The addict must feel himself to be omnipotent. Frustration, loneliness, alienation send him to dope. His addiction is a way of life. Only a total change of outlook can be therapeutic, and admittedly a total change of outlook is very hard to achieve.

In spite of its frequent failures, the particularistic pseudo-surgical approach is in favor. The nineteenth-century scientific outlook still prompts us to seek specific causes for specific effects. The result is an array of theories, concepts, and techniques that arouse scientific fervor—while they last. I have in mind such fashionable concepts as *biochemical imbalance, conditioning, reinforcement, milieu therapy, hypnoanalysis, tension reduction, homeostasis, somatotype, cybernetics, neurological block, cognitive dissonance, stimulus-response,* and certain popular principles of psychoanalysis, such as *transference, Oedipal conflict, oral regression, identity diffusion,* and a vast array of similar conceptual enthusiasms. None of these approaches can be declared wholly erroneous; but they are all partial, some to the point of triviality. Each calls attention to some limited way in which some organisms may react some of the time; but their proponents often imply that their favored theory explains far more than it does.

Note the popularity of the term "organism." This label reflects the impersonal, biological, deterministic outlook of the particularistic investigator. Theorists addicted to partial doctrines seldom speak of the human subject as a man, a woman, an individual, a person—certainly not as a soul.

The theoretical issue, however, is not the truth or falsity of any particular formulation for some particular occasion. The question is rather, *Where do the primary dynamics of a human life lie?* Shall we say that our patient suffers from biochemical imbalance, or from an intolerable loss of self-respect? Both statements may be true; but to science, it seems more objective, less animistic and mystical, to attack the problem at the biochemical level where cause and effect are easier to perceive.

Dr. John Whitehorn tells of his own experience in this

regard. Trained in his laboratory courses to seek specific natural causes for specific effects, he engaged in biochemical researches on schizophrenia. While making his experimental injections, he discovered that his conversations with the patients seemed to do them much more good than did his glucose and sodium acid phosphate. He also discovered that a ubiquitous theme ran through the minds of the patients: a fear of being submitted to coercive influence. They were struggling for integrity in their own way, and were frightened by outside influence.

Yet, as Whitehorn observes, a psychiatrist does inevitably influence his patient; his role demands that he be a leader. And so gradually Whitehorn tested various styles of leadership among psychiatrists and discovered that what he called an "evocative" leadership (a responding, encouraging, sympathetic manner) was more effective than either a directive or passively consultative leadership in bringing about improvement in schizophrenia.[3]

When scientific dogma alone rules the roost, a curious caste system develops, with the patient on the bottom. He alone is not informed, not responsible, not free, and not wise. Just how a patient is to regain these attributes of health when his therapist and even the attendants are supposed to be superior in scientific wisdom is not clear. This sort of condescension is, I suspect, the chief obstacle to cure.

Not all therapists, to be sure, entrench themselves behind their particularistic wisdom. Many of them employ evocative leadership, and in so doing are rediscovering an important chapter in the history of psychiatry. A hundred and fifty years ago, Phillippe Pinel evolved a revolutionary approach to mental illness, which has been called "moral treatment" (although it would be more accurate to retain Pinel's term "morale"). It was a program of planned rehabilitation in a positive, sympathetic, social milieu marked by friendly association, discussion of difficulties, a busy day of occupational work in a family-like environment, during all of which activity the patient was to be treated as a normal person so that he might retain or regain his self-respect. Recently Dr. J. Sanbourne Bockoven has written up this forgotten period of the history of psychiatry. In America, model hospitals employing moral treatment were the Worcester

[3] Whitehorn.

State Hospital in Massachusetts and the Hartford Retreat in Connecticut. In these and other hospitals, compassion had replaced restraint and custody, and the recovery rates, according to Bockoven's analysis, were surprisingly high.[4]

Around 1860, the viewpoint of physical medicine became dominant. Treatment was considered best if it rested on a physical theory. Psychological sensitivity and insight that marked moral treatment were dismissed as mystical, sentimental, and unscientific. Neurological societies ruled out papers dealing with psychological factors in mental illness. And the recovery rate began to go down, reaching its lowest point between 1923 and 1950. Chronic and incurable cases piled up. Although outpatient clinics were being added and the method of keeping statistics was changing, on the whole it seems probable that the success of the earlier moral treatment (what I would like to call "attitudinal therapy") was greater than the success of our more recent scientific and particularistic methods.[5]

Now the cycle is changing again. Pinel and moral treatment are slowly returning to favor. The concept of science is gradually broadening, and within the framework of a broadened science, evidence is accumulating concerning the reasons for the success of the earlier moral treatment. Let me cite one study.

A few years ago, a student of Carl Rogers chose to study factors that would predict the successful reform of juvenile delinquents. The question was, Which factors among many studied in a group of 75 boys would spot the lads who would pull out and be rehabilitated? Possible factors included, of course, the quality of the boy's neighborhood, his parents' attitudes, his friendships, his physique, his past record, his social class, his school adjustments, and a variety of environmental stresses—now fashionably lumped together under the label "psychosocial epidemiology." It turned out that while some of these factors had some predictive power, by far the most important was the degree of self-understanding that the lad displayed concerning his situation. Later, Rogers replicated this finding.[6] And still more recently, Dr. B. R.

[4] J. S. Bockoven, *Moral Treatment in American Psychiatry,* New York: Springer Publishing Co., 1963.

[5] Cf. H. B. Adams, " 'Mental Illness' or Interpersonal Behavior?" *American Psychologist,* 19:191–97, 1964.

[6] C. R. Rogers, "Toward a Science of the Person," in T. W. Wann, ed., *Behaviorism and Phenomenology,* Chicago: University of Chicago Press, 1964, p. 125.

Hutcheson discovered a similar fact: that if a boy regards his antisocial acts as normal, ordinary, natural, the outlook for reform is bad indeed. If on the other hand his attitude toward his misconduct shows that to him it is unnatural and repugnant, he is likely to reform.[7] The generic attitude is of major importance.

### GENERIC ATTITUDES

What do we mean by "generic attitude"? Let me offer a few examples.

President Lowell of Harvard was once asked how he managed to make so many important decisions during a single day of his busy life. He replied in effect, "Oh, it is not too difficult. There are only a few—perhaps half a dozen—principal standards of value by which I make my judgments. Almost every decision fits one of these broad categories."

In trying to classify her patients, Karen Horney found it helpful to distinguish three generic social attitudes: (1) approaching people; (2) avoiding people; (3) being antagonistic or hostile toward people. Each patient, she felt, could be known by the characteristic way in which his social conduct fitted one of these attitudes. Perhaps her typology is too coarse, but the point is there: each of us has a general schema or attitude of our own that selects or "gates" our responses to people.

Even laboratory researches show the pervasive influence of social schemata. Some people are so broadly affiliative that they use many adjectives in describing people, and when rearranging figurines of people they place them closer together than they were in the original arrangement.[8] Thus it is that general schemata guide specific conduct in specific situations. Some years ago, Cantril demonstrated the same primacy that marks generic attitudes in directing activities and in shaping detailed beliefs.[9]

Up to now, I regret to say, neither psychology nor psychiatry, nor for that matter neural physiology, has reached an adequate level of knowledge concerning the nature and

[7] B. R. Hutcheson, *A Prognostic Classification for Juvenile Court First Offenders, Based on a Follow-up Study,* Quincy, Mass.: South Shore Mental Health Center, 1963.

[8] J. L. Kuethe, "Pervasive Influence of Social Schemata," *Journal of Abnormal and Social Psychology,* 68:248–54, 1964.

[9] Hadley Cantril, "General and Specific Attitudes," *Psychological Monographs,* No. 192, 1932.

operation of generalized mental sets. Some slight progress, however, is being made. Neurophysiologists are recognizing the selective or gating force that complex mental attitudes exert upon specific behavioral functions. Hebb, for example, traces this steering influence to what he calls "autonomous central processes" and "central motive states."[10]

Let us take the topic of ethnic prejudice. In most people, ethnic prejudice—or its opposite, tolerance—we now know, is a generalized attitude. That is to say, if John has antipathy toward Negroes, he is almost certain to have antipathy toward Jews, Mexicans, Orientals, Catholics (or Protestants)—almost any group of which he is not himself a member. Correspondingly, if he is tolerant toward one he is almost certainly tolerant toward all.[11]

Let me relate this finding (confirmed by many researches) to the problem of a generalized religious orientation—a topic I have recently been investigating. It is a disturbing finding (but again confirmed by many researches) that, on the average, churchgoers are more bigoted toward minority groups than nonchurchgoers. Our first reaction to this finding is to say, "But that can't be true. Look at the leaders of the civil rights movement; most of them seem to be religiously motivated. One thinks of Gandhi, Father John La Farge, the Reverend Martin Luther King, and many others." We are forced to conclude: if most churchgoers are more bigoted, but if some churchgoers are more tolerant, then there must be a vast difference in the type of religious orientation that people may hold. And such turns out to be the case.

Our research (not yet fully published) shows that churchgoers high in ethnic prejudice tend, on the whole, to have what I have called an extrinsic religious orientation. Extrinsic religion is something to *use* but not to *live*. The extrinsically religious person turns to God, but does not turn away from self. This type of religion is a shield for self-centeredness.[12]

Individuals of this type, it turns out, ordinarily are only

[10] D. O. Hebb, *The Organization of Behavior,* New York: John Wiley & Sons, 1949.

[11] G. W. Allport, *The Nature of Prejudice,* Reading, Mass.: Addison-Wesley Publishing Co., Inc., 1954, Chap. 5.

[12] G. W. Allport, "Behavioral Science, Religion, and Mental Health," *Journal of Religion and Health,* 2:193 ff, 1963.

occasional attenders at church. They are not truly devout. Their religion is a matter of convenience. Some of them, as the saying goes, attend church only thrice: when they are hatched, when matched, and when dispatched. Not surprisingly, it is this type of religion that correlates with high ethnic prejudice.

By contrast, intrinsic religion is not instrumental. It is not a means of handling fear, a mode of sociability and conformity, a sublimation of sex, or a wish-fulfillment. All these motives are somehow subordinated to an overarching motive. One's ethnic relations, one's domestic life, one's quandaries, guilt, and ultimate ontological anxiety are all handled under a comprehensive commitment, partly intellectual but more fundamentally motivational. It is a unifying orientation. Such religion does not exist to serve the person; rather the person is committed to serve it.

It is not surprising that people with this type of generic attitude are tolerant and compassionate toward fellow-mortals.

While I have spoken of these types of religious orientation in relation to prejudice, I feel equally sure that mental health is facilitated by an intrinsic, but not by an extrinsic, religious orientation.

An additional example of generic attitudes is from a recent book by Father John Clifford that sets forth his own strategy for withstanding Chinese communist brain-washers.[13] His points are equally relevant to the strategy by which we ourselves withstand pressures that endanger our mental health: (1) a resolve to be unremittingly and yet passively uncooperative with evil influences; (2) a continual restatement of the positive values and beliefs of one's own life; (3) active planning of counter-strategy; (4) retaining a sense of humor, particularly about the antics and strategems of the captors; (5) remembering that specific indignities are only part of a broader program, and what one does in a given case cannot always affect the final outcome.

Father Clifford's rule that one should continually restate one's positive values and beliefs approaches the heart of the matter. Martin Buber makes the point in a broader way.

[13] John W. Clifford, *In the Presence of My Enemies,* New York: W. W. Norton & Company, 1963.

He writes, "As a condition of the individual soul evil is the convulsive shirking of direction. . . ."[14]

It is not easy for a counselor to know what a given person's own proper "direction" is, or should be; nor is it easy to help him control his characteristic "convulsive shirking." Yet the psychology of the matter is clear: evil is best controlled by affirming and strengthening the generic direction of the life. It is less a matter of specific bad habits or the violation of specific rules, and more a matter of maintaining total orientation. Christ, we recall, worried less about specific legalisms than about pride, self-centeredness, and hypocrisy. His generic formula for mental health and for righteousness was drawn from the Old Testament—to love the Lord God with all one's heart and soul and mind; and to love one's neighbor as oneself.

At the concrete level, we can learn something, I think, from the devices that healthy people use to maintain their "orientation of the soul." Father Clifford's maxims are an example. Some people resort to simple mottoes that distill for them an area of generic wisdom. A hard-working public servant of my acquaintance tells me that his whole life is guided by his generic belief that "if everyone works as hard as he can, and takes only what he and his family need, then there will be just enough to go around." A lovely lady said that her life was pretty much guided by her conviction that she had no right to poison the air that other people have to breathe. She never whined, complained, or gossiped. Many find mottoes in the Scriptures: perhaps, "Be still and know that I am God," or Job's total orientation, "Though he slay me, yet will I trust him." Needless to say, what is effective in one life is not necessarily effective in another; but the principle of discovering and holding fast to one direction is the first law of mental health.

## ROLE OF THE RELIGIOUS COUNSELOR

When we emphasize the importance of man's total orientation, we approach at long last the role of the religious counselor, for this is his specialty.

The aim of attitudinal therapy is to free the individual

[14] Martin Buber, *Between Man and Man,* Boston: Beacon Press, 1959, p. 78.

so that he may know himself—his values, his chosen direction, and his total orientation toward life. Within this context, he has to find a place for his current suffering. No other person has the same context, and no one else has the same problems. It is within this frame of uniqueness that the minister begins his difficult task. Since I am not a pastoral counselor, I cannot speak from experience. Yet a few aspects of the minister's job strike me as especially noteworthy.

For one thing, I believe the advancement of mental health involves a paradox: the tie that binds serious attitudinal orientation with humor. So many tangles in life are ultimately hopeless that we have no appropriate sword other than laughter. I venture to say that no person is in good health unless he can laugh at himself quietly and privately, noticing where he has overreached, where his pretensions have been overblown or pedantic. He needs to note where he has been hoodwinked, too sure of himself, too short-sighted, and above all too conceited. The specific remedy for vanity, says Bergson, is laughter, and the one essentially laughable failing is vanity.

Yet there is an end to laughter. A mature person needs also a guiding philosophy of life. I do not mean that he must be highly articulate about his world view. He need not be a Heidegger, about whom it was said that he wrote his German philosophy in two volumes, the second volume of which contained the verbs.

We hear much nowadays about the tragedy of meaninglessness. Frankl has identified the corresponding neurosis, which he calls "noogenic."[15] I myself believe that this state of vacancy—the "existential vacuum"—is primarily an affliction of the sophisticated and educated (or miseducated) man. In fact, I suspect that existentialism, for all its insights, is pretty much a philosophy written by and for egg-heads. Yet, in many patients, the condition of "existential vacuum" does exist, and the clergy and other therapists have to deal with it. In his pride, the sufferer claims that everything is illusion. He is neither a pilgrim nor even a tourist in life, but only a wanderer.

Here fall the clergy's duty and opportunity. Young people may have to go through a period of vacancy, of rebellion, and of disintoxication with life. I am thinking of the

[15] V. E. Frankl, *Man's Search for Meaning,* Boston: Beacon Press, 1963.

coed who said, beamingly, "I cannot tell you how much I enjoy my existential despair." But what is appropriate for a brief time in late adolescence is no guide for maturity.

Whether we speak of existential vacuum or of total orientation, of generic attitude or of central motive state, the clergyman is a specialist where the scientist is still a fumbler. (*Please note:* In saying that the scientist is still a fumbler, I have in mind psychological research and theory, not necessarily the daily practice of psychiatrists or of clinical psychologists. Many of the latter know from experience the patient's need for a constructive world view; many are respectful toward the religious orientation that constitutes a potential curative direction for a given patient's life. My complaint is rather that the intellectual foundations of the therapeutic professions have not yet been made consistent with the best in therapeutic practice.)

It is probable that the sufferer who comes to the clergyman has some religious ideas to start with. Hence the task is to help him deepen and enlarge them, so that they more adequately embrace his present distress and groping. To employ my earlier terms, the task is to help him move from his relatively extrinsic religion to a mature, all-embracing, intrinsic religion. This, I submit, is the primary assignment of every religious counselor.

Along the way, of course, the counselor may have to bring the sufferer in contact with psychiatric facilities. He may have to interpret such facilities as potential agents of help, and not a seal of doom. But to send the patient to a clinic, a hospital, or a school for retarded children does not automatically solve the problem; in fact, it may increase the strain. No patient or parent can comfortably give up his integrity to a hospital ward or school, where he encounters an array of impersonal treatments—electroconvulsive, hypnotic, pharmacological, or psychotherapeutic—without wanting to put them into perspective. To hand over responsibility to doctors, nurses, psychologists—however skillful they may be—is to surrender one's vital liberty. What the sufferer craves is to be comforted in his extremity, to feel that the spirit of the universe understands his predicament and accepts him. "Is there a place for me, a helpless failure?" This is what he wants to know.

Boisen reports that among sufferers in mental hospitals

religion is seldom an escape from reality. It is much more closely related to the texture of life, and insofar as it brings meaning to the suffering it is a potential asset. But to confront the totality of the patient's distress, his religion must be adequately comprehensive and integrative. For example, as Boisen insists, it is relatively worthless unless it can embrace in some meaningful way the patient's conflicts in the sexual sphere—not in terms of conventional prudery, but in a widely meaningful and integrative way.[16]

One psychiatrist has said that the sense of sin is the chief lesion found in mental illness. If this be true, the clergyman has a clear duty, for the poor psychiatrist and psychologist are ordinarily baffled by sin. More often than not, they view it as they might view an outgrown vermiform appendix—something that ought to be removed by a psychoanalytic scalpel. Here is one place where the minister has a more balanced wisdom. While there is a neurotic type of guilt, there is also in most people a deep sense of their own persistent, sinful, convulsive shirking. William James complained that modern Protestantism does not avail itself of sacramental confession often enough. I think he was right. Except in the Catholic tradition, we seem unready even for private sacramental penance under the seal of secrecy, let alone the open type of social confession advocated by Hobart Mowrer.[17]

The average clergyman has an additional advantage over the psychiatrist in that he is unlikely to close his ears to the religious ideas of a disturbed person. Provided that he does not grow argumentative or angered, he can listen with respect to what may be bizarre religious conceptions. Many patients complain that their therapists never inquire concerning the religious aspects of their turmoil, even though they themselves regard religious issues as central to their distress. Insofar as this is true, the therapist's neglect may sometimes come from his own lack of personal religion; but more often it is the result of his habituation to the grammar of science. He is accustomed to applying the stencils of particularistic theory and the stencils of particularistic treat-

[16] A. T. Boisen, *The Exploration of the Inner World,* New York: Harper & Bros., 1936.

[17] O. H. Mowrer, *The Crisis in Psychiatry and Religion,* Princeton, N.J.: D. Van Nostrand Co., 1961.

ment. In so doing, he may fail to recognize the power of healing that lies in generic faith.

I have been saying that the average clergyman in an average community has several advantages in the relief of distress that comes with mental ill health or into families where mental retardation has struck. He is inclined to view each individual as unique and important, not as an "organism" to which stenciled theories of therapy are applied. He knows that at heart most people (at least most sufferers) have deep religious concerns, and he is by training a specialist in the area of their concern. He can be attentive and intelligent in listening to the mixed-up religious ideas of sufferers and in urging them toward more constructive thinking. He has, or can have, an authoritative method of dealing with the sense of sin. In his heart he believes that an integrative and intrinsic religious outlook is health-giving, and with this basic faith he can go even further in attitudinal therapy than did "moral treatment" a century ago. He can perhaps increase its rate of success.

Of course, there are pitfalls along the way. One is the danger that a minister may exacerbate a disturbed condition by stressing aspects of religion that are pathogenic for a given individual. He may arouse pathological feelings of guilt, an abnormal degree of anxiety, or encourage some futile compulsive ritual. Or conversely, he may offer nothing but spiritual lozenges that are momentarily pleasant but in the long run ineffective.

Another obvious pitfall often pointed out is the danger that a little knowledge of psychiatry or psychoanalysis may tempt the clergyman to abandon his special function and become a second-string psychiatrist.

A more subtle pitfall—one that teachers fall into as well as clergymen—is to throw some solution at the sufferer in one verbal chunk. Any skillful teacher knows that he cannot present his student with a neat, well-formulated conclusion, no matter how many years of experience and labor lie behind it, and expect the student to assimilate it. The student hears what you say, but is unable to digest it.

I recall a case where a counselor prematurely offered advice. He said to his client, "Well, you know that's life. That's the way it is; you have to accept things like that." This bit of summary wisdom at the time fell on deaf ears.

The therapy continued for some months, eventually making good progress. Just before its termination, the patient summed up his hard-won wisdom in the same words: "Well, you know that's life. That's the way things are. You have to accept them." The same words—but with a world of difference.

Change in attitudes comes about only through experience, not through prefabricated and second-hand solutions presented by clergy, teachers, or therapists.[18]

Now these and other pitfalls can greatly reduce a minister's effectiveness and may even damage the sufferer who comes to him for help. (In honesty I must add that other therapists have been known to bring damage rather than help.)

What is needed is training and more training. While many seminaries, of course, are laying good foundations, the need is a continuing one. Especially at this time, the average clergyman in the average community needs to have the whole problem laid before him step by step. The community's health resources should be explained; even more, the relation between the two logics of science and of religion. Training in the techniques of human relations (including the art of listening), theories of personality (including the common forms of mental distress), the place of religion in attitudinal therapy—all are part of the needed curriculum of continuous training. It is encouraging to know that a movement in this direction is now under way.

The main purpose of religion, I repeat, is not to make people healthy but to help them fit themselves into the Creator's context for them. An adequate religion of this dimension serves incidentally to guard, maintain, and restore mental health. It casts out demons. The clergyman knows that a personality, to be sound and fully human, requires a guiding philosophy of life. I have called such a philosophy of life a "generic attitude." By the very nature of his calling, the minister himself is, or could become, a specialist in those generic attitudes that confer and maintain health of mind.

If I have stressed the role of the minister, it is not in order to disparage other helping professions. Many psychiatrists accomplish in practice a true cure of souls. I do, how-

[18] Cf. E. T. Gendlin, in P. Worchel and D. Byrne, eds., *Personality Change,* New York: John Wiley & Sons, 1964.

ever, wish to establish two points. The clergy as such have a valid and valuable part to play in therapy and guidance—a part that few of them (and few psychiatrists) fully understand. As a theorist, I feel that the intellectual foundations of psychiatry are not yet adequately developed. Too much is said of psychosurgical and particularistic factors and too little of the dynamics of the generic attitudes and assumptive worlds of the sufferer.

# 5

# The Impact of the Hospital Situation in Our Understanding of God and Man

*James B. Ashbrook*

### OUR PERSONAL INVOLVEMENT

ONE CANNOT be associated with a hospital without being confronted by the raw stuff of human existence. It is in this setting that the nature and destiny of man thrusts itself into one's consciousness: his sickness and health, his brokenness and wholeness, his sinfulness and salvation.

As long as life runs along smoothly, we can avoid facing the depths of existence. The basic questions of life can go unasked. Joyful abandon can characterize living. When things are comfortable and easy, we can live as though life were shallow. However, in moments when the contradictions

---

JAMES B. ASHBROOK, B.D., M.A., is Associate Professor of Pastoral Theology, Colgate Rochester Divinity School, Rochester, New York.

and crises of life stand forth, these [comfortable and easy things] become strangely irrelevant. The encounter with tragedy and human limitation disrupts surface appearances. We are forced to probe deeper than previously. What was complacently accepted about life must now be re-examined. Despite ourselves, there comes the necessity of participating in man's struggle to find meaning.

In making the rounds of a hospital, on every hand we run squarely into hurt bodies, injured spirits, and distorted relationships. The brokenness of total existence weighs in upon us:

> Sit with a man preparing for a duodenal ulcer operation and he says: "You know, when you get to be around 40 or 45 life begins to let down a little. You need something."

Here we catch the sense of emptiness and meaninglessness overpowering a human being at all levels of his life: physical, emotional, spiritual.

> In maternity there comes the excitement of new life, untold creative possibilities, a sense of mystery and awe at the great drama of creation. In orthopedics we confront the utterly helpless youngster stricken with polio. Here there comes the sense of stunted, distorted, unmerciful, cruel nature.

Here we catch the sense of the disturbing contradictions filling every moment of existence.

> Let a woman suffering with a thyroid growth aggravated by repressed hostility reveal: "There's something inside me that is keeping me from being well."

Here we catch the sense of "internal warfare" destroying a human being.

> Stop long enough for a young single girl diagnosed "incomplete abortion" to confess: "I feel that God could never forgive me for what I've done."

Here we catch an individual's sense of guilt estranging her from all that is necessary for healing.

> Listen to a man in his early sixties agonizing with a skin eruption: "You know, I'm lonely. Nobody cares for me."

Here we catch the sense of utter loneliness isolating a person physically, emotionally, and spiritually.

> A physician reports his reaction to his own operation: "While my *feeling* was one of insecurity, apprehension and at times great pain, I *expressed* euphoria. It seemed to me that it counteracted the anxiety which was undoubtedly present."[1]

Here we catch the sense of anxiety and fear of the unknown and the possible crippling and destruction of one's own life.

> Stand by the bedside of a young woman dying of cancer and she protests: "It's not the pain; it's something deeper than pain and nausea. It's the utter hopelessness—the dying an eighth of an inch at a time. Why? Why? Why?"

Here we catch the sense of utter despair and futility.

The very atmosphere of the hospital forces us out of a shell of detachment into the arena of life to wrestle with the basic issues of life and death: contradictions, meaninglessness, "internal warfare," guilt and estrangement, loneliness, anxiety, fear, despair and futility. These feelings comprise the essential components of religious concern. The questions they raise imply a religious dimension and therefore cannot be fully grasped apart from a religious understanding. For religion has to do with man's most basic concern, his concern with the meaning of his own life and existence in general. It has to do with everything that helps or hinders the realization of that meaning.

The urgency to break through the surface into the depths of life, however, does not stem primarily from the need to help others. Rather it arises from the fact that these experiences bring into sharp focus our own hopes and fears, despair and yearning, doubt and faith hiding in the shadowy corners of our personal lives. If we open ourselves at all in ministering to those who are patients, we cannot help but be influenced by them. And, incidentally, it is only as we are influenced by them that we are able to have an influence on them.

It is possible, of course, to so protect ourselves as not to permit such disruption to break through. By keeping people

[1] M. Pinner, ed., *When Doctors Are Patients,* New York: W. W. Norton & Company, 1952, pp. 111, 114.

at arm's length we avoid having to face the impact of their predicament becoming representative of the predicament confronting every man, and ourselves particularly.

As a father paced back and forth anxiously awaiting word of his son's operation, which was stretching out from an expected half-hour to four hours, he complained: "I think the doctors sometimes operate when it isn't necessary. This one of ours doesn't even give you time to talk with him. You would think he would have told us if he expected to find anything more. It doesn't seem right. He leaves me feeling uneasy." This particular physician was quite brusque with patients and families. He told them as little as possible. The reason seemed to center on his fear of becoming involved with people's deeper emotions. Thus, as a protection for himself, he shut off the opportunity of an involvement, acted condescendingly, and found it easier to handle the annoyance reactions. He eliminated all possibility for the hospital situation to touch the deeper levels of his own being. Yet by such a retreat he diminished the creative impact of life upon life that is so vital in the recovery of health and wholeness.

Those of us who pass in and out of hospitals daily so commonly assume, usually unconsciously, that *we* are not vulnerable to disease. Such a protective feeling prevents us from a widening and a deepening of awareness so essential for creative life. But ultimately we will not avoid an "existential" encounter with human existence. As Dr. Ian Stevenson observed from reflection on his own illness: The patient "has abundant leisure in which to meditate on the function of life on this planet and the laws by which it is governed. He returns to these questions again and again, and finally he may realize that the leisure he has for studying them now is the result of his failure to study them earlier. If a man will not study himself when well, he must when ill."[2] There can be no escape from our examining ourselves, our relationships, our world, and the ground and source of our life.

The place we begin in any consideration of religious faith, consequently, is not in some abstract ethereal realm but in the concrete reality of daily living. Our faith and understanding will become dynamic only as an outgrowth of

[2] *Ibid.* p. 235.

our reflection on our own and others' experiences. As we explore this personal dimension, we shall then be in a position to relate our experiences meaningfully to the historical understandings of the Church and individual Christians.

### THE DOMINANT EXPERIENCE

If we were to pick out the dominant experience that best characterizes the total impact of life confronting us in the hospital, it would seem to be the experience of brokenness. The wholeness of life has been disrupted. Life has become separated and estranged from its dynamic wholeness.

Increasingly we are realizing that this experience of brokenness and separation is not confined to the physical alone. It reaches out to include the emotional and spiritual as well. The most obvious dimension is, of course, the physical level of a sick body, whether it be a broken bone or malignancy. Intertwined with this is the second dimension of the emotional level of the sick mind, resulting from distortions and frustrations in one's significant interpersonal relationships. Finally, infusing both is the dimension of the spiritual level in which a person lacks adequate meaning for life. All three dimensions interpenetrate each other to hinder the individual's fully relating to himself, to others, and to God who is the ground and source of life.

Our generation has rediscovered that which the ancients so clearly perceived. It is not possible to treat illness apart from the carrier of the illness: his feelings, his fears, his hopes, his faith. The condition of man's health always depends upon the quality of his total relationships.

Let us focus our attention on a consideration of this experience of brokenness and estrangement primarily in terms of the individual himself: separation from self.

Due to various configurations of influence a schism develops between our true selves and our immediately apparent selves, between our "essential" selves and our "existential" selves. Paul in the seventh chapter of Romans discusses the problem of his inability to do what he wants and refrain from that which he does not want. He is conscious of the presence of irrational compulsions over which he has no control. This "bondage of the will" envelops every life both consciously and unconsciously. We find ourselves acting against our own best interest. All the destructiveness rampant in the world cannot be attributed to the forces of nature or fate alone. Much of it lies at the door of man himself. Thus, Karl Menninger can speak of "man against himself." We no longer glibly assume that self-preservation is the first law of life, for our hospital experience gives us contrary evidence. Man seems bent on his own self-destruction. Because he is not himself he is at war with himself.

Our hospitals are filled with patients bearing silent testimony to man's separation from himself. J. S. Baker, engineer of the public safety division of the National Safety Council, concludes: "Chance plays but a small part in accidents."[3] Accidents are invited, hence the phrase "accidentally on purpose." Whether we are aware of it or not we actually "choose" to injure ourselves. In similar fashion 50–75 per cent of all illness arises from the fact that we utilize external stimuli to our own disadvantage. Our internal disposition exploits and creates physiological disturbances as a compromise way of overcoming our self-estrangement.

The woman with the thyroid growth provides an excellent illustration. Her early life was filled with rejection and unjustified punishment. "My mother used to spank me and said that I was a naughty girl all the time. I was always getting blamed for things, and I didn't do them. She would come and accuse us kids, and then I would begin to cry, and she would accuse me, and the others would say it was all my fault, and I would get beaten for it. I would cringe if someone raised their arm because I was beaten so much that I had to react that way."

Her entire life, as a consequence, was filled with bitterness. "Once I was so bitter with my sister. In fact, I wouldn't have walked over her body backwards I was so bitter." She talked with a minister about her feelings and he advised her to forgive and "see the Christ in every man." But as she herself reacted to such an easy suggestion: "It is mighty hard to forget and forgive." She told of working in a situation that was terribly upsetting. Increasingly she was forced to do part of the work others should have done. Instead of verbalizing her anger, she would bottle it up. Being a member of a minority group she likewise experienced all of the

[3] Quoted in Karl Menninger: *Man Against Himself,* New York: Harcourt, Brace and Company, 1938, p. 322.

slights, unpleasantness, and downright cruelty of which a dominant majority is capable. Despite the turbulence of bitter and resentful emotion the patient never permitted herself to express it in any overt form. Her fear of physical retaliation (and on a deeper level emotional rejection) caused her to "swallow" her anger. She turned it against herself.[4]

The throat difficulty stretched over a long period of time. A few years after the first signs appeared it became more pronounced. She herself expressed rather keen insight into the nature of her difficulty. "I had so much bitterness against the man I worked for then. I had a lump in my throat, and when I would get mad, I could feel that lump a-thumping. I never let on I was mad, but it was terrible. The worse I got, the more it pulsated. Sometimes when I got mad I would get headaches. A person gets sick," she realistically concluded, "because they are not right inside. . . . Yes, sir, it's what's wrong inside of me that brought me here. . . . It is discrimination. I resent it so and get so mad at times about it. That's why I'm sick like I am. It is something within me that is keeping me from being well. It's my own fault. If I could get rid of this feeling, I wouldn't have this trouble. . . . Because of it I have to have this growth removed."

Here in a necessarily simplified presentation we see illustrated one way in which self-estrangement is revealed in the hospital. While each person is "unique" we find expressed here the feeling all of us have of being somehow alienated, separated from our very selves.

Let us next focus our attention on a consideration of this experience of brokenness and estrangement primarily in terms of the individual in relation to others: separation from others.

Despite the fact that some may use sickness as a way of getting attention and receiving love, it actually serves to isolate the individual. Visiting cards separate the patient from the outside world. Hospital personnel are always so busy there is little time for extended personal intercourse. As a matter of fact, this very busyness—"I don't have time now"—serves to devalue the individual and deepen his sense of loneliness. Many get the feeling, in large hospitals particularly, that "they don't care about you here, just experimenting. If you die, it doesn't make any difference." A

[4] Cf. Edward Weiss and O. Spurgeon English, *Psychosomatic Medicine*, 2nd ed., Philadelphia: W. B. Saunders Co., 1949, p. 476.

person has difficulty keeping himself as presentable as usual under hospital conditions. There is both a psychic and a physical narrowing. Patients "take refuge in unbelievable rigidities of routine, any irregularities in which lead to great irritability and frustration."[5] Where pain has any degree of intensity it shuts out everything else. Said one doctor-patient: "During the first operation I was emotionally reduced to a most primitive level of hope-fear. My attention was focused on concern with my body . . . my interest in the outside world was decidedly restricted to what had direct bearing on my immediate situation."[6] In addition, patients tend to distort other's remarks and actions more than in normal interchange.[7]

The elderly man with the skin eruption helps to sharpen our understanding of this dimension of estrangement. He expressed his intense helplessness and isolation: "No one can help me. The doctors and nurses here can't do anything. You can't do anything." Inquiry revealed the fact he had had no visitors. Although he had been on the critical list for several weeks, his wife had come only once and his children not at all. Over and over again he would moan how he needed someone to talk to. "You know, I'm lonely. Nobody cares for me." His condition expressed his inner feelings of unworthiness and isolation. Beyond the pure symbolism of the disease was the actual illness itself shutting him off from human fellowship. He had no one to depend on, nor anyone who cared for him. In the routines of daily living one can find ways to escape this sense of loneliness, but in the hospital situation its sharper edges thrust themselves to the fore.

Here in this limited picture we begin to catch the sense of the wider ranges of estrangement from others so prevalent in sickness. Surely this is expressive of the feeling all of us have of being somehow alienated, separated from other people.

Let us now focus our attention on this experience of brokenness and estrangement primarily in terms of the individual's relation to the ground and source of existence: separation from God.

[5] Pinner, pp. 78–79.
[6] *Ibid.*, p. 105.
[7] See examples, *ibid.*, pp. 116–17.

Man is a creature that seeks for meaning in life. He is constantly driven to "give account to himself of himself, and of the meanings of his existence."[8] That is why Jung insisted: "The least of things with a meaning is worth more in life than the greatest of things without it."[9] The experience of sickness gives added impetus to this drive. Whether expressed in religious terms or not, the average patient reveals such a need: "Why did this have to happen to me?" "What's the sense of all this?" "Although I don't want the kind of God who would make a person sick, I can't understand why in answer to my prayers I am still sick." "Why am I sick?"

Perhaps no other sickness so acutely forces this dimension upon us as cancer. We all know the agony involved in informing a family and a patient of the presence of incurable malignancy. There is hesitancy and uncertainty in the face of the termination of life and the disruption of relationships. There is the heartache and helplessness of anticipating the indescribable suffering. The woman dying of cancer typifies such response: "I can't understand it! There must be some reason, some purpose to all this! We're born; we live; we die; but it doesn't seem as though that could be all of it. This is bringing out qualities in my family I didn't know existed, but why do I have to go through hell just to make my family better? . . . It's not the pain; it's something deeper than pain and nausea. It's the utter hopelessness—the dying an eighth of an inch at a time. Why? Why? Why?" Where such a response is finally determinative we find a thwarting of positive forces within. Pain becomes unbearable and bitterness poisons every relationship.

The estrangement from God also finds other manifestations in illness. It is to be seen in the case of the single girl diagnosed "incomplete abortion." Undoubtedly neurotic guilt plays havoc with our bodies and produces all manner of disease.[10] Yet in this instance we see the operation of appropriate guilt reaction not to a specific act but to a failure to be her true self. Her story especially reveals this dimension of estrangement from God.

The girl grew up in a milieu of hardships. The father

[8] Erich Fromm, *Man for Himself*, New York: Rinehart and Company, 1947, p. 41.

[9] Carl Jung, *Modern Man in Search of a Soul*, New York: Harcourt, Brace and Company, 1934, p. 75.

[10] Menninger, p. 366.

was ill with tuberculosis, forcing the mother to work. This only increased an already present "nervousness" on her part. The parents never seemed to have enough time for the girl, and so she felt neglected. Whenever she had questions to ask, she became afraid to ask them, and so bottled her feelings up inside. "Mother used to come home from work so tired and tense. The tension at home was something terrific. And you can imagine what it was like to come home tired and have someone like me hanging around underfoot, always asking questions. 'What does this mean?' 'Tell me a story.' She would not answer and pushed me off. At times I would cry because I didn't understand it even if she would explain that she was tired."

Her growth was dominated by the mother. "She just never understood and was always trying to get me to do what she wanted me to do. . . . Mother was always making decisions for me—the clothes I'd buy, the friends I'd have. She even said what kind of boys I ought to go with. She'd outline in detail what they should be like . . . I just couldn't discuss things with her because I knew what she'd do and say. . . . I was always being sat on and slapped around."

The sexual adjustment was not satisfactory. Although the family was intelligent, little real knowledge or understanding of sex was shared with the girl. She herself resisted the process of maturation and insisted she did not want to become a woman, or at least held ambivalent feelings about it. She preferred to be like a boy, playing with the fellows as one of the group even as late as 17 years of age. Denial of her own vital impulses and accompanying feelings of guilt combined to confuse her. As an unconscious way of striking back at her mother and punishing herself, she would go out with boys that were unacceptable. Eventually, she became pregnant.

The presence of a fever kept complicating her recovery. Whenever she was to be examined, the fever appeared and persisted for three or four days. Part of this response sprang from fear that she might have to be operated on, part of it from the unconscious desire to remain away from the distressing family situation, part of it from the punishment of guilt indicative of her sense of estrangement from God. As she confessed: "I feel that God could never forgive me for what I've done."

In this girl and the woman with cancer we find some implications of estrangement from God. Their reactions are expressive of the feelings all of us have of being somehow alienated, separated from the fountain of life, from the very reality that overcomes futility and despair, making life meaningful and worthwhile—God Himself!

The above discussion of brokenness and estrangement in the hospital experience brings into sharp focus the basic problem with which religion deals, namely, the problem of sin.

Unfortunately, "sin" is generally thought of in the sense of "sins"—the sin of lying, the sin of stealing, the sin of killing, the sin of sexual promiscuity, *et al.* A petty moralism results from this kind of compartmentalized living. Religion at its best has repudiated such thinking. It has always maintained that before sin is an act (i.e., lying, stealing, etc.) it is a state. This state is the experience of all existence—brokenness—the experience of being separated and estranged from oneself, from others, and from God.

Consequently, man must be taken as a whole personality. We cannot isolate particular virtues or vices and judge the individual on this basis. Analytic psychology has caused us to shift the emphasis in looking at man from his neurotic symptoms to an understanding of the character structure in which they are embedded. In the same way we do not think of a disease in isolation from the total personality structure of the individual which it expresses.[11] The brokenness we know in the hospital setting, therefore, is a total one encompassing all levels of one's life. Man as "sinner" existing in this ever-present state of estrangement is the dominant experience of religion. To be a part of the hospital experience is to know all too frighteningly well man in this state of brokenness. It is to realize what Paul called "sin abounding."

### THE DOMINANT CONCERN

If we were to pick out the dominant preoccupation and concern—the "ultimate concern," as Paul Tillich would say—confronting us in the hospital, it would seem to be the con-

[11] Cf. Gotthard Booth, "Religion and Health" issue of the *Review of Religion,* 1945–46, pp. 394, 396 ff.

cern with restoring man's health, binding up the brokenness that he might be whole again.

We have seen from our analysis of brokenness that this experience is not confined to the physical alone. A healthy and whole person is the result of the proper functioning of all his physical resources, all his emotional and intellectual resources, all his spiritual resources. By spiritual resources we imply the active presence of a sense of meaning and purpose in life, the realization that our lives are rooted and grounded in God who cares for, accepts, and encourages us in our struggle for life. Actually all three dimensions interact to produce health and wholeness. We separate them for the purposes of analysis and discussion, but they are like the colors in the spectrum in one sense. They run from violet to red with blue, green, yellow, orange, and so on in between. At the extremes we easily distinguish the difference. Yet the point at which the yellows become oranges is impossible to ascertain.

Let us consider the concern for wholeness primarily in terms of reuniting the individual with himself.

We find our reactions, our attitudes, and our behavior governed more than we realize by unconscious forces. Our lives become injured as did my 3½-year-old son's recently. He became frustrated and angry at us for not permitting a certain action. Telling us of his upset instead of being permitted to strike us did not assuage his rage. After a few minutes he quieted down. But a little while later he stumbled and cut his mouth. Unable to give vent to his hostility he released it quite unconsciously by having an "accident." This served the triple purpose of releasing his aggression (although toward a safer object than his parents), punishing himself for his "murderous" impulses, and at the same time receiving the reassuring love which he needed. Adults are injured in similar fashion either by "accidents" or disease. The presence of unresolved conflict and repressed emotion contributes in greater or lesser degree to our brokenness.

Thus, for an individual to become reunited with himself it is necessary to bring to light these hidden destructive emotions. The extent of his self-awareness needs to be widened and deepened. While there are unconscious and discordant elements within him, man is at war with himself. He is only a partial self. As Kierkegaard so acutely observed:

"Generally speaking, consciousness, i.e., consciousness of self, is the decisive criterion of the self. The more consciousness, the more self; the more consciousness, the more will, and the more will the more self."[12] By becoming aware of what is surging within us and accepting it we are able to exercise our own will more responsibly. To the extent this is realized, to that extent we no longer have to "take it out" on ourselves.

Recognition of the existence of these unassimilated forces within is the first step toward integrating them. The woman with the thyroid growth understood this: "I feel the operation will help some, but it must be done in me. I don't know about you but I have a battle going on inside of me. One has to put his house in order in order to get well." If she is really to be whole again, she needs not only the operation and treatment for her somatic difficulties but also something to reconcile and reunite her with herself. She needs an understanding-accepting relationship in which she will be able to examine the conflicting emotions in all their ramifications and incorporate their dynamics into her consciousness. In this way she will be on the way to overcoming her internal brokenness by an integrated self.

Now let us look at the concern for wholeness primarily in terms of reuniting the individual with others.

Although necessary in treatment, the physical and emotional isolation of sickness contributes to the brokenness. Every effort needs to be made by hospital personnel, family, and friends to bridge the separation and loneliness engulfing the patient. In the training of nurses and physicians increasing emphasis is being placed on the importance of ministering to the "person" and not to an isolated organ. We are social beings and unless we are in person[al] "I-thou" relationships our estrangement deepens. What seems of conclusive significance is not so much what may be said or done as mere presence.

Dr. Frederick Wertham, famed for *The Seduction of the Innocent,* has a very relevant personal reaction in this respect: "I remember only two factors which alleviated my general feeling of insecurity while on the operating table. One was the voice of the operating surgeon and one was the reassurance derived from definite physical contact. . . .

[12] Soren Kierkegaard, *The Sickness Unto Death,* tr. by Walter Lowrie, Garden City, N.Y.: Doubleday & Company, 1954, p. 162.

Words spoken by medical friends present. . . . Evidently friendly physical contact of this primitive type is not sufficiently recognized as a helpful procedure."[13]

Only as a patient is supported by communion with others will his recreating resources be mobilized. There must be the reality of genuine concern and care. If the elderly man with the skin eruption is to be whole again, he needs not only ointment and medication for his somatic difficulties but also something to reconcile and reunite him with other human beings. He needs experiences of understanding love to help him overcome his sense of loneliness and separation from others. Without this, all treatment will prove futile. The validity of this was seen in the marked contrast of his scratching pattern. When alone or engaged in superficial intercourse, he would be scratching constantly. During periods when he was sharing with another on a deeper level, the scratching diminished and ceased completely.

The far-reaching effects of reconciliation with others is exemplified in the case of Dr. Max Pinner. For years he suffered from a chronic heart disease which he refused to admit or accept. As a consequence, his life lacked balance. Human relationships were distorted by secrecy and mental isolation. Once the disease was acknowledged and limitations accepted, this all changed. He regained "the receptivity for love, for human harmony, for a close comradeship." There was less cheer and buoyancy and joy. There was more physical discomfort. But in compensation there came "quiet richness, immediacy of relation and a feeling for the presence of deep entwining roots. . . . It is not the measure of joy and pleasure that matters," he concluded, "it is the intensity of living."[14] Such is the wholeness infusing life as we become reconciled with others.

Finally we look at the concern for wholeness primarily in terms of reuniting the individual with God.

Illness forces man to try to make "sense" of his experience in the world. Unlike the animal, he has this tremendous need which results "in an imperative drive to restore unity and equilibrium between himself and the rest of nature. . . . He has to strive for the experience of unity and oneness in

[13] Pinner, pp. 108–9.
[14] Pinner, pp. 29–30.

all spheres of his being in order to find a new equilibrium."[15] The impact of brokenness in sickness demands an explanation. Until he can place his experience in a framework of meaning he is restless and uneasy. Anxiety frustrates the restoration of health. Healing depends upon an individual's capacity to discover the meaningfulness of his disease and thereby restore the dynamic wholeness to life.[16]

Person after person who has fully "participated" in his sickness reports a broadening of understanding and a deepening of awareness. One individual writes: "For years I had no answers, and it is just lately, in my forty-ninth year, *under the threat of losing life prematurely from cancer* . . . that I have begun to feel a contentment and a satisfaction from the growth of a few concepts." Apprehension over new and unexplained pain or feelings of numbness no longer make her unhappy. "Rather, in some strange way, it often gives me a very wonderful feeling of being in touch with the deeper currents of life and nature."[17] Terminal disease clarifies the dynamics in other sickness. It reveals that the patient needs not only medication and treatment to relieve distress but also something to help overcome the separation from the fountain that gives life meaning and worth.[18]

In other times men conceived of sickness and suffering as the result of sin. Today the majority of people tend to scoff at such a notion. Certainly the rigid manner in which it was applied failed to be effective in restoring health. But we must be careful lest in our sophistication we lose an important clue to our understanding of brokenness and restoration. Men may no longer speak in religious terminology of sin, but evidence is everywhere apparent that we do suffer from the consequences of our failures. Observed the psychiatrist Karl Menninger: "Reality cannot be flouted with impunity, and the burden of punishment and consequence ac-

[15] Fromm, pp. 46–47.

[16] "Religion and Health" issue, pp. 344, 346.

[17] Pinner, pp. 169–77. This could give the impression of masochistic roots, but a consideration of the total picture clearly reveals such is not the case.

[18] A comment in the *Journal of the American Medical Asociation,* Nov. 1952, is particularly pertinent at this point: "Finally the aid of the family pastor in incurable cancer is often of greater benefit than psychotherapy of further palliative procedures any physician can offer. . . . A clever pastor by patience and repeated contact may open the mind of the sufferer to religious experiences that will bring a purposefulness to his pain and thereby make it bearable." Quoted in *Pastoral Psychology,* March, 1954, p. 13.

cumulates . . ." Unfortunately, this self-destructiveness often passes "beyond the point of reversibility."[19]

The sense of failure—the conviction of sin, if you will—becomes a necessary and determining factor in restoration. Menninger tells us "wistfulness and sorrow" must replace "blitheness and arrogance" before any effective help can be given.[20] A patient must assume responsibility himself for his condition and recovery. There can be no compartmentalization of life and a passive acceptance of illness such as is exhibited in the statement: "The pneumococcus made me sick, but penicillin made me well again."[21]

The recovery of the girl who had the incomplete abortion is illustrative of the way of the reunion of life with life. Gradually through an experience of understanding-acceptance with a minister she became conscious of many of her previous reaction patterns. The focus of attention shifted from other people to herself and the need to assume personal responsibility for her actions and destiny. Part of the process of reintegration that became foremost in her mind was the importance of changing herself from within. She grew acutely aware of personal failure and a sense of estrangement from God. She yearned for an inner quietness and peace that would enable her to accept herself and handle her conflicts.

There was no verbalization on the part of the minister of her failure and guilt. Instead of condemnation, he was concerned only with helping her enter into a relationship of acceptance. He did not moralize or point out her mistakes. Rather in this new kind of experience he assisted her in her exploration of her own life. Thus, she discovered for herself destructive and creative depths that had been hidden previously. One day she announced spontaneously: "I feel that God has forgiven me for what has happened. I've prayed about it and told Him about it, so there is no need to continue telling Him because He knows. The thing now is to try to live a better life. . . . I didn't have any faith before. In fact, I was really losing any faith that I might have had. But now I'm beginning to get some. To try to change things

[19] Menninger, p. 199.

[20] *Ibid.*

[21] R. May, *Man's Search for Himself,* New York: W. W. Norton & Company, 1953, pp. 107–8.

inside of me. There has to be a change in me, not a pious kind of change, but one that is real . . ." With the realization of being accepted even though unacceptable she experienced reconciliation with God. Once this began to break in upon her, her resistance to recovery diminished, and she started to respond to the medical treatment.[22]

From the above discussion of health and wholeness in the hospital concern we discover that with which religion deals, namely the answer of grace and salvation.

In dynamic terms grace and salvation involve wholeness—the reuniting of life with life, the reconciliation of man with himself, with others, and with the source and meaning of his existence, God, who is the creator, sustainer, and redeemer of life. It implies the acceptance of that which is alienated and the reconciliation of the disharmonious elements within himself.

Healing, consequently, is an experience taking place on all levels of man's personality. Simply to remove a stomach ulcer by surgery does not bring wholeness. An individual's entire life pattern must be healed. His entire personality structure must be scrutinized. This is what Luther saw. There is something more drastically wrong with man than any recital and confession of particular offenses (symptoms) can overcome. The whole nature of man needs to be healed. Luther formulated this by saying a physician has no need to probe each pustule to discover if a patient has smallpox nor does he cure the disease scab by scab.[23] In light of this the concern for wholeness must be a concern with the total health and reconciliation of the patient.

Walter B. Cannon, in *The Wisdom of the Body*,[24] expressed in physiological terms what is true of the total life of man: There is something at work in our bodies always

[22] Cf. Hiltner's statement about spiritual healing: "It brings forgiveness for guilt about things concerning which one ought to feel guilty, after the real guiltiness has been recognized. It brings personality reorganization after the powerful elements of disorganization have been investigated. It brings peace after the causes of 'internal warfare' have been subjected to scrutiny and have been accepted as 'emotional facts.' It brings love after one's capacities for hostility have been seen and diagnosed. It brings security after one's anxieties have been understood and faced." "Religion and Health" issue, p. 101.

[23] Roland Bainton, *Here I Stand*, New York: Abingdon-Cokesbury Press, 1950, p. 56.

[24] Walter B. Cannon, *The Wisdom of the Body*, New York: W. W. Norton & Company, 1932.

driving toward integration and health. The doctor sets the bone, but something greater than the doctor accomplishes the healing. A relationship of acceptance enables one to confront heretofore unfaced dimensions distorting one's relationships, but something deeper than the immediate fellowship undergirds the reunion of life with life. This is not to imply that it is an automatic process, for brokenness will not heal itself. By conscious or unconscious attitudes and actions we can frustrate God's purpose. We can hinder the recovery of wholeness. Thus, there must be this personal knowledge that in the midst of brokenness there is a wholeness capable of realization, a relatedness to life, even though we are separated from it. This is what Paul meant when he affirmed "where sin abounds, grace does much more abound."

## SUMMARY OF AGREEMENT AND DIFFERENCE

We have seen that the dominant experience of brokenness and the dominant concern for wholeness in the hospital are expressive of the religious understanding of man. At the same time we must not be so naive as to assume that there are no fundamental differences between the understanding of the discipline of medicine and the understanding of the discipline of theology.

It is readily recognized that the "person" is intimately related to "his" disease. The prevailing attitude among physicians today is not whether a disease is psychogenic or physiogenic. Rather it is a question of how much "psyche" and how much "soma." It is, as Jung so simply and beautifully described, "the mysterious truth that spirit is the living body seen from within, and the body the outer manifestation of the living spirit."[25]

With such a view religion is in complete accord. The point of tension, however, comes in an understanding of the depth of brokenness and wholeness. For the secular individual estrangement from self can be transcended by an attitude of "man for himself." This fails to recognize the radical distortions resulting from such worship of human self-sufficiency. It fails to acknowledge its own ontological presup-

[25] Jung, p. 253.

position. Likewise, it fails to recognize that man ultimately cannot be his own judge and redeemer. The religious person maintains that after neurotic anxiety and brokenness have been removed man needs to take unto himself the existential anxiety and brokenness which is part and parcel of his being a finite, questioning, responsible creature. Non-neurotic estrangement now becomes the deepest dimension of man's relationship with himself, with others, and with the ground and source of life. Such brokenness man cannot heal by himself.

In similar fashion, religion views reconciliation and wholeness in a deeper dimension. Psychiatry and depth psychology, in many instances, express little concern about the total world structure in which health is achieved. For the most part the question of where the drive for health comes from is never asked. When it is asked, the conclusion is that man's struggle for life is carried on by himself "in a universe indifferent to his fate. . . . There is no meaning to life except the meaning man gives his life by the unfolding of his powers."[26] In the last analysis, man must bear the burden of his own failures and guilt himself.

To the religious man such thinking is limited. The individual who thinks this way fails to see and affirm the drive for recovery as the expression of the basic weave in the cloth of the universe. This reality does not exist in a vacuum. We do not create values; we realize values. Love is not our creation; we fulfill love. We are not the creators of life; we realize life. The universe is so constructed as to support our pursuit and realization of these experiences. Our striving for abundant life, for wholeness, is not carried on against or despite the universe. Beyond the narrow sense of health, although integrally related to it, is this dimension of whether or not life has any "real" meaning and worth. We cannot ultimately avoid asking this basic question.

Our ability to move toward harmony and wholeness between our body, with its physiological needs, and our spirit, with its emotional-meaning demanding needs, adds up in the long run only if the dynamic structure in which these are present is more secure than anything which we alone can

[26] Fromm, pp. 44–45.

determine or control.[27] The Christian focusing only on the fruits and ignoring the roots cannot do. It relates man in a meaningful fashion to the ground and source of life by revealing the framework and dynamics in which wholeness is realized.

[27] O. Roberts, *Psychotherapy and a Christian View of Man*, New York: Charles Scribner's Sons, 1951, p. 115.

# 2

# PSYCHOLOGICAL ASPECTS

# 6

# Behavioral Science, Religion, and Mental Health

*Gordon W. Allport*

ANY GENUINELY HUMAN life is psychologically marginal. It is at best a short span of years compressed between two oblivions, spent chiefly in wonderment, and terminated in mystery. To be human implies moments of delight and glimpses of happiness; but also it implies ordeals of suffering, discord of purposes, frequent defeat of self, and painful reconquest of self. A mentally ill person is one who, at least temporarily, has lost the battle. He regrets his past, abhors his present, and dreads his future. If we ourselves have not gone over this brink, we have been close enough to it to sympathize with those who have.

And such sympathy today is widespread. The many current researches in universities and clinics, frequently supported by the federal government through the National Institute of Mental Health, and the founding and rapid growth of the Academy of Religion and Mental Health with its various activities, including the publication of the *Journal [of Religion and Health]*, are signs of a new understanding and tokens of hope. Our common aim is to fortify the human spirit so that it can withdraw from the brink and to help those who have fallen to regain their footing.

In a general way, we know what mental health requires. It requires that we learn to grow muscles where our injuries were. In the words of the Eighty-fourth Psalm, that man is blessed "who, going through the vale of misery, uses it for a well." One thing we have learned is that a full discussion of mental health requires a rich bilingualism. It requires both the poetic and prophetic metaphors of religion and the precise, hard grammar of science.

This bilingual approach to mental health is something new under the sun. A long-standing gap in communication is closing at last. Richard McCann reports on interviews with a sample of psychiatrists practicing in a large city. Although more than half of them say that they personally are not religious, yet "none is opposed to religion; none expresses the idea that the religious view of reality as such may create problems for his patients; and all welcome the assistance and support that religious affiliations provide for their patients."[1]

On the side of religion, there have sprung up in recent years nearly 400 programs for clinical pastoral training for the younger clergy. Centers for pastoral counseling are mushrooming. Chaplaincies in mental hospitals constantly increase in number. Protestant, Catholic, and Jewish faiths all share in these developments.[2] To be sure, the bickering between psychiatry and religion has not yet ended, but a growing sense of teamwork is evident. Each specialty has wisdom to bring; each now knows that it is handicapped without the aid of the other.

## RELIGION: ITS MERITS AND LIMITATIONS

For many centuries, religion has held priority in the field. By tradition, the church and the synagogue are "therapeutic communities." Throughout the ages, they, more than

[1] R. V. McCann, *The Churches and Mental Health,* Report of the Joint Commission on Mental Illness and Health, No. 8, New York: Basic Books, 1962, p. 206.

[2] *Ibid.,* Chaps. 4 and 7.

other institutions, have concerned themselves with the major crises of life. By comparison, psychiatry and its correlative behavioral sciences are recent upstarts. True, the language of the Scriptures seems dated in spots. (But already the language of Kraepelin and Charcot also seems old-fashioned to our ears.) Fashions in terminology should not deceive us. To say that a sufferer is "afflicted with unclean spirits" is not far from scientific truth.

With its eyes on eternal verities, religion has little difficulty accommodating modern conceptions of psychopathology. When we say that the mentally sick person is one who regrets his past, abhors his present, and dreads his future, religion deepens the issue by adding, "Yes, and I can provide forgiveness for the past, acceptable meaning for the present, and hope for the future." And when we say that mental health requires that we grow muscles where our injuries were, religion echoes, "Yes, our mental health is proportional to the weight of the burden that we can carry." In recent years, psychiatry has been discovering what religion has always maintained: that there is no cure apart from love. Thus do the concepts of therapy and of redemption fuse. Healing follows the path of redemptive love, whether human or divine.

But however modern in principle, religion in practice has many shortcomings. For one thing, churches and synagogues, as they grow in numbers and in grandeur, lose much of their character as therapeutic communities. While 97 per cent of the people profess some form of religious devotion in their lives and 95 per cent say they believe in God, only about 6 per cent of the believers, according to one study, ever take their problems to a clergyman. And hardly any who do so regard their problems as basically spiritual. Even from the clergy they seek chiefly secular help. And among patients in mental hospitals having chaplains, only a few (perhaps 2½ per cent) say that they have received major help from this ministry.[3] From such data we conclude that as of today, church and synagogue fall short in dealing with lives in acute emotional crisis and in helping the sufferer define his problem in spiritual terms.

Another charge that can fairly be laid against some re-

[3] *Ibid.*, pp. 79, 153, 211.

ligion is its use of pathogenic appeals. In some of its forms, religion instills an abnormal degree of terror, injurious especially to sensitive children; it may arouse pathological feelings of guilt; it may inculcate superstition. Or at the other extreme, it may bring superficial happiness, offering only those things that serve as cheap ego-defenses, talismans against reality, medicated lozenges momentarily pleasant but ineffective against the deeper virus of evil. Such religious practices do not make for muscle building.

One final criticism: As of today, we have no firm evidence that religious people on the average are more mentally healthy than nonreligious people. What demographic differences there are indicate that income and education are far more important variables in mental health and illness than is personal religion—at least as personal religion is measured today (chiefly in terms of denominational affiliation).[4] But to this problem I shall soon return.

It is sometimes argued, of course, that religion should not be assessed as if it were merely a servant of hygiene. Its purpose is not to make people healthy, but to save their souls. Even if we grant the theological point involved, our criticism still holds. All religions teach compassion for sufferers here and now, whatever their conception of ultimate salvation may be. Christ himself healed the sick and cast out demons. Religion does have a duty to foster wholeness of personality. When it does not do so, it can be justly criticized.

## PSYCHIATRY: ITS MERITS AND LIMITATIONS

The great achievement of psychiatry and correlative branches of modern behavioral sciences lies in giving us an objective view of the human mind and its workings. Though they are still far from solving mental mysteries, a significant revolution has occurred in comparatively recent times. It was only a little more than a century ago that radical reformers (Pinel and Dorothea Dix among them) started to break down ancient superstitions concerning the nature of insanity.

It took countless ages for man to develop the detach-

[4] *Ibid.*, Chap. 12.

ment required to discover and utilize any of the truths of science. At first, man perceived the world in the light of personal advantage. All truth had to be immediately relevant to the exigencies of survival. Only gradually did a third-person (or objective) point of view become possible. Fire, weather, gravity, man came slowly to realize, obeyed laws not related to personal advantage. Eventually he learned the laws of levers, pumps, steam engines, atomic energy, and of health and disease. Only now at long last are the laws of mental illness and health being discovered. And even today, relatively few people know that such laws exist. Like the cave man of old, most of us still let personal advantage rule our perceptions in our social relationships. Others, we insist, are to blame; we are blameless. The other fellow is always wrong; I am always right. As Emerson said, "What is sin in others is experiment for us." Our strategies of rationalization, of denial, of psychic blindness, of projection, of self-exculpation still show that for us (as for the cave man) what is to our personal advantage is true. We have a long way to go before we are able to apply the same scientific detachment to matters of the mind (our own or our neighbor's) that we apply to the impersonal phenomena of nature. It is to the credit of psychiatry and behavioral science that they lead us forward and focus our attention concretely on wholesome practices in child training, attitude change, environmental reform, and psychotherapy.

But if psychiatry and behavioral science are headed in the right direction, they still for the most part stumble at thresholds. We are still ignorant concerning the etiology of most forms of mental distress. Therapy for the most part is still experimental. Although we are able to give relief, we know we are not yet at the root of the matter. We are still far from being able to fashion balanced and productive lives, even though we take an objective view of our troubles. We rightly ask, "After tranquilizers, what? After energizers, what? After electroconvulsive therapy, what? After psychoanalysis, what?

Here religion enters its claim. When the psychiatrist says, "We must integrate this life," religion replies, "I am the potential integration you need. As a master sentiment, I am able to dominate the nerve network, gating all impulses to accord with my generic motivation; I can dwell deep in the solar plexus; I can knit fragments together; I reach to the roots. When Freud says that anxiety is the alpha and omega of neurosis, I say, 'No: the alpha and omega of neurosis is vanity. And vanity is sin.' "

Here we encounter the characteristic difficulty of bilingualism. Whenever psychiatry and social science employ the hard, precise grammar of science, religion is likely to enter a counterclaim. There is in all religion, says Gabriel Marcel, a "mysterious primacy." It is never a matter of objective propositions amenable to verification. By its very nature, religion demands our participation rather than proof or verification. Religion, being total, contains both us as observers and the objects and events we single out for critical inspection. Working within a religious frame, we cannot expect to objectify entirely the frame that contains us. For example, if we sense that all being is engulfed in divine love, we cannot step completely outside this frame and objectify or measure the operations of this love.

To make the point more concrete: mental patients sometimes complain that their psychiatrists seldom or never inquire concerning their religious faith. And yet the same patients often insist that their religious faith somehow envelops their lives. The psychiatrists' customary neglect of this factor is, in part no doubt, due to their own lack of personal religion. In part it is due to their habituation to the grammar of science. In either case, they fail to recognize the power of healing that lies in generic faith.

## OTHER BEHAVIORAL SCIENCES

Thus it is difficult for many psychiatrists to deal adequately with the "mysterious primacy" of religion. It is equally difficult for many exponents of faith to accept the psychiatrist's grammar of science. The situation is further complicated by the existence of a third voice. Behavioral science agrees with psychiatry in speaking the grammar of science; but it agrees with religion in its desire to broaden the horizon of the therapeutic relationship as it exists in hospitals or consulting rooms.

One of the behavioral sciences is psychology as distinct from psychopathology. Can one study or aid a broken personality without a deep knowledge of normal personality? A patient who recovers from a breakdown does not progress to a new personality. He returns essentially to the personality he had prior to his illness. For this reason the doctor should know the norm for his patient. And he should also know how normal people manage to deal with the evils that befall them. How is it that most of us succeed in growing muscles where our injuries were? (I venture to protest the fact that the great majority of psychiatrists in their course of training are exposed to nothing but psychoanalytic theory. However applicable it may be to some disordered syndromes, psychoanalysis is often a poor, or very partial, fit to lives of normal constitution.)

Sociological disciplines, too, have much to contribute. Ethnic tradition, culture, family pattern, social class all affect the incidence and course of mental illness and are potentially important factors in prevention. We are learning much about the context of treatment in mental hospitals, about the structure of hospitals as small societies, about the therapeutic and pathogenic behavior of hospital personnel, about halfway houses, about ward improvement meetings and group therapy.[5]

Instead of two major disciplines demanding teamwork in the interests of mental health, there are clearly three: religion, psychiatry, and social science. Their interrelations are only now being understood.

## TWO FORMS OF THE RELIGIOUS SENTIMENT

I remarked earlier that we are still ignorant concerning the relation, if any, between mental soundness and the religious sentiment in a given life. To my mind, this is one of two most pressing problems demanding research. The other problem concerns the evaluation of psychotherapy itself—all types of therapy. No one yet knows surely that psychiatric intervention has permanent beneficial effects beyond the course of nature left to itself. But neither have we proved that religion in a life is curative or preventive.

[5] Among recent significant contributions are: M. Greenblatt, D. J. Levinson, and R. H. Williams, eds., *The Patient and the Mental Hospital,* Glencoe: The Free Press, 1957; W. Caudill, *The Psychiatric Hospital as a Small Society,* Cambridge: Harvard University Press, 1958; B. Kramer, *Day Hospital,* New York: Grune & Stratton, 1962; S. H. King, *Perceptions of Illness and Medical Practice,* New York: Russell Sage Foundation, 1962.

I should like to present a hypothesis worth testing. It is my contention that the concept "religion" is too broad for discriminating use. In reality, the religious sentiment varies enormously from person to person. In some it is fragmentary, superficial, even trivial; in others it is deep and pervasive, lockstitched into the whole fabric of being. The religious sentiment varies not only in depth and breadth, but also in its content and its mode of functioning. Indeed, since every personality is unique, I have argued elsewhere that the religious sentiment in every life must take a unique form.[6]

Still, for research purposes it is allowable to select one important dimension of variability. The dimension I have in mind is a continuum ranging from the type of religious sentiment that has only instrumental or extrinsic significance in a life to the type of sentiment that is itself a major motive in life, and thus has intrinsic value. The latter type serves itself alone; it is subordinate to no other motives. If we can locate people approximately on this continuum, and if we are able to establish suitable criteria for mental healthiness, we should then be able to find an answer to our question: Are some forms of the religious sentiment more therapeutic and preventive than others?

For brevity's sake, let us speak then of *extrinsic* and *intrinsic* religion. My hypothesis is that extrinsic religion is less therapeutic or preventive than is intrinsic religion.

### *Extrinsic Religion*

For many people, religion is a dull habit, or a tribal investment to be used for occasional ceremony, for family convenience, or for personal comfort. It is something to *use,* but not to *live.* And it may be used in a variety of ways: to improve one's status, to bolster one's self-confidence, to enhance one's income, to win friends, power, or influence. It may be used as a defense against reality and, most importantly, to provide a super-sanction for one's own formula for living. Such a sentiment assures me that God sees things my way, that my righteousness is identical with His. I see the nature of being as conforming to the facts of my particular being. Two pious aged sisters were quarreling. One said

[6] G. W. Allport, *The Individual and His Religion,* New York: The Macmillan Company, 1950.

with asperity to the other, "The trouble with you, Jane, is that you lack the grace of God in your heart." The grace of God, it seems, is hers, not Jane's.

One hypothesis already successfully tested is that this utilitarian or extrinsic form of religiosity correlates positively with racial and ethnic bigotry that is unfortunately widespread among churchgoers.[7] There is no reason why the same measures used in this research on religion and prejudice should not be applied to research on religion and mental health.

In theological terms, the extrinsically religious person turns to God, but does not turn away from self. For this reason, his religion is primarily a shield for self-centeredness. Had Freud been more perceptive, he would have seen that it is only this kind of religion that resembles a neurosis. It defends against anxiety. As with the cave man, religious perceptions serve personal advantage.

In motivational terms, the extrinsic religious sentiment is not a driving or integral motive. It serves other motives: the need for security, the need for status, the need for self-esteem. In terms of developmental psychology, the formation is immature. Like Piaget's children, the possessor holds an egocentric view of the universe. Habit, custom, family tradition are not critically re-evaluated and recentered into an adult outlook.

If you ask, "But isn't religion legitimately a source of comfort?" I reply, "Of course it is. But the comfort it supplies can never be on our own terms—only on *its* terms. The burden cannot be evaded, nor can it be trimmed down. It must be borne. The comfort comes with courageous acceptance of the burden."

Like all defenses, and like all instrumental habits, extrinsic religion is in danger of breaking down when the cross-purposes of life grow too discordant. It is for this reason that my hypothesis does not expect extrinsic religion to be either preventive or therapeutic in the long run, for life has a way of shooting its poisoned darts through defensive armor.

[7] G. W. Allport, *The Nature of Prejudice,* New York: Doubleday Anchor, 1958, Chap. 28. See also G. W. Allport, "Religion and Prejudice," Chap. 16 in *Personality and Social Encounter,* Boston: Beacon Press, 1960.

### *Intrinsic Religion*

Our hypothesis holds that, though religion of the extrinsic variety may hinder mental health, religion of the intrinsic variety may help. Each of us has known lives that remain serene in spite of inner turmoil, courageous in spite of the shattering shafts of fate. We have also known religious people who, in spite of neurotic fragments in their own lives, manage somehow to maintain control of their sanity—apparently because of a generic and embracing and guiding religious motive.

Intrinsic religion is not an instrumental formation. That is to say, it is not primarily a means of handling fear, or a mode of conformity, or an attempted sublimation of sex, or a wish-fulfillment. Earlier in life it may have been all these things. But now these specific needs are not so much served by, as they are subordinated to, an overarching motive. Quandaries, predicaments, cross-purposes, guilt, and ultimate mysteries are handled under the comprehensive commitment. This commitment is partly intellectual, but more fundamentally motivational. It is integral, covering everything in experience and everything beyond experience; it makes room for scientific fact and emotional fact. It is a hunger for, and a commitment to, an ideal unification of one's life, but always under a unifying conception of the nature of all existence.

It is important to note that this conception of intrinsic religion has nothing to do with formal religious structure. There are intrinsic Catholics and extrinsic Catholics, intrinsic Protestants and extrinsic Protestants, intrinsic and extrinsic Jews, Moslems, and Hindus. It is for this reason that I would not expect to find denominational or sectarian differences in the incidence of mental illness. My prediction rather is that mental health will vary according to the degree to which adherents of any faith are intrinsic in their interpretation and living of their faith.

It should be noted that intrinsic religion, according to our hypothesis, cannot exist in order to be therapeutic or preventive. Intrinsic religion is not a mustard plaster. The sufferer can aim only at religion; he cannot aim at treatment. If he has deeply interiorized his religion, he will find sanity and soundness as a by-product. Such is our hypothesis.

I have already conceded that there are pathogenic strains

in some religions, such as excessive terror, superstition, a built-in hostility to science, or a palliative defensiveness. But these pathogenic strains are not found in the great creeds of the world religions; rather they are extrinsic accretions that lead some worshippers away from the intrinsic possibilities of their faith. If I am not mistaken, most of the damage that religion does and most of the criticisms directed against it are related to these accretions. They aim to make religion easy and palatable, but they fall short of the total outlook of the creed in question.

### SANITY IN WORLD SOCIETY

Our approach, being psychological, has been person-centered and needs, therefore, a certain enlargement. To seek one's own mental health smacks of hypochondriasis. Hence we ask a final question: "Can one be truly sound in mind unless one takes upon himself some of the redemptive duties in the world today?"

Physical science has already made it possible for all men to die together. Is it not the task of psychological and social science to discover ways by which we can live together? If we do not soon do so, the last human survivor may write the epitaph: "Over the whole earth lie the irradiated ashes of *Homo sapiens,* the only species to have committed self-extinction. Man learned too late that his sapience, his pursuit of private mental health, was fatally one-sided."

Not long ago an editorial in a Southern newspaper caught my eye. Titled "Science Isn't God," the editorial opens with the question:

> Is it possible, as has been proposed, that a new science could be created to keep society from committing suicide with nuclear weapons? Can a science of human survival be developed, or is one necessary?

The writer says "No."

> We do not need a new science of human survival. What we need is to use the solution for human conflicts and failure handed down to us by Christ and the Christian churches. . . . Human nature, upon which human survival depends, can be changed for the better and controlled only from within by the promptings of conscience and faith in God. We do not need a science for survival; we need faith.

At first, I dismissed the piece as just one more item of religious obscurantism. Then there came to my mind what Bertrand Russell said, although he himself is a salty foe of religion: "An indispensable condition of survival," he wrote, is "the kindly feeling toward others which religion has advocated."

The editorial writer and Bertrand Russell are right in saying that religion has given us the guideline for international amity just as it has for personal mental health. No one can doubt this fact.

But religion by itself, in this complex world, simply cannot specify the means. Indeed, throughout the ages religious authority has often combatted every increment of technical knowledge gained through the study of astronomy, of evolution, of vaccination. Some religion has held to belief in witchcraft, to the demonic theory of mental disease, to bigotry. Always available to man were the miracles of antibiotics, heart surgery, atomic energy, electronics, and the objective techniques of psychotherapy and social science. But these latent miracles were not available until scientists diverged from theology and commenced in their own way "to think God's thoughts after Him."

The editorial writer denies that scientific miracles may lie ahead in the realm of human relations. It is inconceivable, he says, that the new science may some day help man to control his aggressive impulses, improve relations in industry, in neighborhoods, between nations and races, and eventually to weave a firmer texture into all human character.

Fortunately, such obscurantism is on the wane. Religion is beginning to realize that it needs to team firmly with psychiatry and all the behavioral sciences in order that its vision may find implementation. How to love one's neighbor (or one's enemy) effectively is a question not of good-will alone, but of knowledge derived from psychological and social science. Furthermore, scientific exploration, critically employed and applied to oneself, can help to clarify, sift, and test the purity of the religious motive, so that it will become more and more an intrinsic possession of aspiring man.

May it not be that the health (or wholeness) of any system—whether it be personal, national, or international—can be the product only of concerted wisdom, wherein the insights of religion and behavioral science blend? May we not hope that the present bilingualism of religion and behavioral science—good so far as it goes—may eventually lose its duality and emerge as a universal language suited to a final theory and implementation of both individual health and planetary peace?

# 7

# The Voice of the Body

*Gotthard Booth*

### THE BODY AS SYMBOL

MANKIND has known intuitively since early times that the body speaks a very basic and very honest language through the healthy and unhealthy functioning of its organs. Our expressive gestures, the color of our skin, and the behavior of our heart and our bowels, of our lungs and our genitals, unequivocally spell out our existential situation. The lie detector, reading the body directly, triumphs over the faculty of words to hide the truth. As Ludwig Klages, the founder of scientific graphology, described the relationship: "The body is the expression of the soul, the soul is the meaning of the body." In the course of the past 40 years scientific research has accumulated more and more evidence that this intuitive insight is correct.

More important than the mass of empirical material,

---

GOTTHARD BOOTH, M.D., is a psychiatrist in private practice, New York, New York.

however, is the theoretical insight into the lawful nature of the relationship between body and mind, an insight made particularly clear in the work of F. S. Rothschild[1] who applied the principles of semantics to the evolution of life. Retracing life's stages from the organization of the human brain back to the amoeba, he classified all physical structures in their role as carriers of specific forms of communication between subject and object. Each organ not only supports the life of the body but also serves a specific relationship between body and environment. The different forms of the nose in the bulldog, the anteater, and the elephant are obvious examples, but the principle also is responsible for differing brain structures in such mammals as the porpoise and the horse. Both the appearance and the inner anatomy of an organism reflect its place in the context of nature and are therefore symbols of its specific life in the same way a wheel is a symbol of motion or a letter of a certain sound.

The meaning of an organ and its functions always transcends its physical elements, just as the meaning of a word transcends the letters which compose it or the meaning of a sentence transcends the words which compose it. The growing complexity of organisms in the course of evolution is the expression of an expanding range of communication between subjects and objects. The intricate structure of the brain of the higher mammals represents the syntax which organizes these manifold interrelationships into rational patterns. For the needs of man, however, the brain has proved inadequate. He has developed a system of nonbiological structures of communication, language, which enables him to interpret and control the levels of prehuman communication which are expressed only through bodily forms and organ functions and which have remained the biological foundation of human existence.

When the human organism is seen in this light it is understandable that the language of the body is straightforward and unequivocal in contrast to words. The syntax of the body has been structurally fixed since prehistoric times; language proper, on the other hand, is still in flux. Nothing illustrates this point better than the King James Version of

[1] F. S. Rothschild, "Laws of Symbolic Mediation in the Dynamics of Self and Personality," *Annals of the New York Academy of Science,* 94:774–84, 1962.

the Bible. Although it has stayed a living part of English literature for the past 350 years, its message can no longer be completely understood by the modern reader, because many of its words and usages have either disappeared from contemporary English or have radically changed in meaning. This is not true of the word "illness," which still has the same general meaning. When we come to the problem of defining "psychological illness," however, we immediately get lost in the quicksands of the idiosyncratic use of words which Siirala discusses in his book *The Voice of Illness.* Illness has an unequivocal meaning only in the context of the body. In the context of verbal communication the same description of an experience may be regarded by some as a sign of spiritual health and by others as a symptom of a mind out of touch with "reality" or God. A physical symptom, however, always has the same immutable meaning in the communication between the individual and the world. *In the state of illness the person is alienated from the object of the affected function.*[2] One may describe physical disease as insanity of the body. This purely negative formulation is inadequate, since even a psychotic process does not annul the individual personality, but only disturbs communication with others. The body always expresses the soul, in illness as much as in health. One may even say that illness expresses the soul more impressively than health in the same way that a good caricature expresses essential aspects of a personality more clearly than photographs taken in uncharacteristic situations.

## ILLNESS AS ALIENATION

The essential character of disease is illustrated most clearly in the dramatic event of an epileptic attack. In a moment the patient makes the transition from normal social relatedness to an unconscious state in which the whole organism concentrates on the convulsions of the motoric system. After the storm has exhausted its fury, consciousness and normal rapport with the environment are re-established. This sequence of events defines a specific personality type:

[2] Gotthard Booth, "Health From the Standpoint of the Physician," in Paul B. Maves, ed., *The Church and Mental Health,* New York: Charles Scribner's Sons, 1953.

a person endowed with both a strong tendency toward aggression and the capacity to control it ordinarily, subordinating it to constructive social behavior. Only an intolerable accumulation of aggressive tensions can occasionally overwhelm the conscious personality to such an extent that the tensions are discharged in the form of socially harmless fits. In the rare cases when an epileptic has committed murder, he has done so while unconscious. The accumulation of aggressive tension is visibly dependent on events in the life of the epileptic. For example, I once saw a ward patient go into a seizure while he was signing his name to a birthday card for his brother, the oldest son of the family. Consciously he had accepted the fact that the brother had inherited the family farm, but to carry goodness to the point of celebrating his brother's birthday proved too irritating to be confined within conventional behavior. The seizure expressed a compromise between respect for the brother's personality and the need at least symbolically to act out the aggressive impulse.

The contrast in the epileptic personality between generally overcontrolled healthy behavior and the evident violence of the fit earned epilepsy the name *morbus sacer* in antiquity. A demon seemed to take possession of the body. It was Hippocrates who introduced the notion that epilepsy is a disease like any other, the result of "natural causes." His causal interpretation was not so much of an advance in the theory of disease as it may appear at first sight. The father of rational medicine retained the primitive concept that external agents overwhelm the victim and harm his body. Even today, physical injuries, chemical substances, bacteria, and viruses are considered enemies of man ready to take advantage of any neglect in the defensive system of the body, no different in character from the demons of old. Diseases have assumed individual characters in Western medicine. Science has delighted in naming each frequent combination of symptoms as if it belonged to some mysterious organism—epilepsy, tuberculosis, cancer, etc.—each as if it had its own natural history and would have its own way with the patients unless they could fight it off. Are such national campaigns as "Fight cancer" and "Fight tuberculosis" really more scientific, more sophisticated in spirit, than the exorcistic rituals of ancient medicine men? As Freud discovered, and Siirala documents, the Inquisitors were well informed about "witches" from the point of view of disease description; they were only mistaken in their interpretations. They argued very logically and very simply that every event must have a cause, and that an evil event must be caused by a power hostile to the victim: the devil.

Modern medicine has followed this line of thinking; it has gone all out in tracking down "disease demons" which have one thing in common: they are all defined as something destructive which attacks the otherwise healthy body in the form of bad genes, birth injuries, faults of nutrition, germs, toxic substances, etc. Psychoanalysis has added various forms of damage which civilization, specifically religious moralism, inflicts on the "normal instincts" which seek oral, anal, and sexual gratifications. It is not difficult to see that the underlying concept of man as "naturally healthy" represents a Manichean dualism of good and evil as warring cosmic powers. Careful observation of sick persons reveals, however, that the negative aspect of illness, the reduction of the affected function, does not exhaust the significance of sickness. The example of the epileptic attack shows more than an unconscious man, his muscles given over to useless thrashing around. It shows an episode in the life of a man who practices self-control to such an extent that he expresses his capacity for rage only in symbolic form. The biological function is used as a mere gesture, but *a gesture which realistically affirms a social attitude.*

## ILLNESS AS COMMUNICATION

The interpretation of organic disease as *social communication* may appear strange to many readers who have been subjected to the concept of communication as a function which serves individual interests. The popular notions of life in the raw employ clichés like "struggle for survival," "self-preservation," "sexual hunger," and "cruelty of nature." They represent a narrow and tendentious selection from the life of subhuman nature and from so-called primitive human cultures, a selection of more or less correct observations which can be used to rationalize the individualistic mores of modern industrial man. Scientific observers have established clear evidence that Darwin's observations about the utilitarian bias of "natural selection" cover only part of the complexity of nature. *Social organization* of life and quasi-artistic *self-expression in the service of communication* are actually as much an integral part of biological forms as self-preservation. As Spitz[3] demonstrated clearly, even the best physical care of bodily needs does not keep a baby alive unless it is related to a mothering human being. Harlow[4] has added the observation that rhesus monkeys can be kept alive if the warmth and softness of a maternal body is replaced by a dummy to which the baby can cling. Nevertheless such babies grow up into defective adults: they are incapable of carrying out the sexual act because they have not developed the function of interaction with another organism. The *gestures* "Yes" and "No" are patterned by the reflex activities of the baby which take place when the baby has found the nipple and when it has failed to find it, respectively.[5] As far as body *forms* are concerned, the predominance of self-expressive over self-preserving needs is seen most strikingly in the fact that on the highest level of evolution the testicles have left the protection of the abdominal cavity. Nothing could possibly be gained for the survival of the individual or of the race by exposing the male germ cells to such danger.[6]

Communication between the members of the same group as well as communication with members of different symbiotic groups is thus the fundamental principle of biology. The utilitarian functions of feeding, fighting, mating, and breeding have all been used as material for the elaborate social *rituals* of animal life. The latter, like the head-nodding and the head-shaking of the human infant, are forms of symbolic communication by means of the body. They are apt to replace effectively the need for physical action on the object. In many animal species fights between rivals are

[3] René A. Spitz, "Hospitalism," in Ruth S. Eissler *et al.*, eds., *Psychoanalytic Study of the Child,* Vol. 1, New York: International Universities Press, Inc., 1945.

[4] H. F. Harlow, "Development of Affection in Primates," in E. L. Bliss, ed., *Roots of Behavior,* New York: Harper & Row, 1962. See also Harlow, *Nature and Development of the Affectional Systems* ("Salmon Lectures"), New York: Academy of Medicine, 1960.

[5] René A. Spitz, *No and Yes: On the Genesis of Human Communication,* New York: International Universities Press, Inc., 1957.

[6] Gotthard Booth, "Values in Nature and in Psychotherapy," *Archives of General Psychiatry,* 8:22, 1963; A. Portmann, *Biologie und Geist,* Zurich: Rhein Verlag, 1956.

ceremonial in character and do not seek the death of the vanquished. As a great animal ethologist formulated it, the end of purposive behavior is not the attainment of the object but the performance of the consummatory action: "Not the litter or the food is the animal striving towards, but the performance itself of the maternal activities or eating."[7] Self-preservation, in other words, is a by-product of the activities of the organism. Under normal circumstances all organisms, not only man, feed and fight in their characteristic ways as an expression of living, not in order to keep their own body alive as an end in itself.

In the state of illness nothing changes as far as the principle of self-expression is concerned. Illness differs from health only with respect to *the form in which the individual relates to his specific environment.* Whereas healthy behavior patterns use the body organs, social conventions, and language in a manner which establishes and maintains positive interaction with others, *the symptoms of illness serve only as self-expression.* Usually this is not understandable to others or to the patient himself, because the conscious mind is generally out of touch with the deeper self. This deeper self asserts itself in the form of illness when the existential situation frustrates a specific need of the personality. If these needs cannot be expressed in realistic, "healthy" form, symbolic organ language takes over. This is illustrated by our previous example of the epileptic. Under the average conditions of his life he is, for all practical purposes, healthy, although he is identified with his specific liability by the pattern of his brain waves and by his unconscious reaction pattern. Only when his personal problem is excessively intensified does the expression of controlled rage change from rigidity of social manners to abnormal physical behavior, the seizure. The term "abnormal" requires qualification. Every human being is capable of going into an epileptic fit, but most people do so only in reaction to extreme stimulation, e.g., as it is applied in the form of electroshock therapy. What sets the epileptic apart is his constitutional tendency to react thus extremely to situations which do not affect the majority of people in this way.

It is probably true of most diseases that they are de-

[7] Nikalaas Tinbergen, *The Study of Instinct,* New York: Oxford University Press, 1955.

termined decisively by specific combinations of genes. This does not mean that the genes directly cause the pathological symptoms, but that *they excessively favor the use of one normal biological potential over others.* Even the very abnormal behavior of the cancer cell represents a regression to the earliest level of life when energy was derived from fermentation rather than oxidation.[8] Before examining more examples of the relation between disease and physiological functions, it is necessary to point out that constitutional dispositions must be understood as involving not only the body but also its environment. The principle that the inner and outer world are systematically interrelated was demonstrated first by the biologist Von Uexküll. As he formulated it: "There are as many worlds as there are subjects. These subjective worlds are formed by limited numbers of spatial elements, movement patterns, time elements and qualities of content."[9] Insofar as the subjects belong to the same species, their worlds are similar but apparently, even on primitive levels, not identical. Constitutional dispositions in human beings, often inherited independently, carry the implication of certain corresponding worlds of their own. One may describe them as Von Uexküll describes animal species: "independent organisms with their own characters and extremely long durations of life."

The specific worlds of constitutional types have been analyzed and described very fully by Szondi.[10] Through clinical description and through his personality test[11] he demonstrated that the difference between healthy and sick carriers of the same genes is of a quantitative nature. Epilepsy, for instance, is the most extreme form of a way of life which is concerned with the control of aggression, and the same way of life may also take a healthy form such as religious or medical vocation or fire-fighting; paranoia is an excessive development of a tendency to get involved in the personalities of others, etc. The constitutional types tend to attract each other sexually, thus perpetuating the group because

[8] O. Warburg, *Über den Stoffwechsel der Tumoren,* Berlin: Springer, 1926.

[9] J. Von Uexküll, *Theoretical Biology,* New York: Harcourt, Brace and Company, 1926.

[10] L. Szondi, *Schicksalanalyse,* Basel: Benno Schwabe, 1944.

[11] L. Szondi, V. Moser, and M. Webb, *The Szondi Test,* Philadelphia: J. B. Lippincott Co., 1959.

the latent genes are combined in the offspring and become more effective. If it were not for this unconscious attraction of latent tendencies, some rare hereditary diseases probably would have become extinct, since the mating of the carriers due to chance encounters is statistically unlikely.

In organic diseases the differences between the constitutional types can be classified by means of the Rorschach test. The same ten standard inkblots are perceived differently by different clinical groups. This does not mean that there is no overlap; hardly any response is unique for any one group. If one evaluates all of the responses of one patient, however, it nearly always appears that the majority of his responses fit the clinical type rather than the type of the control group.[12] It is self-evident that the consistency of the inner and outer world of each individual provides the conditions for a specific life-pattern. Each human being represents a mosaic of different hereditary dispositions whose dynamic influence varies according to the dominant or latent character of the specific genes. The total of these dispositions accounts for the phenomenon Freud described as "the striving of the organism to safeguard its own individual path toward death."[13] He gave it, because of his pessimistic outlook, the unfortunate name *Todestrieb,* translated even more misleadingly as "death instinct." Actually it is not death but the *way of life* which is meant. Illnesses are part of the individual way of life; they represent the individual mode of approach to the natural end of physical existence.

## ILLNESS AND VALUES

The preceding remarks about illness as expression of personality may impress the reader as mere speculative generalizations of psychoanalytic theory. To illustrate the practical importance of the concept, a few of the most impressive examples may be described which indicate that since prehistoric times mankind has been developing a few clearly distinguishable personality types which are related to major forms of physical illness.

[12] Gotthard Booth, "Organ Function and Form Perception," *Psychosomatic Medicine,* 8:367, 1946.

[13] Sigmund Freud, *Beyond the Pleasure Principle,* New York: Liveright Publishing Corp., 1922, and Bantam Books, Inc., 1959.

The first of these types can be traced back to the period 30,000 years ago when the prehistoric *hunters* left the pictorial record of their heroic lives on the walls of caves in France and Spain. Their pattern of culture has been preserved into the present by primitive tribes of the Old and the New World. What distinguishes the hunters from the earlier food gatherers is their pursuit of big game like the ancient mammoth and cave bear, the modern elephant and buffalo. Such a daring innovation as tackling creatures of far superior physical power presupposes the evolution of a breed of men distinguished by individual initiative and prowess. The religions of the hunters reflect an emphasis on *personality*. The spirit of man is experienced as transcending his physical existence; he is considered individually immortal. Leadership is exercised by men or women who feel moved by spontaneous visions to assume the role of shamans. Their inspiration is accepted as genuine by the tribe.

A contrasting personality type became distinguishable in the subsequent emergence of the *planters* about 10,000 years ago. Here survival becomes based not on the capacity to fight individually against acute threats but on the *subordination of the individual* to the seasonal demands made by the plants he cultivates. The planter community entails a carefully structured collective organization of life which must be attuned to the cosmic order; the role of the leader himself becomes a matter of observing laws. Not individual inspiration but traditional ritual confers priesthood in planter societies. The emphasis on the group is expressed in a concept of immortality which differs from that of the hunters. Immortality is identified with the survival of the tribe in this world rather than the survival of the individual in the spirit realm. Nothing expresses the difference between hunters and planters more convincingly than the fact that ritualistic human sacrifice has been discovered only among planters in widely separated parts of the world. This point is further stressed by the fact that the victims have been selected for physical perfection or for high social rank.

The preceding descriptions of the individualistic hunters and the collectivistic planters[14] correspond in great detail to the conclusions derived from the psychological study of

[14] Joseph Campbell, *The Masks of God,* New York: Viking Press, Inc., 1959.

*the two most frequent forms of chronic illness in the United States.* Rheumatic diseases on the one hand and afflictions of the heart and the circulation on the other shared about equally in accounting for 14.5 million out of the total of 25 million persons who were found in 1937 to suffer from chronic ailments.[15] The similarity between the anthropological and the clinical findings is particularly convincing because the clinical findings were published 13 years before Campbell brought the anthropological ones to the attention of a wider public.[16]

*Rheumatic disabilities of muscles and joints* affect those who have lived in their days of health as much like the primitive hunters as modern culture allows. The members of this group are characterized by enjoyment of physical activity for its own sake, not for prestige or health. Their actions are motivated by the need for individualistic self-assertion even in the face of social opposition and great odds against practical success.

*Diseases of the heart and blood vessels* are typical of those who, like the planters, have been motivated by social expectations—physical activities, whether work or competitive sports, having been undertaken only in order to comply with outside demands. To give two clinical illustrations: An arthritic clerk used to carry his light briefcase "as if it were a bucket full of water." On the other hand an arteriosclerotic clerk continued for a whole year after the loss of his job his daily routine of going to the business district and returning in the evening so that nobody in the neighborhood would know of his social failure.

The connection between disease symptom and personality is understandable. Since rheumatism goes with a condition of intensified muscular tension and effort, it expresses symbolically a predominant need for action. When illness, old age, or overwhelming obstacles have defeated the self-assertion of the individual, the organ of action becomes the center of self-expression and its pain becomes a heightened form of self-experience.

The diseases of the cardiovascular group express dependency on the given environment because the bloodstream represents the primordial environment of all life. The blood is

[15] Booth, "Organ Function and Form Perception."
[16] Campbell.

a bit of encapsulated and developed seawater pulsing through the higher organisms even as the ocean supported the first living cells. When internal or external conditions deprive individuals of a milieu toward which they have been primarily oriented, the organs serving the blood circulation become diseased: the muscles in the walls of the arteries become tense, the walls degenerate, the heart fails. The meaning of milieu for this personality type is expressed most drastically in cases of sudden death. Instances have been observed both in human beings and in animals in which the heart of an organically healthy individual stopped because of panic when he was faced with the loss of the supporting social environment—the so-called voodoo death.[17] The most frequent form of interdependence between milieu and heart disease was illustrated by the heart attack of President Eisenhower; it came at a time he felt uncertain whether the majority of the American people wanted him to run for reelection. After his experience of a "heartening" popular reaction there was no recurrence for eight years (i.e., to the time of this writing), although age is a definite factor in heart disease.

The manifestation of the two major prehistoric value systems in two major contemporary clinical groups is understandable, for modern populations are derived from both hunter and planter ancestors. Each cultural group apparently inbred and developed specific gene constellations. As the research by Szondi indicates, even in a mixed population the mutual attraction between carriers of latent genes perpetuates specific variants of mankind. The survival of the two types is obviously no longer based on the external necessities which favored their origin. The complex and manifold opportunities of industrial society allow each type to select his individual world either of self-assertion or of conformity. This is illustrated very clearly by means of the Rorschach test. Each type selects from ten non-representational inkblot pictures the features which are congenial to his attitude toward the world at large, just as a zoologist and a botanist walking together through the woods will observe more animals or more plants, respectively.

[17] C. P. Richter, "The Phenomenon of Sudden Unexplained Death in Animals and Men," in Herman Feifel, ed., *The Meaning of Death,* New York: McGraw-Hill Book Co., 1959.

The continued presence of the two prehistoric personality types is very obvious in our Judeo-Christian tradition. Although the forms of religion have developed far beyond shamanism and the rituals of human sacrifice, the essence of both has stayed in evidence in the coexistence of prophetic individualism and priestly conservatism. We have Moses, Jesus, and Luther who defied the formidable powers surrounding them, but we also have our high feast days which are synchronized with the annual rhythm of nature. Christianity as the individualistic departure from Judaism generally emphasizes the immortality of the soul, whereas Judaism has survived 2,000 years of minority existence because it has been committed since Moses to the responsibility of preserving the chosen people.

The elaboration of the two contrasting types of relationship between man and environment may have diverted attention from the feature they have in common: both have been formed by a dependency on subhuman organisms. Only those of our primitive ancestors survived who were capable of observing "religiously" the laws by which animals and plants exist. There was a great deal of identification between the hunters and their game, between the planters and their plants. That they all inflicted death on one another was part of existence. It was acceptable as a dramatic episode in a life which transcended *physical* existence. This faith was not unrealistic. Measured and tested pragmatically, the religions of the hunters and of the planters have proved themselves adequate to maintain their adherents since prehistoric times.

The emergence of technological man has added a new perspective to the relationship between way of life and liability to disease. Nature was once regarded as the awe-inspiring manifestation of a divine spirit. Survival demanded a worshipful attitude toward nature even when that attitude was intellectualized as the scientific study of natural laws. Now that modern science and industry have made it possible to interfere with the natural order to an extent beyond the imagination of previous generations, man increasingly sees himself as the conqueror of nature, and in the field of medicine specifically as the conqueror of disease. During the past hundred years, the latter undertaking has seemed to achieve spectacular success in the war against microbes. Antisepsis, asepsis, vaccines, and chemical compounds have contributed to reducing infectious disease and extended the average life expectancy of the population. This success has been a Pyrrhic victory, however, for as more and more researchers have realized cancer is steadily increasing as the infectious diseases decrease. It has become apparent that this phenomenon is due not to the fact that more people reach the "cancer age," as was at first supposed, but rather to the fact that cancer is directly related to the antibacterial defenses of the body.[18] In previous ages man lived in generally peaceful symbiosis with bacteria. Only under special circumstances, as when the body had been weakened by malnutrition, emotional frustration, or old age, did the bacteria gain the upper hand. By contrast, cancer has never been connected with any living organism. All known cancerogenic agents are either inanimate substances or viruses, which are inanimate chemicals unless they are brought into contact with living cells.

The connection between technological progress and the changing balance of infectious and cancerous diseases is not simply an unfortunate by-product of certain scientific inadequacies of medicine. The root of both developments is found in the emergence of a new personality type. The so-called conquest of nature is not the result of intellectual advance but of a different motivation in the use of the intellect. The question has often been asked why the Greeks and the Romans did not develop industrialism, since they had the necessary scientific and intellectual sophistication. The answer is suggested by a psychological comparison between two disease groups which are representative of the old and the new type of man: tuberculosis and cancer.[19]

The use of the Rorschach method, as in the previous study of individualism and collectivism, has led to the following conclusions.

In *tuberculosis* the patient's personality has been originally and predominantly directed toward the establishment of *mutual* relationships with other human beings. Such relationships can be sublimated into involvement with imper-

[18] H. C. Nauts, G. A. Fowler, and F. H. Bogatko, *A Review of the Influence of Bacterial Infection and Bacterial Products in Man,* Stockholm: Acta Med. Scand., 1953.

[19] Gotthard Booth, "Cancer and Humanism," in *Third International Conference on Psychosomatic Aspects of Neoplastic Disease,* London: Pitman, 1964.

sonal causes and ideals, but the striving is always toward that which is valued as much as the self. The closest biological example of this type of relatedness is obviously the sexual striving for union in which both partners are of equal importance. Psychoanalysis has described personalities in which this motivation predominates as *genital* types. Tuberculosis may be understood as the expression of a frustrated need for affectionate involvement with another person. The destructive symbiosis with the tuberculosis bacterium takes the place of an unobtainable human partner.

In *cancer* one finds that the patient has originally been concerned with the establishment of *control over objects,* in the broadest sense of the word object. Not mutuality and partnership but the security of the particular relationship valued by this individual is needed. This trait does not imply that these patients have been selfish or possessive, nor that they have necessarily been aggressive in their attitudes toward others. Many have been self-sacrificing parents, physicians, or nurses, or religious and political idealists, although in one-sided, inflexible ways. Disease strikes them when their particular object seems to have been irretrievably lost, a fact suspected since antiquity and documented abundantly in modern times by LeShan.[20] Psychoanalysis has defined this personality type as the *anal* character. The designation is based upon the observation that in the psychological development of these individuals the dynamic pattern of the anal function, that is, the earliest infantile experience of controlling an inanimate object, retains particular importance. In later life the connection between the bowels and social attitudes is usually forgotten, although served.[21] This unconscious association is probably one of the causes of the widespread reluctance to consider the role of personality in the predisposition toward cancer.[22] The contrast between anal and genital character is well documented in the work of Freud. As a scientist he devoted himself to the study of sex as the basic life force, but as a cancer personality he could never overcome his defensive reaction to the fact that sex makes the mates interdependent. Even in one of his last

[20] Nauts, Fowler, and Bogatko.

[21] R. Abrams, and J. E. Finesinger, "Guilt Reactions in Patients With Cancer," *Cancer,* 6:474, 1953.

[22] Booth, "Cancer and Humanism"; G. Engel, "Selection of Clinical Material in Psychosomatic Medicine," *Psychosomatic Medicine,* 16:368, 1954.

essays[23] he concluded that for both male and female sex inescapably involves an injury to the individual. He assumed that both sexes unconsciously are *anxious for control* over the penis: castration fear and penis envy are considered the "organic rock bottom of psychoanalysis."

A cancer can be understood as a symbolic substitute for the lost object. In the earlier life of the cancer patient *the object has played the role of an extension of the self,* even when it has been another individual. The tumor, as an outgrowth of the body, symbolizes the lost object.[24] The cells of the tumor do not interact with other living organisms as is the case in bacterial infection. They react to inanimate substances which become part of the cell chemistry, changing the cell's metabolism so that the cancer becomes independent of oxygen. Thus even on the cellular level cancer symbolizes the autonomy which has been the predominant aim of the patient in his days of health.

## SACRIFICE

The rise of cancer and the decline of infectious disease express a shift to a different value system. It can be understood as parallel to the change from a theocentric to an anthropocentric orientation of humanity. These terms are used in a purely descriptive sense: the concept of God implies a living being who transcends human power and on whom man therefore depends for his own existence. The image of God has changed in history as human awareness of the world has changed its focus: from the large animals of the hunters to the crops of the planters and finally to the image of the creative power of man himself, the being with whom man can entertain dialogue in spite of the difference in power. In all stages of this development man has existed by virtue of his ability to subordinate his individual life to his image of the divine realm: the hunter risked his life in contesting powerful creatures, the planter in accepting human sacrifice, the Jew and Christian in bearing witness against worshipers of subhuman gods.

[23] Sigmund Freud, "Analysis Terminable and Interminable," *Collected Papers,* Vol. 5, London: Hogarth Press, 1950.

[24] Booth, "Cancer and Humanism"; W. B. Quisenberry, "Sociological Factors in Cancer in Hawaii," in Vera Rubin *et al., Culture, Society and Health, Annals of the New York Academy of Science,* 84:795, 1961.

In the preceding section it was pointed out that the secularized descendants of religious ancestors continue to subordinate themselves to the old values. These values have retained a numinous quality for them. Individualists are still lamed in the contest with the superior powers of their environment; conformists are still victimized by failure of their blood circulation as they struggle to keep up with conventional standards; those needing to share emotions with other persons are still made sick by bacteria and parasites. Many of them have been made aware by doctors that their way of life is unhealthy, but they continue even though no shaman or priest can be held responsible. *Life is sacrificed for the sake of values which are natural to the individual.*

The increased life span of modern man expresses a new attitude toward physical existence. This new attitude is the result of the spreading gospel of humanism which asserts against all previous theistic concepts that man must assume full responsibility for his fate and that his physical existence is his highest good. Scientists and politicians have therefore concentrated on improving material conditions for the greatest number of people in order to preserve life for the longest possible time. These efforts have succeeded spectacularly. Whereas all classical antiquity and medieval England added only 8 and 12 years respectively to the 20 years average life expectancy of prehistoric man, contemporary man has added 38 years more within just the past 400 years. In other words, the threescore and ten years that formed the highest limit of natural life in biblical times is now within the reach of almost everyone.

This success story is all too often told with no mention of the price. In the periods in which man was integrated into the living forms of nature, individuals consciously or unconsciously sacrificed their lives for the sake of participating in nature's values. As the humanists asserted the superior value of the life span, they sacrificed the old values. The new values of inanimate nature as increasingly controlled by technology and science have gained ascendancy. Man as the master of nature surrounds himself more and more with inanimate objects and machines which he can manipulate and dispose of. Activities are synchronized with clocks, results are measured in money. Art has become "nonobjective" and "nonrepresentational"; medicine has accepted the ominous word "antibiotics." The "No" to symbiotic life has invaded even sexuality. The union of man and woman has turned into the use of the partner for the achievement of a sexual outlet, a purpose for which a member of one's own sex may often be preferable. Dancing, which used to express various aspects of natural sexuality, has developed into the "twist," the motions of which run counter to all directions associated with copulation. In this dance, the equality of the sexes and their independence from each other is emphasized. For many the womb has become as expendable an organ as the appendix.

All such phenomena illustrate an estrangement from living nature which is inherent in the increase of the anal at the expense of the genital personality type. The industrial process is in many respects an elaboration of the digestive aspect of the organism: animate and inanimate parts of the world are transformed into materials which can be used for personal survival without creating new organisms. It appears therefore consistent that those who are predominantly dedicated to values inherent in self-preservation will be rewarded with longer lives, but will also transform some vital organ into a self-sufficient object. It is also consistent that the common forms of therapy in cancer rely specifically on machines and on discoveries concerning the physicochemical aspects of biology. The cancer patient in the midst of the machinery of the modern hospital is a sad postscript to the volume of more than 200 years ago in which a physician highlighted the medical aspect of the Enlightenment and humanism: *L'Homme machine.*[25] The author expected that the mechanistic approach would lead to the unimpeded enjoyment of life. Experience has taught us otherwise. Machines do not enjoy themselves, and to the extent man has identified himself with machines he has sacrificed the joys of his pretechnological ancestors.

## HEALING

Physical disease seems to teach a negative lesson, that man comes through sickness unto death by living according to his own individual nature. It is the function best en-

[25] J. O. de La Mettrie, *L'Homme Machine,* Leyden, 1748.

dowed for life which becomes sick and causes the fall from health. We have seen that this development cannot be blamed on the environment. The individual selects his own way of relating to the environment even as he selects specific imagery from the many possibilities suggested by Rorschach's ten inkblots. This individual bias is the organic counterpart to what Kierkegaard [26] described as "sickness unto death," the will to be one's own self and to create one's own life according to a personal hierarchy of values.[27]

The negative aspect of illness, however, is only part of the story. Illness also affirms positively that man lives not only on the strength of his preferred function but also by virtue of all those functions and values he has taken for granted. No matter whether his endowment is that of a genius or of an ordinary person, physically he cannot exist unless all his organs are relating to the environment according to their purposes, in action and in dependent existence, as autonomous body and as symbiotic partner of many other organisms. Socially man is also enmeshed in many ways: no matter how individualistic he is, he must find some place in society; no matter how conformist, he must also act individually. He may be aware chiefly of his uniqueness, but he can express that uniqueness only in relation to his fellow man; he may feel only his solidarity with the group, but he must live as a person.

Illness sets the balance straight between preferred and neglected functions: the crippled arthritic has lost the power of independent action, but he continues to live thanks to the orderly function of the other organs and to the milieu of family or state which supports him. The cardiac patient is prevented from conformity with the social order, but he can use his limbs freely enough to move in a restricted sphere of life. The tuberculosis patient is too weak to participate emotionally in symbiotic existence and must concentrate on his own self. The cancer patient loses control over his self-created world, but he experiences the fate of being subject to the control of others.

These examples of disease as compensation are not oddities but illustrate a general principle. This principle was not

[26] Soren Kierkegaard, "Sickness Unto Death," in R. Bretall, ed., *A Kierkegaard Anthology,* Princeton, N.J.: Princeton University Press, 1946.

[27] Booth, "Values in Nature and in Psychotherapy."

discovered with respect to physical illness but in psychiatry by Jung,[28] who was the first physician to point out the full medical significance of the different psychological types of mankind. These types are distinguished by the overdifferentiation of one's function. One-sidedness leads to illness because sooner or later each type encounters a situation which cannot be met realistically by the leading function, but rather requires one of the undifferentiated functions; e.g., feeling might be required from a thinking type. In consequence the neglected function does take over although it is poorly prepared for the task. All this is bearing out the prophecy that "many that are first will be last, and the last first." (Matthew 19:30)

If we view health in its basic meaning as *wholeness* then the way through sickness to death is a way of health. Through the laws of nature we sacrifice those conscious attitudes which have set us apart as individuals. This formulation may appear excessively psychological since it disregards common concepts of physical health and makes the psyche alone significant, whether it be conscious or unconscious. It should be considered, however, that the decay of the body, whether rapid or retarded, is an inherent part of man's participation in life. The statement in the General Confession of the Book of Common Prayer, "There is no health in us," has given expression to this concept that man does not find his fulfillment in his own person.

Religions have at all times and in all places expressed an intuitive insight into the meaning of illness and death. Ritualistic sacrifice seems to be a conscious and deliberate anticipation of the effects of the natural process intended to give death the dignity of a free human act.[29] In this respect it is noteworthy that the sacrifices of prehistoric and contemporary hunting tribes consist in the amputation of finger joints "although" hands are particularly important for the hunter, whereas the planters sacrifice human lives "although" existence on this earth is their main concern.[30]

The concept of sacrifice in voluntary or involuntary form is not a part of modern secular thinking. Man as the

[28] C. G. Jung, "Psychological Types," *Collected Works,* Vol. 6, New York: Pantheon Books, Inc., 1958.

[29] Gotthard Booth, "Variety in Personality and Its Relation to Health," *Review of Religion,* 10:385, 1946.

[30] Campbell.

conqueror of nature strives for an ideal of total personal health. Illness is therefore conceptualized as damage inflicted by the still unconquered parts of nature. To accept illness as the expression of an intrinsic limitation of the personality represents a fundamental denigration of the image of man. Modern medicine has therefore flagrantly sidestepped the insight which was so evident to religious ages, that man is "[his] own executioner" (John Donne, *Devotion XII).*[31] In the hope of controlling disease, after the example of scientific victories over inanimate matter, the body is regarded as a machine which is supposed to function only according to the laws of physics and chemistry. This automatically excludes personality from consideration. An example of this intellectual blindness is provided by research on cervical cancer. Several investigators have established that this disease is nonexistent among nuns, but particularly frequent in women who have started sexual activities early in life.[32] The attempts at explaining this have considered physical trauma and virus infection, but have not even mentioned that there must be a difference between the personalities of girls taking vows of lifelong chastity and those who start an active and often promiscuous sex life in their teens.

The recognition of disease as an expression of personality gives the art of healing a wider scope than that provided by physical theories. The latter theories often deal very effectively with the physical agents which are involved, but they do not answer the question of why a person became ill in a specific form and at a particular time. Certainly many people recover from illness as a result of physical therapy without gaining any psychological insight. When we deal with serious conditions, however, such as those described in this chapter, it becomes important to inquire into the way of life which has been involved in the sickness. This inquiry gives the physician an opportunity to help the patient in achieving a healthier way of life instead of merely strengthening him for the continued pursuit of the old one-sided values which led to illness. The attempt to effect such inner change in a patient is certainly more difficult than the treat-

[31] John Donne, in John Hayward, ed., *Complete Poetry and Selected Prose,* Bloomsbury: The Nonesuch Press, 1929, p. 529.

[32] I. D. Rotkin, "Relation of Adolescent Coitus to Cervical Cancer Risk," *Journal of the American Medical Association,* 179:486, 1962.

ment of physical symptoms, but its success can mean a great deal for the future. Not only is it important for the physician to understand the patient, when a cure can be effected, but, since every person must die, it is most important that death be understood as a meaningful conclusion to the trial by life. This part of illness has been much neglected in the development of powerful physical methods. Specialists have more and more replaced the family physician who observed the personalities of his patients in their normal environment and who saw it as his task "to watch over the life *and death* of [God's] creatures."[33]

The death of every human being expresses in a unique way the message of the Crucifixion. The mortal body and personal initiative are brought to their end on the cross of the superpersonal *law,* the law of biological existence. The vertical beam may be seen as the symbol of the hierarchical order of the world in which the individual is contained, the horizontal beam as a symbol of the symbiotic dependency of man. It has concerned me for many years that the cross is seen so often without the body of the Christ. Is not this the body through which the evolution of all men has passed from generation to generation, transcending forever the law which would endlessly repeat the same patterns of life? It is the dignity of each human being which is expressed by the voice of illness and death, the dignity of having chosen his own way to end. The person may seem insignificant, may be unconscious of any meaning, but he has participated in the physical fate of Christ even as the two thieves did. Contemplating the sick and the dead we learn that there is always a meaning which transcends the law that calls on us to understand and to act with as much purpose as we can. "The Son of God suffered unto the death, not that men might not suffer, but that their suffering might be like His."[34]

[33] A. E. Cohen, "The Daily Prayer of a Clergyman-Physician," *Journal of Religion and Health,* 1:64, 1961.

[34] G. MacDonald, Quoted in C. S. Lewis, *The Problem of Pain,* New York: The Macmillan Company, 1944.

## ADDITIONAL REFERENCES

"Irrational Complications of the Cancer Problem," *American Journal of Psychoanalysis,* 25:41, 1965.

"Krebs und Tuberkulose im Rorschachschen Formdeuteversuch," *Ztschr. f. Psycho-somatische Med.,* 10:176, 1964.

"The Cancer Patient and the Minister," *Pastoral Psychology,* Feb. 15, 1966.

Gotthard Booth, "The Psychological Examination of Candidates for the Ministry," in Hans Hofmann, ed., *The Ministry and Mental Health,* New York: Association Press, 1960.

E. Wittkower, *A Psychiatrist Looks at Tuberculosis.* London: National Association for the Prevention of Consumption and Other Forms of Tuberculosis, 1949.

# 8

# Religion and Psychopathology

*Orville S. Walters*

RELIGIOUS FAITH and practice play a tremendous role in the patterning of the emotional life, the thinking, and the behavior of men. After declaring this fact, an authoritative psychiatric body advises the psychiatrist to look most seriously at religion and learn to take it adequately into account in understanding and treating sick men.[1]

Religion and psychopathology are not infrequently found together. Religious preoccupation in incipient psychosis is well known. Religious ideas may also be interwoven with neurosis. This occasional mingling of religion and pathology makes it important that the psychiatrist be able to

ORVILLE S. WALTERS, M.D., is Psychiatrist and Director of Student Health Service, University of Illinois, Urbana, Illinois.

[1] Psychiatry and Religion: Some Steps Toward Mutual Understanding and Usefulness, Rept. 48, New York: Group for the Advancement of Psychiatry, 1960.

differentiate between normal and pathologic in religious expression.

Starbuck, one of the earliest students of the psychology of religion, stated the need of criteria for differentiating between normal and pathologic.[2]

> The value of the study of persons in groups is that it *establishes certain standards by which to judge individual instances.* To have well-established types by which to estimate religious phenomena is as important in the sphere of spiritual things as to have standards of distance in physics and astronomy, or laws and principles and formulas in mathematics and chemistry. It is of even greater importance, inasmuch as the data are intangible (p. 409).

Many students of personality deny the possibility of drawing a definite distinction between normal and pathologic. Jahoda's review[3] recognizes the difficulty of finding a basis for agreement on the concept of mental health but acknowledges that the individual's relation to reality is an essential criterion.

Starbuck was aware of the difficulty of establishing criteria of normality.

> No two persons will agree upon the limit at which normal religious experiences pass over into pathological. Where the line of demarcation will fall depends largely on one's general attitude toward religion, and on one's temperamental attitude toward human experiences, which allows them a wide or narrow range. There are the alienists, too, who are constantly on the lookout for some abnormal tendency, and, consequently, are sure to find it (p. 163).

### VARIETIES OF RELIGIOUS PSYCHOPATHOLOGY

The best known study in the psychology of religion is William James's *Varieties of Religious Experience.*[4] James described his Gifford Lectures as "a laborious attempt to extract from the privacies of religious experience some general facts which can be defined in formulas upon which everybody may agree" (p. 433). After passing in review a large

[2] E. D. Starbuck, *The Psychology of Religion,* New York: Charles Scribner's Sons, 1906.

[3] M. Jahoda, *Current Concepts of Positive Mental Health,* New York: Basic Books, Inc., 1958.

[4] W. James, *Varieties of Religious Experience,* New York: Longmans, Green, 1902.

number of widely diverse personal histories, he undertakes "to reduce religion to its lowest admissible terms" as a basis for broad agreement upon the validity of religious experience (p. 503). James concludes, "I only translate into schematic language what I may call the instinctive belief of mankind: God is real since he produces real effects" (p. 517).

James had no interest in differentiating between normal and pathologic in religious expression. In the process of cooking down religious experience to determine its essential components, he made no effort to screen out the atypical and bizarre to eliminate the influence of psychopathology upon the final result. Instead he took as his major premise, "If there were such a thing as inspiration from a higher realm, it might well be that the neurotic temperament would furnish the chief condition of the requisite receptivity" (p. 25).

Those "best able to give an intelligible account of their ideas and motives," James contended (p. 3), are the "religious geniuses" who have invariably been "creatures of exalted emotional sensibility," subject to melancholy, obsessions, trances, voices, visions and "all sorts of peculiarities which are ordinarily classed as pathological" (p. 7). Frankly acknowledging his study as a "pathological programme" (p. 21) James asserts that "in the psychopathic temperament we have the emotionality which is the *sine qua non* of moral perception (p. 25). . . . We learn most about a thing when we view it . . . in its most exaggerated form. This is as true of religious phenomena as of any other kind of fact" (p. 39). The essence of religious experience, he insists, is most prominent in those which are most one-sided, exaggerated and intense (p. 45).

This selective bias which granted a higher order of authenticity to the more extreme forms of religious expression sprinkled James's pages with psychopathology. These "violenter" examples were by no means essential to the fulfillment of his objective. He acknowledges in introducing one of the more ordinary of his documents, "Probably thousands of unpretending Christians would write an almost identical account" (p. 70). James himself asks, "Why not leave pathological questions out?" In answer, he pleads his own irrepressible curiosity and the dubious premise that a thing is better understood in its exaggerations and perversions (p. 21).

James's logic was sound up to the point of selecting his data. Since religion reports what claim to be facts, it is only proper to examine the evidence. The objective truth of the experience will hinge upon the reliability of the reports (pp. 507, 509). At this point James begged the question of reliable reporting by enunciating the premise that psychopathology enhances capacity for religious insight and interpretative authority.

James was immediately criticized by Starbuck, according to Perry,[5] because the examples he selected were too extreme (p. 346). Pratt stated flatly that "the great majority of those possessing dissociated mind states have none of the superiorities set forth by James. . . . The highest type of man, in the religious life as well as elsewhere, is the unified and rational self."[6]

The idea that genius is linked with insanity and creativity with illness has been closely examined by Kubie.[7] Taking sharp issue with Freud and many others who have held this view, he concludes, "No critical studies exist which would make of such claims anything more than superficial and somewhat dubious guesses" (p. 3). Rather, Kubie finds, the processes of illness corrupt, mar, distort, and block as the creative potential of the preconscious is captured, imprisoned, nullified, sterilized, and stereotyped by unconscious neurotogenic forces (pp. 52, 141). He speaks of "the insidious, destructive influence of the neurotic process" which arises out of deeper levels of conflict and pain (pp. 13, 55). "The unconscious is our straitjacket," Kubie writes, "rendering us as stereotyped and as sterile and as repetitive as the neurosis itself." He asks, "Can there be wisdom even about the objective world around us (considering how many distorting fantasies we project onto this outer world) in the absence of wisdom about the inner world from which these projections arise?" (pp. 132, 143).

The indiscriminate mingling of reports of religious experience tainted by psychopathology with the experiences of normal persons has tended to stigmatize the whole as pathological. James himself foresaw this possible consequence when he recognized that in using extreme examples "we may

[5] R. B. Perry, *The Thought and Character of William James,* Vol. 2, New York: Little, Brown and Company, 1935.

[6] J. B. Pratt, *The Religious Consciousness,* New York: The Macmillan Company, 1944, p. 67.

[7] L. S. Kubie, *Neurotic Distortion of the Creative Process,* Lawrence: University of Kansas Press, 1958.

thereby swamp the thing in the wholesale condemnation which we pass on its inferior congeners" (p. 22).

The terms "sick soul" and "healthy-minded" coined by William James at first appear to designate categories signifying the presence or absence of psychopathology in religious experience, and have come to be used extensively in this way. However, those who use the terms to convey such meaning have stopped short of grasping James's intention. As his thesis develops, James acknowledges at length that these categories are "somewhat ideal abstractions" that do not exist in fact. "The concrete human beings whom we oftenest meet," he recognized, "are intermediate varieties and mixtures" (p. 167).

> From this point of view, the contrasts between the healthy and the morbid mind, and between the once-born and the twice-born types . . . cease to be the radical antagonisms which many think them. . . . In many instances, it is quite arbitrary whether we class the individual as a once-born or a twice-born subject (p. 488).

Indeed, James understood at first hand the lability inherent in these categories; his biographer acknowledges,[8] "James had his times of healthy mindedness and his times of soul-sickness, and he knew both. . . . There were deeper alternations of mood. . . . Oscillation . . . is profoundly characteristic of James's nature" (pp. 671, 680).

James recognized the inadequacy of "healthy-mindedness" as a way of meeting life and accepted the cogency of the ascetic view. "Healthy-mindedness pure and simple can hardly be regarded by any thinking man as a serious solution. . . . Asceticism must, I believe, be acknowledged to go with the profounder way of handling the gift of existence" (p. 364). This personal affirmation of faith is supplemented by the statement of Perry[9] that James himself experienced "a feeling of renewed life similar to that of the twice-born" (p. 324).

### RELIGION AND PSYCHOPATHOLOGY IN FREUD

Like James, Freud had a far-reaching influence upon the psychology of religion. His views on religion are still

[8] Perry.
[9] *Ibid.*

commonly found in close association with the thought and practice of psychoanalysis. But the search for criteria to differentiate between normal and pathologic in religious experience receives little help here. Freud's conclusions upon religion were based more upon speculation and theory than empirical observation. His first paper on religion drew an analogy between obsessional neurosis and religious practices. The description of obsessional neurosis is clearly based upon empirical observation, but the constricted concept of religion reflects Freud's unfamiliarity with its nature. The result is a tortured analogy, only one side of which is grounded in acquaintance with the subject.

In 1907 he wrote,[10] "An insight into the origin of neurotic ceremonial may embolden us to draw by analogy inferences about the psychological processes of religious life" (p. 25). At the end of the same paper, by an even bolder flight of analogical speculation, he writes, "One might venture to regard the obsessional neurosis as a pathological counterpart to the formation of a religion, to describe this neurosis as a private religious system, and religion as a universal obsessional neurosis" (p. 34). In 1928 Freud wrote,[11] ". . . the true believer is in a high degree protected against the danger of certain neurotic afflictions; by accepting the universal neurosis he is spared the task of forming a personal neurosis." The "bold analogy" of 1907 became an unqualified assertion in 1928 and by 1960 was considered an established relationship, empirically based:[12] "It was clinical experience that led Freud to see the dynamic relation between neurotic and religious phenomena" (p. 358).

Freud himself may be an example of the distorting and blocking effect of neurosis described by Kubie. Zilboorg,[13] taking note of Freud's lifelong death anxiety (p. 225), described his pessimism and gloominess as symptoms of a depressive neurosis (pp. 133, 134) which permeated much of his thought and which deeply colored his attitude toward religion. Although he is a stout defender of psychoanalysis,

[10] S. Freud, "Obsessive Acts and Religious Practices," *Collected Papers,* Vol. 2, London: Hogarth Press, 1924.

[11] S. Freud, *The Future of an Illusion,* New York: Liveright Publishing Corp., 1949, p. 77.

[12] Psychiatry and Religion, *op. cit.*

[13] G. Zilboorg, *Psychoanalysis and Religion,* New York: Farrar, Straus and Cudahy, 1962.

Zilboorg believed that Freud's view of religion was astigmatic (p. 241), "a caricature which Freud created in order to demolish it with greater ease" (p. 240). He traces by numerous examples the distortions in Freud's own thought resulting from an "unconscious ambivalence which Freud showed in relation to the Hebraic tradition" (p. 231). Zilboorg concluded that Freud cut religion to a size chosen by himself in order to "abolish" it.

Many analysts have expressed agreement with Freud's declaration that his philosophical views on religion were not bound to the clinical data and conclusions of psychoanalysis. Nevertheless, Ginsburg[14] commented that many psychiatrists and psychoanalysts believe that religious acts express neurotic helplessness and sick dependence, inevitably resulting in warped attitudes and crippling experiences. Zilboorg[15] stated that "a great number, if not the majority, of Freudian psychoanalysts look upon atheism as an earmark of scientific superiority, and upon religious worship as an atavism left over from primitive magic and animism" (p. 227). Although psychoanalytic psychiatry is still proposing to learn more about the psychology of religion from "our patients"[16] (p. 358), clarification is needed as to what an analyst with these presuppositions can bring from pathologic personalities to a normative psychology of religion.

### RELIGIOUS CONCERN IN SCHIZOPHRENIA

An understanding of religious symptoms in psychosis is also important to the psychiatrist. Linn and Schwarz[17] have written, "Resemblances between the onset of acute schizophrenia and religious experience are almost a byword." In support of this comment they refer to the writings of Anton T. Boisen as being "of the first importance."

Boisen formulated an explanatory theory following his own schizophrenic illness in 1920 and has supported his hypothesis with extensive writing over the past 40 years. He draws upon the anamnestic material of his own five separate

[14] S. W. Ginsburg, "Concerning Religion and Psychiatry." *Child Study*, 30:12 (Fall), 1953.

[15] Zilboorg.

[16] Psychiatry and Religion, *op. cit.*

[17] L. Linn, and L. W. Schwartz, *Psychiatry and Religious Experience*, New York: Random House, Inc., 1958, pp. 206–7.

psychotic breaks which he describes as "madness of the most profound and unmistakable variety"[18] (p. 9). His explanatory theory has had considerable acceptance and influence, especially within the clinical pastoral training movement that he pioneered.

According to Boisen's hypothesis, psychosis is a religious process in which the disturbed person is trying to assimilate some aspect of ultimate life philosophy. Boisen believes that the emotional upheaval of schizophrenia is a purposive, problem-solving experience[19] (p. 297) that may either make or break personality. Psychosis, therefore, is not to be regarded as evil[20] (p. 69), for it has creative potential (p. 4). Following the breaking up of the psychotic's world, Boisen contends, there may be a reconstruction more splendid than the original[21] (p. 104). He is convinced that this was true in his own experience: "It was necessary for me to pass through the purgatorial fires of horrifying psychosis before I could set foot in my promised land of creative activity"[22] (p. 208). Boisen rests his theory upon deep personal conviction, even though he has not found any clear-cut instances where psychotics have risen to a higher level than before[23] (pp. 114, 115). The idea that psychosis is a potentially constructive, essentially religious process is a theme that runs through all of Boisen's writings.

One group friendly to Boisen's theory believes that psychosis may throw some new light upon normative religious experience. Boisen has actively promoted this idea in his writings,[24] declaring that some persons have emerged from such experiences with new insights. Their eyes have been opened to unsuspected meanings (p. 192), hence mental patients have much to tell us about religion[25] (p. 53).

Clark[26] appears to accept Boisen's idea, asserting that "schizophrenia in its catatonic form may actually favor the

[18] A. Boisen, *Out of the Depths,* New York: Harper & Bros., 1954.

[19] A. Boisen, *The Exploration of the Inner World,* New York: Harper & Bros., 1936.

[20] A. Boisen, *Religion in Crisis and Custom,* New York: Harper & Bros., 1954.

[21] Boisen, *The Exploration of the Inner World.*

[22] Boisen, *Out of the Depths.*

[23] Boisen, *The Exploration of the Inner World.*

[24] *Ibid.*

[25] Boisen, *Religion in Crisis and Custom.*

[26] W. H. Clark, *The Psychology of Religion,* New York: The Macmillan Company, 1958, p. 344.

facing and thinking through of issues." Oates,[27] a pupil of Boisen's, reflects a somewhat similar view:

> The mentally sick person quite often has religious ideas that comment meaningfully upon the sickness of his culture. His own personal grasp of religious reality bursts through the duplicities . . . therefore, the illness itself may have a prophetic element in it. . . . Oriental reverence of the mentally ill as being a bit closer to God at times than other people has just enough truth in it as a superstition to persist in one's own primitive awareness.

Hiltner,[28] also a former pupil of Boisen's, believes that "We are beginning to catch up to the depth of Boisen's original insights." Mowrer,[29] reviewing his own experience, agrees with Boisen that psychosis "may ultimately provide the basis for a firmer grasp upon reality." However, Boisen's view of schizophrenia as a religious process that may inform the psychology of religion begs the question of whether the religious experience of a psychotic is commensurable with that of normal persons, and whether the individual with abnormal perception and thought processes may give a reliable account of spiritual reality.

The most important characteristic of the schizophrenic is impairment of reality testing. However great the distortion produced by neurosis, the neurotic patient does retain his essential orientation to reality. In contrast, the schizophrenic has difficulty in distinguishing between fantasy and reality. His thinking may become illogical and disconnected, with impaired associative activity. Often he is beset by delusions. In addition to his defective thought processes, he is frequently unable to interpret external events correctly because he is the victim of abnormal perceptions. Therefore, the schizophrenic cannot be depended upon for reliable reports. His bizarre thinking and hallucinatory perceptions frequently lead to grotesque distortion of reality.

Schizophrenia is often studied by attempting to assemble or reconstruct prepsychotic patterns and to correlate these with psychotic productions and symptoms. This process may lead to the inference that the two are not only continuous

[27] W. E. Oates, *Religious Factors in Mental Illness,* New York: Association Press, 1955, pp. 99, 100.

[28] Boisen, *Religion in Crisis and Custom,* p. xii.

[29] O. H. Mowrer, "Even There, Thy Hand," *Chicago Theological Seminary Register* 52:1, 1962.

but they stand in the relation of cause and effect. Upon this *post hoc* judgment rests the theory that schizophrenia has a psychogenic etiology.

Boisen[30] not only assumes such an origin for schizophrenia but regards the condition as an essentially valid religious process, citing the schizophrenic's "sense of mystery . . . ideas which he had never before heard and with which he himself seemed to have nothing to do . . . feeling themselves in touch with some mighty personal force they call God."

This approach not only assumes that the psychotic shares a common ground of religious experience with normal people but also that schizophrenic reports of religious reality are trustworthy and that they may enlarge the religious understanding of normal persons. Since the reality testing of most schizophrenics is not reliable, there seems to be no reason for considering their religious observations any more valid than their other reports of reality.

Lowe[31] concluded after studying a series of patients with religious delusions that religious preoccupation was an aftermath of severe personality disturbance, not its cause, and represented severe anxiety rather than truly religious mystical experience.

Bleuler's classic monograph[32] records religious ideation and delusion among schizophrenic patients, but not as a common or prominent feature of the disease. Factors looked upon as causes of the disease are often its consequences, Bleuler believes, if there is any connection between them at all (p. 345).

Bleuler emphasizes the fact that the schizophrenic is going through "thousands of peculiar experiences" with his abnormal perceptions, delusions, and fantasy. If he retains any residue of healthy logic, the psychotic is constrained to construct "explanation-delusions" (p. 131) to justify his deviant thinking and behavior. Bleuler noted that schizophrenics refer abnormal perceptions to whatever complex may happen to be in the foreground of their interest (p. 133).

[30] Boisen, *The Exploration of the Inner World*, pp. 169, 170.

[31] W. L. Lowe, "Psychodynamics in Religious Delusions and Hallucinations," *American Journal of Psychotherapy*, 7:454, 1953.

[32] E. Bleuler, *Dementia Praecox*, New York: International Universities Press, Inc., 1950.

He found, for example, that schizophrenics with previous religious inclination tended to have religious delusions, and doubted whether such delusions ever appear in those without previous religious interest. He acknowledged the possibility that such delusions might arise in persons not religiously inclined originally, but stated, "as yet this has not been proven to me" (p. 391).

Bleuler acknowledged that some patients seem to be better after an acute schizophrenic illness than before, but regarded their insight as defective since the connection between the pathological experiences and the "improved" ego is lacking (p. 257). He was never able to substantiate the evidence for a full, complete rectification of schizophrenic delusional ideas. "As yet," Bleuler wrote, "I have never released a schizophrenic in whom I could not still see distinct signs of the disease" (p. 256).

Both Boisen[33] and Hiltner[34] deprecate Starbuck's insistence upon a distinction between normal and pathologic. Hiltner states that Starbuck refused to concede a religious label to abnormal phenomena. The inclusion of persons with defective reality testing is bound to give a distorted view of modal religious experience. The schizophrenic's impaired perception and association does not bar him from participating in religious worship, but to incorporate the reports of his experience into a normative psychology of religion is comparable to treating the responses of the schizophrenic to questions about bodily functions as illuminating human physiology, or his comments on a meal as contributing to our understanding of nutrition.

The idea that religious symptoms in schizophrenia are the consequence of premorbid religious concern is supported by Boisen's own life history. In his autobiography[35] he traces clearly the strong religious influence of his family and early environment. Premorbid religious concern is also traced clearly in the histories of five VA hospital schizophrenics with religious concern in the series described below, corroborating Bleuler's view.

[33] Boisen, *The Exploration of the Inner World.*

[34] S. Hiltner, "The Psychological Understanding of Religion," in O. Strunk, *Readings in the Psychology of Religion,* Nashville, Tenn.: Abingdon Press, 1959, p. 79.

[35] Boisen, *Out of the Depths,* pp. 34, 38.

## CULTURAL FACTORS IN RELIGIOUS CONCERN

Cultural influence may be responsible for changes observed in the incidence of religious concern among schizophrenics. Boisen's long-time interest in the religious implications of schizophrenia has provided an accumulation of mental hospital data that extends over a considerable period of years. Studying the incidence of religious symptoms in one series of 173 schizophrenic patients, most of whom were chronically ill, Boisen[36] found that 42.8 per cent had no religious concern, 51.4 per cent had moderate, and 5.8 per cent had marked religious concern. Religion was incorporated in the patient's delusional system in nine patients or 5.2 per cent.

In a later series of 78 patients, most of whom were schizophrenic, Boisen found religious concern accentuated in 35.9 per cent, while unaffected in 64.1 per cent. Over a longer period, Boisen[37] has observed that about 10 per cent of newly admitted schizophrenics are likely to have some sense of mystical identification.

A somewhat similar study was made of 68 state hospital patients by a group of theological students under the direction of Oates.[38] Over half of these patients showed an absence of religious concern. An additional 20.6 per cent had very little, if any, religious concern in the prepsychotic experience but turned to religion as a "last straw" measure.

Southard,[39] a hospital chaplain, made a similar survey of 170 state hospital patients, based upon his own admission interviews. Two-thirds of these patients showed no interest in religion.

The present author tabulated religious concern found in the psychiatric examination of 105 unselected patients admitted to the acute intensive treatment service of a VA neuropsychiatric hospital over a two-year period.

Diagnoses were distributed as follows:

| | |
|---|---|
| Schizophrenia | 37 |
| Psychoneuroses | 34 |
| Personality disorders | 29 |

[36] Boisen, *The Exploration of the Inner World,* p. 51.

[37] A. Boisen, "The Genesis and Significance of Mystical Identification in Cases of Mental Disorder," *Psychiatry,* 15:287, 1952.

[38] W. E. Oates, "The Role of Religion in the Psychoses," in *Religion in Human Behavior,* New York: Association Press, 1954, p. 88.

[39] S. Southard, "Religious Concern in the Psychoses," *Journal of Pastoral Care,* 10:226, 1956.

| | |
|---|---|
| Chronic brain syndrome | 4 |
| Psychotic depression | 1 |

Of the 105 patients, seven or 7.7 per cent manifested religious concern. Two of these were diagnosed as anxiety reaction and five as schizophrenic reaction. Considering schizophrenic patients separately, five or 18.5 per cent of the 37 displayed religious concern. The great majority of those psychiatric patients showed neither religious symptoms nor concern.

Klaf and Hamilton,[40] in a comparison of schizophrenic symptoms in the nineteenth and twentieth centuries, were struck by the fact that religious preoccupations were three times more common in the earlier period than now. They deprecate the view that analysis of schizophrenic symptoms is likely to illuminate the cause of the illness and believe that if contemporary psychoanalysts had been considering patient material of the mid-nineteenth century, they would have been forced to consider religious disturbance as a prime factor in the etiology of schizophrenia. Klaf and Hamilton are convinced that both the religious and the sexual preoccupation of the schizophrenic are culturally determined. Tracing the strong religious influence that pervaded nineteenth-century England, they conclude:

> Small wonder, then, that the schizophrenics of the period were preoccupied with religion, when nearly every other member of the society was. It does not seem strange that a mid-nineteenth century adult, having been trained to flee the fires of Hell since childhood, should hear God's voice and fear His retribution after developing a schizophrenic illness. Or, to draw an analogy that may or may not be far-fetched, the mid-twentieth century adult, exposed to our society's preoccupation with sex, may be expected to develop sexual preoccupations during a schizophrenic illness. We wish to point out that such preoccupations may be culturally determined. Looking for the aetiology of schizophrenic illness in a detailed analysis of religious and/or sexual delusions or hallucinations appears to be a futile search.

A similar cultural transition may be seen in the nonreligious explanations invoked by the schizophrenic to account for his abnormal sensations and perceptions. Tausk[41]

[40] F. C. Klaf, and J. G. Hamilton, "Schizophrenia—a Hundred Years Ago and Today," *Journal of Mental Science,* 107:819, 1961.

[41] V. Tausk, "On the Origin of the 'Influencing Machine' in Schizophrenia," *Psychoanalytic Quarterly,* 2:519, 1933.

in 1918 gave a classic description of the "influencing machine" so common in the schizophrenic's delusional system. Tausk's patients attributed their changed thoughts and feelings to machines utilizing invisible wires, electricity, magnetism, or X-rays. Visual hallucinations were often blamed upon the effects of a "magic lantern." Tausk concluded, "With the progressive popularization of the sciences, all the forces known to technology are utilized to explain the functioning of the apparatus." The continuing popularization of science has indeed brought a corresponding change in schizophrenic explanation-delusions. Radio, radar, and TV are now commonly invoked to account for contemporary hallucinations and abnormal thought processes.

## RELIGION IN A CONTEXT OF HEALTH

Psychology of religion has become preoccupied with psychopathology. Clinical pastoral training has been permeated extensively by psychoanalytic psychology and has been strongly influenced by the view of its founder that schizophrenia is a religious process. When William James enlarged religious experience to include religious pathology, and Freud extended psychopathology to include religion, the boundaries between normal and pathologic were submerged in the process. In consequence, the psychology of religion has come to appear as a melange of health and disease without reliable criteria to tell which is which.

No such dilemma exists. Both psychoanalytic and operational criteria have been offered. Kubie[42] holds that conduct is neurotic when the unconscious dominates and is normal when the conscious-preconscious alliance is dominant. Redlich[43] states that the extremely abnormal, both psychotic and severely neurotic, can usually be clearly recognized by both lay and expert. He proposes the "social agreement" that leads to psychiatric treatment as an operational approach to the concept of normality, whether it comes through external pressure or voluntary private arrangement. DeSanctis[44] as-

[42] L. S. Kubie, "The Fundamental Nature of the Distinction Between Normality and Neurosis," *Psychoanalytic Quarterly,* 23:167, 1954.

[43] F. C. Redlich, "The Concept of Normality," *American Journal of Psychotherapy,* 6:551, 1952.

[44] S. DeSanctis, *Religious Conversion,* London: Kegan Paul, Trench, Trubner & Co., 1927, p. 203.

serts that "mental pathology almost invariably offers criteria by which we can distinguish the morbid case from the individual who is not morbid."

Zilboorg[45] acknowledged the importance of differentiating abnormal from normal when dealing with religious problems but asserted that what goes on in the human mind has been learned mostly through psychopathology. The normal cannot be observed directly, he contends, but must be reconstructed from the pathologic (p. 64). This would reverse the usual order in which the abnormal is identified as such by its discordance with a broadly based standard previously established as a norm. Zilboorg's logic would construct the baseline by using deviations from the baseline.

It is true that the normal is not likely to be seen in the consulting room. Psychoanalysis has always been vulnerable to the criticism that its observations are made or its inferences drawn upon sick persons who are paying for treatment. The heuristic role of the analyst has always been limited by the psychopathology of the patient and the expectation of improvement implied by the treatment contract. Observations upon religion made in the one-to-one relationship are subject to distortion by the analyst himself as well as by the psychopathology of the patient.

The factors that make for health and stability in personality should be studied in the healthy and stable where they are operative, not in the sick where they are absent or inoperative. Freud acknowledged that religion has a stabilizing influence upon human personality, but his speculative explanatory theories hardened into categorical declarations without his ever having turned toward this stable group in serious empirical investigation.

Increasing collaboration between psychiatry and religion has brought the clergyman and the psychiatrist closer together. Programs of clinical training have made the minister better acquainted with mental illness in its various forms. But there has not been any comparable movement to acquaint psychiatry with religious experience in its healthy expressions.

Many psychiatrists have submitted without protest to the mandatory act of faith in Freudian principles required

[45] Zilboorg.

for initiation into psychoanalysis, who would reject any religious affirmation of faith or refuse any formal affiliation with the church. By this disaffection, psychiatrists who are frequently obliged to make authoritative discrimination between normal and pathologic religious elements in personality are shut off from a comparable acquaintance with religion in its constructive and wholesome expression in normal persons.

Elsewhere I have emphasized the value of collaboration between clergyman and psychiatrist[46] and the necessity of supplanting concepts of religion formulated in a context of psychopathology by an understanding of religion viewed in a context of health.[47] If such collaboration is to grow into a broad relationship of mutual respect and confidence, it is important to correct a perspective that is presently deeply tinctured with the pathological.

## SUMMARY

As the psychology of religion has given increasing attention to psychopathology, a blurring of the boundary between normal and pathologic has occurred. Current psychiatric attitudes toward religious experience have been based upon generalizations drawn from patients or populations altered by psychopathology.

Evidence is adduced to indicate that defective reality testing invalidates the religious ideation of the schizophrenic patient as a source of illumination for normative religious experience. Neurosis also distorts religious experience and vitiates data for inclusion in studies of normative religious phenomena.

The incidence of religious symptoms in schizophrenia is relatively low and has declined in this century. There is evidence that such symptoms are culturally determined. Their occurrence appears to be a function of previous religious interest in the life of the patient.

Discrimination between normal and pathologic by the psychiatrist requires an acquaintance with normative religious expression.

[46] O. S. Walters, "Metaphysics, Religion, and Psychotherapy," *Journal of Counseling Psychology,* 5:243, 1958. See also Walters, "The Psychiatrist and Christian Faith," *Christian Century,* 76:847, July 20, 1960.

[47] O. S. Walters, "The Psychiatry-Religion Dialogue," *Christian Century,* 78:1556, Dec. 27, 1961.

# 9

# Man's Original Sin

## (Attempt at a Psychological Interpretation)

*Arthur Jores*

THE DOCTRINE of man's original sin that results in illness and death is a Christian dogma that has to be adopted by the believer. It is, however, very difficult if not impossible to bring forth a real understanding for this dogma. That the "guiltless" newborn child suffers already from the original sin and that the illnesses of this child derive, finally, from the same original sin have steadily aroused an opposition and a protest from those of weaker faith, and particularly from those who doubt or do not believe at all. Even if it is always somewhat awkward and only partially possible to interpret doctrines of belief with the help of scientific judgment, this chapter will make an attempt to interpret the doctrine of original sin.

This doctrine declares, first of all, that man is imperfect.

ARTHUR JORES, M.D., is Psychiatrist, Medizinischen Universitäts Klinik und Poliklinik, Hamburg-Eppendorf, West Germany.

With the perfection that we find all around in nature, this is a surprising statement. But modern anthropology can only ratify this declaration. Developments in forms of life below man rest on gene mutations *(genmotationen),* i.e. sudden alterations of the original material; with man for the first time a new principle appears. Man enters this world with the complete fullness of his possibilities, but it takes him several thousand years to unfold and develop these possibilities. So, for example, the unfolding of the spiritual powers of man—that is, of powers and possibilities that basically had slumbered in each man—began only 2,000 years ago, with Greek civilization and with Christianity. This is not difficult to recognize today in the fact that the sons of parents who live in inner Africa among magic study in Western universities, just as the sons of the Western tradition. This thought of the increasing unfolding of man's possibilities has been convincingly worked out by Teilhard de Chardin, with Christ as goal and end of history. What actually unfolds is the conscience. It was the Western man who first became conscious of his own spiritual capabilities and possibilities and who first succeeded in applying them. In this form, circles of culture in the world at large, just as the particular men within a circle of culture, are differentiated among themselves through the broadness and intensity of their conscience. The more this process is advanced, the more man approaches perfection—the image of what the Creator intended him to be.

We see then that man is in reality imperfect, that he is steadily and continually developing, and that life is given him as task and mission. This is the consequence of his freedom. Freedom—as expressed by the word itself—is meant here first of all purely in the sense of the natural sciences, insofar as man, contrary to the animals, becomes free from the compulsory quality of action suggested by the instincts. The value concepts distinguish between right and wrong, good and evil, and are developed into a culture that is transmitted to the children through a process we call education.

Though we certainly have to acknowledge that, if men want to live in peace in society, the directives that correspond to the Ten Commandments ought to have validity, yet beyond that we are also offered an uncommon variety of human existence. The decisive question is whether man can lead his life completely according to his own discretion or not. Were that so, then life would be no real task for man. What could be that task? Could it be anything other than that of bringing the abilities and predispositions embedded in a person to their best development? Which other interpretations can we give to the words that one should not put one's light under a bushel, or to the parable of the pounds that one should deposit the pound on interest and not bury it in the ground? The heaviest penalties of Hell are pronounced in the parable upon him who has buried his pound. So for the first time in the history of mankind, the "become what you are"—formulated by the Greeks—is no longer merely a philosophic demand but rather an undischargable natural law. For a plant or an animal, life is not a task because all the conditions for a right fulfillment of life are finally determined in the inherited substance. But it can happen also with plants and animals that, as the result of unfavorable outer conditions of life, the development of the possibilities is decidedly hindered. This has for consequence disease, sickliness, and finally death.

As I have elsewhere discussed in detail,[1] with respect to man we soon arrive at the fact that we have here diseases that among animals pass as spontaneous diseases and are not observed at all. I have called them therefore specifically human diseases. They have something to do with the particular manner of existence of man, and this particular manner of existence is based precisely in the fact of his freedom and in the fact that life is presented to him as a task. These diseases are hardly noticed in that stage of man's development which is connected with the magical; but in the present stage of development of Western man they are steadily increasing, and they constitute today the main group of diseases. Such are the great number of nervous disturbances and all those that today are called psychosomatic diseases. It is with this group of diseases that we should deal first. A medicine that observes and investigates in purely somatic terms can hardly make any pronouncements upon the causes of these diseases. Under psychological investigation they all show individually a great differentiation in details and a unified fundamental

[1] Arthur Jores, *Der Mensch und seine Krankheit,* 3rd ed., Stuttgart: Klett Verlag, 1963.

principle. With these patients the question always concerns people who are thwarted in the development of their possibilities, and who—less out of outer than out of inner causes—cannot become what they actually are. We should investigate more closely these inner causes.

Since the directives for the action of man—unlike of the animals—are not congenital but rather are acquired in childhood, there is no phase in the development of man that has greater significance and is more decisive because of all its possibilities than childhood. Each person is born, it goes without saying, with certain dispositions and abilities; but how he can realize them later will be decided by influences of the environment of his early childhood. These influences impress him in a very particular sense and transmit to him determined patterns of behavior that later become authoritative for his whole life. These patterns of behavior were once conditioned by the society in which he grew up but have beyond that another character conditioned individually by the parents. Man is in a much higher measure than any other animal dependent upon his environment and stamped by it. This is an acknowledgement of modern anthropology that has not yet sufficiently been recognized in its entire significance.

So national characteristics have nothing to do with the inherited substance but are entirely conditioned by the environment. Each newborn child, as the zoologist Portmann once emphasized, is capable of learning all the languages of the world. He can also acquire all the patterns of behavior of the various nations if he grows up precisely in a corresponding national environment. It is perfectly possible that in a society certain patterns of behavior are being developed that basically stand in the way of an adequate unfolding of man. It is possible that the decline of certain civilizations is connected with this fact. It might be concluded from this that the number of people within a society suffering from a specifically human disease is a standard of measurement for whether in that society the patterns of behavior that are developed are right or wrong.

The psychotherapist Erich Fromm has pointed to these circumstances and has taken for a standard of measurement not so much the specific human diseases but rather suicide and alcoholism. It is a very striking fact that in those countries in which—considered from outward appearances—men live at leisure, in which poverty is almost unknown, namely Sweden, Switzerland, and the United States, the number of cases of suicide and alcoholism is steadily increasing. It is clear therefore that "guilt" (this word is not meant here unconditionally in a moral sense) for the state of disease has to be ascribed to society. One can ask oneself whether the particular care that is devoted to the ill person in all Western civilized countries—aside from the fact that these countries are considerably influenced by Christianity—is not actually the expression of a deeper awareness that we all become somehow guilty of the ill person's condition.

In addition to the directives imparted by society, there are also those modes of human behavior that are imprinted through a determined parental behavior. Here also there are naturally many individual variants.[2]

Fundamentally important is love—love that finds its precipitation in the environment, in the atmosphere of the parental home (which through an unhappy marriage can to some extent be disturbed), and more important, love that does not wish to make anything particular out of the child but only aims at letting the child unfold and develop according to his natural dispositions and abilities. Unfortunately very often the parents have determined notions and preconceptions of what their child should be, and they try to influence him and bring him up in this direction, even if the child has primarily different dispositions. A particular misfortune is to be an unwelcome child because then, in part certainly unconsciously, the child comes to feel this, and the parents are not in a position to meet him with true love. There are still many other grounds that lead to distorted development, into which we cannot enter here in detail. Parents are guilty of such maladjustments, whereby again the word "guilt" is not to be understood in a moral sense. We want now to look more closely at the causes for such failure in education.

Somatically oriented medicine has for a long time pointed out that with many of the specific human diseases treated here, the so-called factor of predisposition is a condition for their development. Under predisposition one under-

[2] See H. E. Richter, *Eltern, Kind, und Neurose,* Stuttgart: Klett Verlag, 1963.

stands the fact that there are newborn babies who in their heritage contain certain particularities that make them more susceptible than others to acquire later determined diseases. This thesis was formulated on the incontestable fact that many such diseases, as for instance an ulcerous condition or asthma, appear in certain families with greater frequency than in the population at large. We want to determine now whether this familiar patterning of certain diseases has necessarily to be traced back to a hereditary peculiarity. We have already seen that psychological research has proved that in all these diseases some failure in rearing played an essential role. It happens, however, that most mothers endeavor to bring up their children according to the principles by which they themselves were brought up. Sometimes the opposite occurs when the mother experienced a very difficult childhood. In these cases the pattern is to some extent reversed into its opposite. This means, in other words, that there are familiar educational singularities which, with certain transformations, are transmitted in their fundamental characteristics through several generations. There is still a further circumstance that we shall best consider with an example. Let us select an ulcer condition. A very characteristic psychological trait of many people suffering from ulcers is what one calls oral inhibition. That is, these are people who find it very difficult to make demands, particularly upon themselves. They appear under superficial observation to have relatively few wants. This lack of need is, in reality, not a genuine one. On the contrary, they make very high demands, but they are hardly ever in a position to realize these inner desires. Thus such a person is usually not in the position to demand for himself a raise in salary; and at Christmas time or at his birthday he can hardly manifest any wishes for himself. He himself, however, finds this condition normal. In this regard he has what in psychology one calls a "blind spot." It is very probable that he will carry over this sort of distortion into the rearing of his children, since this appears to him to be the normal and correct manner of behavior. If we now ask ourselves how such a person comes to such a kind of maladjustment, we would again have to go back to his childhood and his parental home. Thus it follows in reality a sort of distorted behavior that certainly often is transmitted through many generations and which may be the basis for the development of an ulcer condition in later life. The ulcer condition appears thus conditioned by the family circle. One has fallen into the misinterpretation of assuming here the existence of a hereditary factor. In reality, however, it is an environmental factor existing in the families and in their educational methods. The predisposition is thus conditioned by environment and not by heredity. Summing up, we may assert that in the behavior patterns of human communities, of societies, and of families there are factors which yield, through the intervention of false directives, an important basis for the genesis of diseases. These factors are transmitted over many generations.

Not without purpose was the word "guilt" so often used here, i.e., "guilt" primarily in the sense of causality, rather than in the sense of culpability. Now we have to ask ourselves whether a genuine guilt does not, in a certain sense, lie in the background. It is obvious that it is not the sort of guilt for which I can hold somebody immediately responsible, since neither society nor the parental home is aware of this guilt or of possibly trespassing a law, such as disobeying the Ten Commandments. Consciously trespassing God's commandments belongs to the definition of guilt in a Christian sense too. There is certainly no conscious trespassing in this case. But there is also the tragic offense that man commits without knowing it. Greek tragedy deals again and again with the problem of man becoming tragically guilty. Tragic guilt is something other than genuine guilt. We realized this at the end of World War II in Germany. At that time the word appeared in Western newspapers about the collective guilt of the German people. This immediately brought about violent protests on behalf of the Germans. The reproach raised against the German nation was false if it was meant in the sense of genuine guilt for which one could immediately hold somebody responsible and even pass judgment. In this respect the protest on behalf of the Germans was justified. But the reproach was proper in the sense of tragic guilt, for who would dispute that all the terrible things that Hitler had done were possible only through the support of the whole German nation? This tragic guilt that is passed on over generations plays a very great role in human history. How often is a nation found guilty in history for things that had been done generations before!

In this tragic sense we all stand in a guilt entanglement in relation to many sick people. Can we designate that tragic guilt in the Christian sense as a "sin"? I think we can, since it has already been explained that basically all educational failures that eventually could become roots of human diseases prove to be an offense against love. Also, love is the highest Commandment, and an offense against love may well be marked as sin. Life is given to man in terms of a task; man carries responsibility for his life. In this respect we may speak here of existential guilt which is tragic guilt.

One should still prove whether these statements agree with the assertions of the New Testament. First of all we ought to establish that the New Testament also knows of diseases that have nothing to do with personal sin or with sin of the parents. At the healing of the man born blind (John 9:1–41) this is expressly stated. Not every disease is, according to biblical conception, an immediate consequence of sin. Further, it is noteworthy that in the New Testament forgiveness of sin does not follow in all cases the cure of the sick. Yet, when forgiveness follows cure (with perhaps the exception of John 5:14), it is never referred to as particular sins which the person in question had committed. It seems, therefore, that we are not concerned with an immediate personal guilt. Also it is difficult to imagine that care for a sick person would have been made a Christian duty if disease were always a consequence of personal, genuine guilt. It is highly probable that disease is considered in the New Testament also as a consequence of original guilt—i.e., tragic guilt—although it is not said so expressly at any particular place.

At the beginning of the original guilt is the genuine guilt of the first human couple, the guilt of Adam and Eve. It is characterized by the fact that the first man wished to be Godlike. Adam made himself the measure of things and began to lead his life according to his own discretion, outside of the order set by God. Basically this has remained *the* guilt of man to this day. Had parents taken their children for what they are, the gifts of God, and had they understood that their task is to protect them and to let them grow, it would have perhaps been possible to avert to some extent this excommunication. But most people today are still like Adam;

they want to be Godlike, they want to "make" something out of "their" children.

For those diseases which man shares with the animals, especially the infectious and parasitic diseases, the present interpretation is hardly possible, since here a harmful element that enters man from outside represents the cause of the disease. There is only the question of the disposition here, and the disposition is again very much depending on psychological factors. The question in which group the tumors should be classified is still open and cannot for the moment be decided.

We see therefore that it is possible to advance a certain interpretation of disease as a consequence of original sin.

# 10

## Mental Health in Christian Life

*Andre Godin*

ADOPTING THE IDEA that mental health is the ability to work and to love, while adjusting constructively and creatively to a changing environment objectively perceived,[1] I have divided the subject of this chapter into two distinct questions:

1. Is the Christian religion capable of serving mental health, of strengthening or restoring it? As a theologian, I would be inclined to answer affirmatively; but the answer seems to me extremely difficult to justify or even to approach scientifically.

ANDRE GODIN, S.J., M.A., is Professor of Religious and Pastoral Psychology, International Center for Religious Education, Brussels, Belgium.

[1] On the concept of normality and mental health, see F. Duyckaerts, *La notion de normal en psychologie clinique,* Paris: Vrin, 1954. E. Fromm, *The Sane Society,* New York: Rinehart and Company, 1955, p. 69; A. Snoeck, *L'hygiène mentale et les principes chrétiens,* Bruxelles: Assoc. Catholique d'Hygiène Mentale, 1953.

2. Can mental health assist Christian life? Can it bring to the spiritual life of Christians the possibility of becoming more Christian? This question, in my opinion, calls forth a clear "yes." Scientifically controlled proof of this answer can be presented, though one may wish that the question had been studied with greater precision than it has been up to the present.

## EFFECTS OF CHRISTIANITY ON MENTAL HEALTH

*Can the Christian religion serve, strengthen, or restore mental health?*

This question, very difficult to approach scientifically, may even rest upon a misunderstanding that it is important to clear up.

We are not concerned, obviously, with the use of religion (and still less Christianity) as a means of assuring mental health to individuals or groups. God is never a *means,* but an end. And the religion that keeps us in a living relation with the Divine Presence should never be regarded as a means or as if it were to be used for the acquisition or restoration of a human balance. To consider it so would be to deprive religion of its deepest meaning (according to which God is not at our service); and a religious person would risk not reaching his full maturity, which assumes, beyond a primitive and affective egocentrism, a preoccupation with a quite free gift of God (eternal salvation) and an adaptation to transcendent realities. It is indeed *salvation* in the moral and spiritual sense that we are offered in Christ. Psychic *equilibrium* can be only an additional benefit, and one that is not always achieved, because biological, social, and psychological conditioning, on which such equilibrium depends, is not (except through a miracle) modified by the grace of God.

An improvement of mental health, then, assuming that it could be scientifically proved, would be to the theologian only a *possible* consequence, an eventual and progressive restoration of man to a state of natural "integrity," which does not constitute an end in itself.

This quite general theological remark implies the granting of complete freedom to scientific research. At the start of scientific research, it removes certain apprehensions and assures better collaboration between religionists and psychologists.

The difficulties of scientific research into our subject are real; but they are sometimes underestimated. A kind of euphoria, arising from great good will, often pervades the atmosphere of groups studying this subject and obscures the hard work that must be done. People talk as if practical applications were the only consideration, as if planning and a program of improvement would be enough, as if deep problems (that is, scientific knowledge about the relation between religion and mental health) had been solved, or at least were on the way to being solved. As a matter of fact, I wonder whether these problems have been seriously approached and even whether we are in agreement about the way to approach them.

Here are a few examples of some uncertain methods of procedure and of some still unsolved problems.

### *Correlations Among Sociological Statistics*

There have been attempts to throw light upon the influence of religion on mental health by means of correlations between dependence upon an established religion and the kinds of behavior indicative of mental health.

Durkheim and the early members of his school[2] thought that a study of the statistics of suicide and homicide might reveal the religious element as a distinct and active sociological factor. They found a high rate of suicide in some predominantly Protestant countries (Denmark, Sweden, Switzerland, England) and a high rate of homicide in countries with Catholic majorities (Italy, Spain, and South [as compared with North] Ireland)—countries that also have a high rate of alcoholism.

We know that apparent relationships often fall apart when statistical analysis takes into account the developmental factor of age. "Suicide" and "homicide" are found to vary not so much in relation to the religious structure of the society, as Durkheim first suggested, but rather in relation to age, the kind of life (industrial or agricultural, urban or rural), social circumstances (wars), and the cultural condi-

[2] Three studies on suicide summarize this development: Durkheim (Paris: Alcan, 1897); Halbwachs (Paris: Alcan, 1930); Deshaies (Paris: Presses Un. de Fr., 1947).

tions of an environment. At first glance, it seems that *the influence of religion, as such, upon mental health has never been demonstrated by means of simple sociological correlations.*

One might approach the question *indirectly* through study of forms of moral conduct, which are, in their turn, related to mental health. A well-planned study of this kind would be made in two stages.

For example: first, one would find, for a country or a socioeconomic class, the statistical relation between the religious practice of married couples at the beginning of the marriage and conjugal stability. (Positive correlations would probably be easy to determine; some are found in the Kinsey report.) Then one would try to find out the relation between broken marriages and the mental health of the children. This second correlation would be more difficult to establish correctly. Indeed, one might suspect a priori that, in certain psychologically troubled homes, the material separation of the parents could have a *favorable* influence on the equilibrium of the children; at any rate, separation would be better for the children than the perpetual disputes of parents living together. In addition, the hereditary factor must not be overlooked.

A frequently cited statistic in a study by Maud Merrill[3] shows that the proportion of juvenile delinquents to nondelinquents is practically the same among children of divorced parents and in families deprived of the father by death. This is another example of the difficulties encountered by careful research in this direction. Besides, many statistical studies cited in this area have not employed control groups taken from the general population and hence have little probative value.

It is regrettable that there are so few good studies in this area. Of course, such studies would not yet put us in contact with the influence of the religious life as such, since the religious factor would be fragmented into moral conduct and external, controllable kinds of behavior, and these factors are obviously clothed with and motivated by other forms of social conditioning. Nevertheless, such studies would pro-

[3] Maud Merrill, *Problems of Child Delinquency,* London: Harrap, 1947, p. 66. See also John Bowlby, *Soins Maternels et Santé Mentale,* Genève: Organisation Mondiale de la Santé, 1954.

vide a serious presumption in favor of an influence of religion on mental health.

But are there not religious groups in which a particularly fervent and authentic Christian life would constitute a protection against mental troubles?

Such might have been the conclusion of a research by Father Thomas Verner Moore (psychiatrist and at that time a Benedictine in Washington) when he studied the proportion of American priests and nuns who were or had been treated for mental troubles.[4] Compared with the proportion in the general population, the proportion of mental illnesses among members of the clergy and of religious communities showed two characteristics that almost entirely counterbalanced each other. In most of the communities or groups, the incidence of mental illness was lower than in the general population, but in other communities or groups (chiefly certain religious communities devoted to the contemplative life), the incidence was abnormally high. Evidently one cannot overlook the facts that the persons in seminaries and convents pursue studies more advanced than the average (which brings an increase of troubles), that these groups are strictly selected (which should lower the incidence of troubles), and that they live in a setting in which there is considerable tolerance of slightly abnormal behavior of others (a fact that would reduce the number of troubles officially reported).

Father Thomas Verner Moore noted the attraction for certain prepsychotic personalities of the idea of a cloistered life, isolated, absorbed by prayer, etc. Thus we are turned back to the consideration, not of the religious life itself, but of the particular significance that certain individuals attach to it, either in desiring it or in living it. If they are neurotic or prepsychotic, this significance is altered or not clearly perceived. The psychological mode of assimilating the religious life therefore remains the central problem, and this would escape statistics.

Father Thomas Verner Moore's recently published book[5] affirms that sanctity, viewed as heroic possession of

[4] Th. V. Moore, "Insanity in Priests and Religion," *The Ecclesiastical Review,* 95:483–98 and 601–13, 1936.

[5] Th. V. Moore, *Heroic Sanctity and Insanity,* New York: Grune & Stratton, 1959.

virtues, could have a therapeutic value and could effect a progressive normalization of an initially neurotic condition. The conclusion is based on a study of special, individual cases, beyond the statistical questions we have been considering. But in an appendix the author publishes a limited statistic (Massachusetts, 1935) showing that "the insanity rates per 100,000 of priests and Sisters in the United States in 1935 were distinctly lower than for the married in the general population." Unfortunately, this table, favorable as it is to the author's conclusion, is a limited excerpt from more complete figures. The isolated group considered in this table is not compared with a group of persons having approximately the same cultural and social background and living in an environment approximately as tolerant of mental illness as are religious institutes. Therefore the table is not convincing. One would better trust the more complete tables published by Father Moore in 1936, in which the conclusion with regard to the protective effect of the setting of the religious life upon mental health was not positive.

A statistical table compiled by Leah Gold Fein and published in *The Academy Reporter* for December 1957,[6] comparing 55 normal adults, 31 alcoholics, and 50 mentally ill persons, indicates that religious practice within the family is a factor in mental health. In each group, the persons were divided into three categories on the basis of their memories: their early education in the family had been in an *orthodox, liberal,* or *purely formal* religion. The differences are statistically significant. Far more of the alcoholics and the mentally ill reported that they were brought up in a religion that was only a "token observance."

Regrettably, in this interesting little pilot study, one is not informed about the composition of the group of "normal" adults, of whom 32 said they had had orthodox religious practice within their families, 17 liberal, and 6 purely formal religious observance. As the findings rest entirely on comparison with this group of normal persons, ignorance of its composition weakens one's acceptance of the author's inference that "normal adults come from homes in which religion was respected and observed, while adults with affective and mental troubles come from homes in which religion was

[6] Leah Gold Fein, "Statistical Evidence That Religious Observance Is a Factor in Mental Health," *Academy Reporter,* 2, 9:3, Dec., 1957.

treated lightly, looked down upon, or completely neglected." We believe that findings based on childhood memories cannot lead to such a conclusion. The alcoholic, especially, can easily say that his education was "purely formal" in the attempt to blame his parents for his pitiable situation. It is remarkable, too, that none of the alcoholics or the mentally ill reported having belonged to a family with "liberal" religion. Hence this category (which seems to have had meaning only for the normal) introduces grave doubt of the statistical calculations and completely contradicts the apparent conclusions. But, as I have noted, the fault lies rather in the choice of the 55 normal adults who served as the point of comparison.

It is not easy, obviously, to find out accurately the influence of religious education, and still less easy, we shall see, to discern the influence of religion itself.

### *Careful Interpretation of the Psychological Effects of Religion*

Turning to positive observations, individual or clinical, one sees with equal force problems of method and interpretation that seem insurmountable in any collective study and that show the inadequacies of any purely statistical approaches to our problem.

In a well-known book, Henry Murray presents a conclusion that is at first glance a cause of rejoicing for Catholics.[7]

"The Catholic subjects," he remarks, "were conspicuously more solid and secure [than average]. There was relatively little anxiety-linked material bubbling in the minds of the Catholics. . . . They were relatively happy, free from neurotic symptoms. . . ."

But one must not rejoice too quickly. Here is Murray's interpretation, well justified according to Father Edward Nowlan,[8] and based on the special type of Catholic students living at Harvard and participating voluntarily in this research.

> Their repressions were firmer, and what occurred in their depths could only be inferred indirectly by interpreting their projections.

[7] H. A. Murray, *Explorations in Personality,* New York: Oxford University Press, 1938, p. 739.

[8] Edward Nowlan, "The Picture of 'the Catholic' Emerging From Attitude Tests," *Lumen Vitae* (International Review), No. 2, Brussells, 1957.

It was as if their faith in an ultimate authority relieved them of the necessity of independently resolving fundamental issues. Their unconscious fears, one might say, were quieted by the hovering presence of the maternal Church. If they were unable sometimes to live up to the precepts of religion, they knew that forgiveness was always at hand. A secret, remorseful confession and once more they would be beneficently accepted members of the flock. It might be supposed that the irrational unconscious tendencies of these Catholics were so satisfactorily interpreted by a wise, human, and altogether forgiving Church that they never knew what it was to feel themselves alone and forsaken in a maelstrom of incommunicable feelings and ideas. . . . The problem of good and evil is settled and only the problems of moral will remain . . .

So the happy effect of this religion, or pseudo-religion, on the "psychism" is not an unmixed blessing. In his interpretation, Murray passes over the influence of religion in the area of the superego, favoring thereby not a truly human development, but rather a certain sterilization of the creative potentialities of religious persons.

In any case, the problem thus posed exists and brings with it a methodological question linked to a question of real depth. If Christian life operates as a factor only of appeasement, only of adaptation to the Christian group, only of balance, it is because it may have been assimilated through certain not very authentic contacts in a partial perspective, and not according to the totality of its inherent values. Hence the difficulty: Does religion act on mental health, or on the repressions?

Therefore, with respect to the objective meaning of religion (with which philosophers and theologians are concerned), we are constantly forced, as psychologists, to take account of the *special meanings* that each individual attaches to religious values and to his perception of them. If alcoholism can be used as an escape from reality, religion also can have the meaning of an escape. The quality is different, certainly. But if it is a question of an unauthentic religion, one not conforming to Christian values, it matters little to us to know whether that religion produces good psychological effects.

So it would seem that only a clinical method, studying individual development of health or of neurosis, can reveal the eventual influence of authentic religion (motivations, attitudes, conduct) upon mental health. Psychological literature offers certain descriptions along these lines,[9] but they are not very well systematized.

### *Christian Life and Mental Health of Children*

Would the psychological development of the child lead us to evaluate the influence of Christian life as a mental health factor?

Certainly it would do so if the religion corresponded to a strictly instinctive need. But can one say, from the psychological, affective point of view, that the child has an instinctive need that would be frustrated outside a religious formation? Or does that formation, notably the Christian formation, represent a luxury, morally imperious perhaps (if God speaks and calls), but one of which the child has no *psychological* need? In this case, religion would bring him a richness, but it could also represent a handicap that would burden him, sometimes prematurely, and in certain cases hinder his purely human development.

On this point, let us look at some conclusions set forth in a report on mental health and religious formation at the preschool level presented by the child psychiatrist Dr. Jacques Schurmans at the meeting of the Belgian Catholic Association of Mental Hygiene in 1955.[10]

In the absence of precise and systematically conducted studies, we must admit that, at first glance, there appears to be *no important difference, from the mental health point of view, between young people brought up in religious or non-religious surroundings.* Everything else being equal, one cannot say categorically that the Christian formation responds to an affective need of the child nor that its absence interferes with his psychological development.

However, the fact that children brought up without religion are as well as others does not permit one to conclude that religious formation is not important. We know, indeed, that all preschool-age children, even those raised in atheistic surroundings, develop a certain embryonic and spontaneous religion. According to studies of genetic psychology, those of

[9] There are, for example, articles by Caruso, Daim, Frankl, *et al.* in *Journal of Psychotherapy as a Religious Process,* Jan., et seq. (Institute for Rankian Psychoanalysis, Dayton, Ohio), 1954.

[10] J. Schurmans, "Santé mentale et formation religieuse au niveau préscholaire," in *Santé mentale et formation religieuse,* Brussels: Association Cathol. d'Hygiène Mentale, 1955, p. 16.

Piaget for example, one may well say that *there is no child without religion.* Spontaneously the preschool-age child lives in a marvelous artificiality, in magic; his world is entirely animated by psychic life, by rather punitive purposes, etc. This primitive religious life develops no matter what are the spiritual opinions of his parents.

Hence the problem is not to know whether one should give or not give a religion to the child, but to know whether one should cultivate and favor the development of his natural religion or rid him of it, inhibit it as quickly as possible. For a Christian, the problem will be to know how this spontaneous religiosity of the child can be led and ripened into the divine mystery revealed in Christ and finally structured through Him.

From the scientific point of view, in relation to mental health, religion is part of a surrounding culture that the child must assimilate. One must, then, if possible, compare not two groups of children but three groups of selected adults: the first brought up in a neutral atmosphere without any religious influence; the second having been reared from earliest years in an antireligious environment; and the third having received a religious formation favorable to their psychological and spiritual growth.

Without such research, nothing can be firmly established. But it is evident that we can foresee certain aspects, favorable or unfavorable, to the religious preparation of children.

### *The Religious Factor in Psychotherapy*

Another doubtful point related to the positive influence of religion brings up the difficult problem of the systematic use of beliefs, of behavior, and of moral and religious commitments as direct therapeutic factors, i.e., in terms of the relationship between the psychotherapist and the patient. This question, related to psychotherapeutic technique, is at present controversial.

Most French, English, and American psychoanalysts and psychotherapists favor techniques aimed at modifying the "psychism" (defined as the "field of forces" in which the bio-socio-affective conditionings of the personality come together) by specifically psychic means, without explicit evocation of moral commitments or discussion of religious values.

A strong Germanic current, on the other hand, is sensitive to the unity of the personality, to the totality of interpersonal rapport between the therapist and the patient, and to the possibility of effectively utilizing the subjective aspect of religious realities as well as values of health and restorative forces.

The first current is a typical derivative from Freudian analysis. The second, without always being historically dependent upon Jung, could nevertheless claim connection with many of the perspectives of the master of Zurich.

The religious meaning of a therapy should never be considered as the special privilege of the therapists following the second tendency. They sometimes tend to believe it; but one will observe, on consulting the works of those Freudians who are preoccupied with religious values, that religion is rather well (if not better) respected by them.[11]

From the Catholic point of view, there are the words of Pope Pius XII speaking to Catholic psychotherapists and psychoanalysts: "These questions, which lend themselves to scientific psychological examination, belong to your competence."[12]

We hope that the finding of these perspectives, sometimes divergent, will bring about appreciable progress, notably the possibility of approaching scientifically (i.e., clinically) the question considered in this chapter: Can the religious attitude, as such, have a direct influence that is empirically discernible upon the cure of a neurosis?

### *Conclusion*

Let us end here our answer to the first question. If religion has an influence upon mental health, it is only in the individual clinical area, through a longitudinal examination of motivations, attitudes, and commitments, that it can be, if not easily recognizable, at least correctly posed as a problem. Psycho-sociological statistics would furnish only a presumption.

[11] On this subject, see various communications to the VIIth Congrès Catholique International de Psychothérapie: Conducta Religiosa y Salud Mental (Actes du Congres), Madrid (Olivos 18), 1957.

[12] Pie XII parle de psychologie et de santé mentale, 1 vol., Edit. de *Lumen Vitae,* Brussells, 1960, p. 32; *Acta Apostolicae Sedis,* 45:278, 1953.

## EFFECTS OF MENTAL HEALTH ON CHRISTIANITY

*Does better mental health favor Christian life, offering it a possibility of becoming more Christian?*

The answer to this highly interesting question seems easier to arrive at. And one may hope that there will be more methodical studies in this area.

The important point would be to know to what degree children or adults whose mental balance is disturbed are handicapped in regard to their religion, either in expressing it outwardly, or living it within themselves, or even in perceiving the fullness of the Christian message (biblical, liturgical, doctrinal) correctly presented.

Here there are more precise studies.

To limit our consideration, let us take a scientific approach to the third type of influence: the neurotic person's difficulty in correctly perceiving the appeal of Christian values, an aspect of deficient perception that probably lends itself best to investigation.

In the Christian education of young children, one can see that all psychic deficiency, reaching the deepest layers of the affective life (under the age of four years) has terrible repercussions on the assimilation of religious themes included in a Christian education. A lack, for example, in the child's security (chiefly in his relation with his mother), an increase of psychic fear, a rigid strengthening of the superego, and unfortunate structuring of the Oedipal relation with his mother or father—all this profoundly affects the later development of his understanding of God.[13] All that is learned in the catechism, at the age of 6 or 7, about the authority of God, about His goodness, about His pardon that is always offered, etc.—all that must first be lived in the relation with the father and mother. Where the great affective images lack a basis in personal experience, the concepts learned in the catechism touch only the intellect, never reaching the depths of affectivity. The religion of charity, of love, of pardon, is learned by memory, but it does not penetrate the personality. One becomes aware of this fact when adults communicate the infantile state in which their image of God has re-

[13] L. Ancona, "Aspects de la conception religieuse en rapport avec le développement de l'ego," Bonn, XVIme Congrès International de Psychologie, Volume des Communications, XVII, 1.

mained:[14] in many cases it is a root of possible disbelief. God, no longer fulfilling the psychic functions assigned to Him by a religion acquired in a neurotic manner, soon becomes an object of doubt, of crisis, or a rejected image. The fundamental transition in Christian education has not been made; the human being is caught up in an egocentric, largely illusory image of God and does not accept (affectively at least) the mystery of divine charity as a value to which all else is morally and spiritually subordinated.

It would be interesting to know more precisely what are the critical periods of the child's development in which sensitivity to the religious factor is particularly acute, in harmony with his affective maturation: spontaneous anthropomorphism of an omniscient God strengthened by a rigid superego (5–7 years); prolonged fixation of the stages of animistic magic so well described by Piaget, a condition nourished by certain marvelous or miraculous aspects of biblical stories (6–8 years); reflexes strengthened by insecurity prolonging the expectation of "an inherent immediate justice";[15] partial contamination of the religious attitude by an anxious, adolescent moralism growing out of obsessive neurosis (scrupulosity); development of intergroup prejudices (racial, for example) of which certain American inquiries have revealed the connection not with Christianity but with the aggressiveness that is falsely compared with it in certain partial aspects.[16]

Studies in this area should be very precise.

Working with Melle Vandercam, we were able to show that the understanding of a biblical story (Abraham and Isaac) told for the first time in simple terms to children six to eight years old was completely altered by children suffering from insecurity and personality disturbance. The drawings showed that these anxious children identified rigidly with Isaac and perceived the menace of the story much more

[14] R. V. McCann, "Developmental Factors in the Growth of a Mature Faith," *Religious Education,* New York: May-June, 1955.

[15] J. Piaget, *Le jugement moral chez l'enfant.* Paris: Presses Un. de France, 1957[2]; I. H. Caruso, *La notion de responsabilité et de justice immanente chez l'enfant,* Neuchâtel: Delachaux, 1943.

[16] Besides the classic work of Gordon W. Allport, *The Psychology of Prejudice,* Boston: Beacon Press, 1954, see the communication of M. A. Jeeves, "Contributions on Prejudice and Religion," XVme Congrès Intern. de Psychologie, Brussels, 1957, *Actes du Congres,* Amsterdam, North-Holland Pub. Co., pp. 508–10.

strongly than the divine protection, the latter being the fundamental meaning of the story: rejection of all human sacrifice.[17]

In the mind of the neurotic child, many religious subjects are distorted. Françoise Dolto has described cases of disturbed children whose thought processes have been so violently invaded by the idea of the devil as to threaten psychological disassociation and hindrance of maturation.[18] Hanna Colm, another child psychoanalyst, has written a remarkable article[19] in which she describes three children whose idea of God was involved in neuroses: Anne (12 years old), on the basis of her neurotic claim that others should take the responsibility for meeting her every want and need, could not establish real relationships with the people around her, particularly with her father; she would angrily demand from God all that she failed to get from her parents and others within her circle. Peter (10 years) projected onto God his self-condemnation for a secret hatred of his father; he would act out his aggressiveness by shooting arrows toward the sky for long periods. Jim (6 years), constantly pushed back and forth between trust in God and doubt of His existence, felt the need to compete with God and to check on His reliability. He would frequently run outdoors in the evening to see whether the stars were all where they belonged. At one time he crawled into a dresser drawer, making himself very small and saying he was Jesus, the Christ Child; then he jumped out, screaming, "Now I am Christopher Columbus."

Clinical analysis of religious symbols in cases of neurotic children should be pursued.

The religious vitality of adults also is impeded by a lack of mental health. It would be interesting to know what elements of religion are most often seized upon and contaminated in neuroses and psychoses.

Wayne E. Oates has studied the role played by religious ideas in the cases of 68 psychotic or prepsychotic persons.[20]

[17] A. Godin, "Isaac au Bûcher Recherche sur des dessins d'enfants," *Lumen Vitae* (International Review), No. 1, Brussels, 1955.

[18] F. Dolto, "Le diable chez l'enfant," in Satan, *Etudes carmélitaines,* Paris: Desclée De Brouwer, 1948.

[19] Hanna Colm, "Religious Symbolism in Child Analysis," *Psychoanalysis,* 2, 1:39–56, 1953.

[20] W. E. Oates, "The Role of Religion in Psychoses," in *Religion and Human Behavior,* New York: Association Press, 1954, pp. 88–106.

He found that 17 per cent of the cases had been troubled by moral-religious conflicts of long duration; in 10 per cent of the cases a "pseudo-religious" experience had been the precipitating factor; 20 per cent of the cases had borrowed from religion the content of their thought. About half of the psychoses had developed in connection with religious themes, almost all resulting from poor education in childhood or from deviant perception of religious faith or practice.

For my part, in pastoral and psychotherapeutic counseling, I am more and more struck by the repercussion of neurotic tendencies upon partial or false perception of religious teaching. The neurotic person, one might say, is incapable of living the totality of Christian truths in a rich synthesis that, for the healthy person, combines the vital paradoxes of religion. For the neurotic, one aspect of religious teaching or message devours all others: the aspect of conquest (aggressive) of the Kingdom of God, for example, conceals the infinite patience of divine charity; vengeful and intransigent justice overshadows the compassion that ceaselessly offers pardon; the Virgin, as gentle, protecting mother, hides the woman who is actively the co-redeemer, and so forth.

Obviously it is not the transcendent meaning of religious symbolism that is in question but the relation of the religious message with the affective tonalities whereby mental health deficiences eventually stifle certain resonances and sharpen others.

One may still considerably broaden the perspective by comparing, in this respect, the action of different religions. In an interesting discussion held by the group on religion and mental health of the World Federation for Mental Health,[21] psychiatrists and psychologists of four great religions expressed the belief that these four religions offered somewhat different sustenance to various neurotic troubles. Christianity, lived in the Western world, is most often used in the line of obsessive neurosis (moral scruples), and the Asiatic religions and Judaism in the line of hysteria. These are only generalities, depending upon the surrounding culture and social level of the patients seen by these psychiatrists and psychologists. But some psychiatrists, having had experi-

[21] World Federation for Mental Health, Annual Conference, Istanbul, Aug., 1955, Study-group on Religion and the Family (mimeographed reports).

ence with groups of patients of the same culture but different religions, agree in assigning certain particular religious contents to certain neuroses in keeping with a particular religious orientation. These questions deserve scientific study; it is unnecessary to add that they are a distant goal for research; more immediately accessible topics ought to have priority.

### *Conclusion*

The influence of mental health upon the perception, assimilation, and expression of religious values is very apparent. As the precision of our knowledge increases, there is no lack of evidence for an affirmative answer to the question posed for the second part of this report.

If the proper methods for studying the influence of religion on mental health have seemed to us to be full of ambiguity, it has also seemed to us that the future development of our scientific knowledge relative to the influence of mental health upon religion is entirely feasible and highly desirable.

To work for better mental health is to permit believers (and this is equally valid for all religions and all faiths) to gain better understanding of the call of their religion in all its authenticity. The very perception of the religious message, in its richness and complexity, would be enhanced if one could raise the level of balance and of psychological maturity in a population. Mental health does not automatically make men more religious (we have no interest in an automatic, conditioned religion), but it prepares a better background in which the word of God may be heard, received, and more fully assimilated.

It is in this perspective that we all must work together—doctors, psychologists, educators, priests—toward improvement of mental health.[22] Let us, however, avoid unenlightened enthusiasm; let us keep ourselves from undertakings of which the practical applications would be directed toward illusory purposes. An effective program demands precise objects: these can be formulated only on the basis of methodically conducted research and scientifically established conclusions.

[22] On the specific role of the priest, see also A. Godin, *The Pastor as Counselor,* New York: Holt, Rinehart and Winston, 1965.

# 3

# MEANING *and* HEALTH

# 11

# The Quest for Meaning

*Russell J. Becker*

THERE HAS BEEN a series of revolts in the controlling anthropological point of view within the psychotherapeutic world in the last 70 years. The latest, the existentialist revolt, is the one which we are calling the "Quest for Meaning." In order to understand this latest revolt it is necessary to trace the meaning of the earlier psychological revolutions. These contemporary perspectives of psychology and psychotherapy on the nature of man invite detailed attention for two major reasons. In the one instance, we in the Christian fellowship believe we have an anthropological perspective which is both distinctive and important for man's understanding of himself. Any alternative view of the human situation places the Christian's self-understanding on the defensive insofar as there are differences. This is the crucial issue in our relation to Freud. In the second instance, we are compelled by the

RUSSELL J. BECKER, Ph.D., is Associate Professor of Pastoral Theology, Yale Divinity School, New Haven, Connecticut.

comprehensiveness of the Christian image of man (nothing less than the whole of man before God is entertained) to regard every clue found in nature and history as having a place in God's creation. Consequently we look with interest to whatever scholarly inquiries unfold, for we are prepared by our doctrine of creation to accept that whatever is scientific data is also theological data; that is, it is the "given" of God. Thus we are simultaneously apologetic and open when we stand as Christians in this area of understanding man. Standing as Christians before the modern anthropological revolutions of psychology we are open to new data as God's gift to us, but we are apologetic with respect to the primordial data, God's gift of Himself in Jesus Christ.

To consider the current continental existentialist revolt in psychotherapy we need first to fix its meaning in relation to the Freudian revolution against which it stands primarily.

Freud launched contemporary psychology in a revolutionary direction. We must credit him with effecting the disenchantment of man's view of himself. Ripping at Victorian veils he relentlessly exposed the subterranean components of much of man's behavior. Working as a physician treating the neurotic ills of his patients, he discovered and elaborated a theory about man's behavior which related everything higher (art, philosophy, religion, and even science) to the lower instinctual drives of the organism.

## EARLY DEVIATIONS

It is interesting to note that there were early disagreements with Freud's interpretation of human psychological experience. Disagreements were offered by both Adler and Jung. They stood close to Freud at the early point of the century but each of them had broken with Freud by 1911. Adler insisted that sex is not the definitive motivational force within the individual but rather a thrust toward the assertion of self which roughly might be thought of as the will-to-power. He himself thought of this as a compensatory instinct or compensatory mechanism rooted in the primal and universal human experience of infant insignificance in the presence of all-powerful adults. Because no human can come into being without having to suffer the ignominious position of littleness, inadequacy, and helplessness, which is the infant's condition and the child's condition in the adult world, *everyone* has this drive to compensatory assertion of self. Life is one long attempt to compensate for this humiliating insignificance into which we are born and live out our early years. So all that goes on later is not simply because the sex life of man is unfolding in this way and that but because the indignities of this initial human situation are still felt and are being compensated against.

Jung's disagreement with Freud took a little different direction. As a matter of fact it seemed to religious people generally to be a direction which gave the forces and cause of religion a more reasonable appreciation than Freud afforded. Jung tried to take the Freudian instinctual interpretation of man and add to it a larger understanding of man and his total cultural experience. What he did though was more closely tied to Freud than he may have been willing to recognize or acknowledge. He did give a place for man's strivings toward a spiritual and religious interpretation of the world, but the place he gave was located in the unconscious. He asserted that these religious forces are imbedded in some kind of "collective unconscious." Through these forces there is an accumulating residue which is larger than the life history of a single individual. When we talk about factors and forces that extend beyond the life of the individual and yet shape and form him, we are talking about cultural factors in contemporary terms. However the cultural anthropologists had not as yet provided their analyses at the time Jung began trying to reach this larger-than-individual factor which shapes, forms, and affects character. He sought to interpret a social reality beyond our individual selves which needed to be taken into account. Freud had not taken this into account. Jung therefore posited a "collective unconscious" in which archetypes exist which pattern all human thought. Archetypes are primal types of human experiencing so that regardless of where you are born or in what particular culture you are raised, you will end up sharing in some variation of a *primal type of thought form.* So religionists thought, "Now psychoanalysis recognizes religion *is* located in the human soul." Many religionists drew Jung to their bosoms as one who was their kind of psychoanalyst. Jung had affirmed a place for man's search for significance and man's search for meaning and man's larger-than-individual understanding of himself. But Jung's locating of man's religious life—either in the unconscious of the race or in the collective experience of the community—really does no credit to the objective reality of God as a Being apart from human experience who is the Creator of the world and who in Christian thought reveals *Himself* to man. The God of the Christian revelation *is*. He discloses Himself to men first in the history of Israel and then in Jesus Christ. The essential assertion of the Christian community is not that we have made ourselves one of the finest types of God that man could ever want but that there is a God that is the Sovereign and Supreme Creator of all that is and who Himself provided the unifying principle of all that is in terms of the Logos that was with Him from the beginning. The climactic disclosure of Himself is in the Logos made flesh which dwelt among us, the man Christ Jesus. Jung does not help us to see religion in its peculiarly Christian form as *historical revelation* when he roots religion in unconscious or communal forces.

### THE FREUDIAN VIEW

Even though Adler and Jung deviate from Freud they stand with Freud in the scientific outlook of reductionistic materialism which prevailed at the close of the nineteenth century. All aspects of the human spirit are treated by Freud and his compatriots as expressions of hidden, root forces in the human organism. The basic structure of psychic life is a set of warring regions identified as ego, id, and superego. The interplay between these antagonistic regions is interpreted through the model of hydraulic mechanics with repression as the central inner force. Now each of these Freudian ideas is a novel theoretical construction:

1. The construct of the unconscious
2. The construct of the id, ego, superego
3. The construct of repression

The Freudian revolution has been so effective that we widely use these constructs as though they were the reality of human experiencing.

It is this situation of thorough absorption and acceptance of the Freudian map of the human psyche which provokes the revolt of the existential psychotherapists.

### THE HUMANISTIC REVOLT

Before I come to the existentialist revolt more narrowly conceived—by which I mean the people who have used this approach as their basis for criticizing Freud—let me indicate another group of people who are existentialists in a broader sense. These are a group who have not necessarily taken an existentialist philosophy as a basis for their interpretation of the human situation but who have nonetheless been led to the same or similar kinds of reinterpretation of the nature of human experience and the requirements of psychotherapy. This is a group that Abraham Maslow has called a "third force in psychology." It is a force that does not stand with the animal experimental psychologists nor with the Freudian clinical psychologists. It is a group who stand for a clinical and humane psychology which is oriented around humanistic ideals and values.

I would like to term this group a "humanistic revolt" (against Freud). Essentially what they have done is to contend with orthodox psychoanalytic thought in the name of a more humane understanding of man. They hold a view of the human situation which includes and partakes of human values as noble forces within the human situation rather than as ignoble forces transmuted into "seeming" nobility. They are a reaction against the reductionist tendency of the scientific materialism of the nineteenth century which so formed and shaped the attitude and outlook of Freud upon human psychological phenomena.

There are five factors which contribute to this humanistic revolt against Freud. One of these is democratic political philosophy. This affirms the dignity of man as man. The respect for persons as persons is in some way required when we view the human situation under a democratic political philosophy. The human situation is not to be seen solely in terms of the instinctual and animalistic forces. Something genuinely new has evolved in the spirit of man itself.

The second factor in this humanistic revolt is the advancement of the concept of the self in social psychology during the first half of this twentieth century. George Herbert Mead, building on insights of William James and John Dewey, offers us the idea of the self as a product of the human social process. *To understand man as man you have to take account of man as an interactive social being.* Selfhood is not given at birth and is not imbedded in the genes. It will vary radically in its form depending upon the character of the social environment that relates itself to man, and this is the difference of one culture from another culture.

The third contributor to the humanistic revolt against Freud is a group of socially oriented psychoanalysts. These people accepted the new thinking about the social factor in human personality as selfhood but still had a general psychoanalytic outlook on behavioral dynamics. Fromm, Horney, and Sullivan are the most prominent of these. Each of them uses the term "self" which Freud himself never used. They begin to see man in a new social dimension.

A fourth factor that needs to be registered came from a strange quarter. It came from the brain surgeon Kurt Goldstein who tried to understand the experience of man as man revealed at the point of crisis and tragedy which brain damage represents. He worked with brain-damaged patients of World War I for several decades. Goldstein asserts that the unifying factor in man's behavior is the drive toward self-actualization and the anxiety over any threat to the self's continued actualization of itself. He noted that even with the limitation of human potential which brain injury imposes upon the human organism, what makes sense of all that is occurring is the fact that the individual is still trying to cope with his existence as a whole within the limits available to him.

The fifth significant contribution to the humanistic revolt in psychology has been made by Kurt Lewin. Lewin offered a field theory of personality and motivation in behavior. The behaviorally significant factor in human interaction is the total set of perceptions and meanings (the *Gestalt*) which each individual organizes within his own mind as his life-space. A true psychology of behavior must therefore be an individual and phenomenological psychology. We do not behave because of instinctual forces impelling us in ways beyond our control. We behave in terms of the complex set of meanings and values we attach to the world as we peculiarly view it. Lewin offered a consistent phenomenological approach to psychology.

## HEIDEGGER'S EXISTENTIALISM

Strangely, though, this humanistic revolt has been untouched until recently by another revolt against Freud which roots itself in philosophy. This is the more narrowly conceived existentialist revolt against Freud. The philosopher responsible for this revolt is Martin Heidegger. The psychoanalysts who have used Heidegger in order to reinterpret the meaning of human existence are chiefly continental figures. Among them Ludwig Binswanger and Medard Boss are the most available and significant. Because Heidegger leads the transformation of thought for both Binswanger and Boss, we cannot understand them without looking first at Heidegger.

Heidegger is one of those rare phenomena of human history—a philosopher who in rethinking the problem of philosophy comes up with a genuinely novel understanding of what philosophy is and what man is. His book *Sein und Zeit* was first published in 1927. Its English translation appeared in 1962. That is a gap of 35 years between the German edition and the English translation which can only be explained by the strange and difficult use of language by Heidegger. Heidegger not only reshapes philosophy as he philosophizes but he reshapes the German language as well. What Heidegger's basic contribution is can be seen in a preliminary way by the one word he uses for speaking about human existence. When we use the phrase "human existence" in English, we have in mind the totality of that which is distinctively what I am. Heidegger uses one word to describe human existence—a German word which is simply accepted and used constantly by Heideggerians in its German form—*dasein. Dasein* when broken down into its parts means *da sein*—"being there." This may seem like a strange way to phrase the quintessence of the human situation—"being there"—but with this word Heidegger seeks to transcend the epistomological problem in modern philosophy which Descartes posed. Heidegger takes the position that the Cartesian dualism is an erroneous understanding of our fundamental being. For Descartes there is an assured subjectivity *(Cogito ergo sum*—"I think, therefore I am.") and there is objectivity, things in the world about which we think. This dichotomy of the subjective and the objective poses the problem for all modern philosophy of how we (who are subjective) *know* that which is objective or outside us. How do you get from the subjectivity of your being to that which is "outside" to be known? The Kantian solution of Descartes' problem posits in the mind of the knower various a priori categories. Because the categories of knowing are a priori to experiencing the world, we are always involved in constructing the world we know. We never know the world as it is apart from the constructive action of the knower upon it. Thus we can know only the phenomenal world, never the numenal world—the thing as it is—for our action in knowing affects all we know.

Heidegger attempts to transcend the subject-object problem by saying man's experience is essentially always an experience of having the world as a given. He posits what can be called an existential a priori. There is no possibility of human experience in any way apart from relatedness to the world. Our being is always being there (in the world)—*dasein.* Both our being and the being of the world are given a priori to human experiencing and knowing. Heidegger breaks through the subject-object dualism and sees man as a transcending being. Man transcends the categories of subject and object at all times—he is *dasein,* "being there"—he is being-in-the-world. This means there is always a givenness of the there, the world, for man. As the being who transcends the subject-object relation, man is never to be dealt with in his essence as an object or a thing. He is always an "existing" rather than *vorhandenheit.*

There are two essential aspects of this *being there* of which Heidegger speaks. One is *facticity* and the other is *potentiality* or possibility. He similarly speaks of these two as "thrownness" and "projection."

These are interesting words to struggle with and to take as serious descriptions of *dasein*—of human existence. *Facticity* or thrownness means our present state in the world is always a given set of limited, factical conditions. Man is in this world as a "thrown" creature. His being is not of his doing. Why do you have two eyes rather than one? This kind of stature rather than that? Some kind of parent rather than another? That is a part of the facticity of our being—the thrownness of our being. Our being is always in the world—has to be in the world in some particular way at some particular moment. That is a part of what human being is. But another part of what human being is, is to be the creature who projects—not in the psychoanalytic sense but as the creature that reaches beyond this moment of thrown, factical being and reaches toward a variety of other things that he might come to be. Another way of capturing this projecting quality of man is to say man is the creature of *potentiality*. He is in Heidegger's terms "the self-creating creature." Potentiality is always to be understood as a crucial dimension of man—just as crucial as thrownness. Let me illustrate these two with Viktor Frankl. When Frankl sees man even in the concentration camp brutally treated with nothing to do but to suffer brutal treatment, he still conceives of the person as having one thing left to do. He can take an attitude towards that which is happening over which he otherwise has no control. When Frankl says man may create attitudinal values as well as productive values he means there is always the possibility of making something new of any situation man is in. There is always a potential—a projection he may make of that which is thrust upon him, that which he is thrown into—even though the potential is narrowed to what attitude he will take toward this whole brutal circumstance.

We have been looking at the term *dasein* in Heidegger in order to see the depth of his probing of the problem of being (ontology) and the sweep of his understanding of human existence as "thrown projection." There is much more to his thought than this, and even so he considers his anthropology to be incomplete. For instance, he insists on the utter individuality and uniqueness of each life and, therefore, of the necessity of dealing with reality from the perspective of the individual, that is, phenomenologically. Or again, the nature of man's relation to the world is care. Care is what distinguishes man qua man from all other things. Or again, the twofold possibility of our existence is to be authentic or to be inauthentic. We become inauthentic when we "fall into the world," becoming just another object or thing in the world, losing the leverage of our transcending relation to the world around us. The anxiety of our being is the anxiety of the creature who transcends his creatureliness in the core of his being.

Perhaps the fact of death is the most telling instance for Heidegger of the human situation. Death is both a possibility and a certainty for *dasein*. We flee from death. The highest affirmation of meaning in life, however, must come in the response we make toward the possibility and certainty of death as non-being. Rather than despair in the face of death or flight from it, Heidegger counsels a form of authentic living as that living which anticipates death but has the courage to go on living nonetheless. Anticipatory resoluteness is resoluteness to live in the face of the certain possibility which man anticipates—death. The affirmation of meaning in life comes in this paradoxical circumstance of facing and not fleeing the nothingness of our being.

This is not intended to be a complete review of Heidegger's philosophy, but it is a tracing of the circle of ideas which have influenced a group of psychoanalysts in a profound way. Both Ludwig Binswanger and Medard Boss have been as deeply influenced by Heidegger as by Freud. As a consequence they have produced an existentialist revolt against the Freudian interpretation of man. They have attempted to ground their work as psychotherapists in the fuller understanding of man offered by Heidegger rather than in the narrow circle of reductionist scientific materialism which framed all of Freud's ideas about the human situation. Each of these, therefore, sees man as a creature who must come to grips with the meaning of life, not simply as an organism which needs to resolve tensions, conflicts, and complexes but as a transcending creature who must come to grips with his own being-in-the-world.

Boss's recent work[1] offers a view of the way a psychoanalyst influenced by Heidegger's anthropology reinterprets his task as a psychoanalyst. Boss makes a selective appropriation of Heidegger. For that matter, Binswanger does too. Only if you have struggled with Heidegger do you begin to appreciate why anyone who wants to come to terms with him ends up being selective. The quality of the description of the human situation that Boss takes from Heidegger and

[1] Medard Boss, *Psychoanalyse und Daseinsanalytik*, Bern and Stuttgart: Verlag Hans Huber, 1957.

utilizes most significantly derives from the fact that Heidegger is essentially a phenomenological interpreter of the human situation. He interprets man as phenomenal, and phenomenon means that which shows itself—that which discloses itself. Man as phenomenon is a being who discloses himself, has disclosing power, or has luminosity. "Openness to the world" is the way in which Boss deals with man as *dasein* whose being is in the world, who is always the being who is there, who always has the world as that which is given.

Taking man as *dasein*—as a unique self-disclosing phenomenon in his own right—Boss finds his therapeutic approach to man being simply that of wanting to get into the uniqueness of *dasein* and letting it disclose itself. That is what it means to take the phenomena that are there. Take *dasein* as human phenomenon, as self-disclosing, light-shedding reality, and what you end up with is what the Rogerians talk about as client-centered acceptance—permissiveness. The difference is that Boss utilizes an ennobled philosophical and psychological appreciation of the fullness of human existence. By contrast the phenomenological approach which the Rogerians have spoken about is a perspective derived more narrowly from perceptual and social psychology alone. Heidegger offers a phenomenological approach which understands man as *dasein,* the self-disclosing being-in-the-world.

Another aspect of psychotherapeutic practice which Boss discovers in this phenomenological and *dasein*-analytic appreciation of *dasein* is worthy of mention. The question the psychoanalyst usually poses to a patient when he says this or that is "Why?" The typical psychoanalyst is interested in analyzing or in having his patient analyze the causes of his behavior. The analyst views the patient as a resultant of various causal forces playing upon an object. When the patient is viewed as a self-disclosing, self-transcending event, the question to be posed more appropriately, says Boss, is "Why not?" rather than just "Why?" The patient struggling with this problem or that—who wonders if he can do this or that—is thrust out by this "Why not?" towards the potential of his own being. He is thrust in the direction of the future projection he may be. He is treated as one who has possibilities. The "Why not?" invites and encourages a courageous attack upon life for the patient who might otherwise struggle and turn inward and devour himself in analyzing causation. The patient is moved toward exploration, investigation, and creative living. "Why not?" rather than "Why?" accomplishes quite a shift in orientation toward life.

Binswanger takes a little different clue from Heidegger. He stresses being-in-the-world, as the nature of man. He perhaps gives a more consistent stress towards the phenomenological quality of what it means to be man, on the one hand, and an awareness that the root category for understanding man is the category of transcendence, on the other. Man is a creature who transcends himself. He is both creature and *aware* of his own creatureliness at one and the same moment.

Binswanger is genuinely interesting to and significant for the Christian because of a number of additional categories beyond this one of transcendence. One of these is the category of *extravagance.* It is a fascinating notion. The German word for extravagance is not easily translated. It is *verstiengenheit* and it is taken from the word meaning "mountain climbing." It refers to a process of going too far and means a point beyond which one cannot turn back or go forward. That kind of extravagance has a lot of similarity with the Christian concept of pride—that self-transcendence which is *hybris.*

Another term which he sees as a category by which we must understand the essentialness of man actually goes beyond Heidegger. He lifts up the category of love. Man in his relationship to the world has a loving potential in relation to other beings. At some points he uses the New Testament word *koinonia* for describing that quality of human fellowship with other men that is distinctively human without realizing its New Testament significance.

A third category that strikes us in a fascinating way from a Christian perspective is the ability and necessity which man has to come to terms with his finitude.

> Only he who scorns these limits who—in Kierkegaard's terms—is at odds with the fundamental condition of existence, can become "neurotic," whereas only he who "knows" of the unfreedom of finite human existence and who obtains "power" over his existence within this very powerlessness is unneurotic or "free." The sole task of "psychotherapy"

lies in assisting man toward this "power." It is only the ways to this goal that are various.[2]

Here Binswanger suggests that the goal of the psychotherapist is to help the patient to be free. But it is a freedom obtained by acknowledging and accepting the unfreedom of finite existence. In other words, freedom for man is secured in the recognition of the limits which are given by the terms of his birth and development. Freedom is never an escape from the "thrownness" of our life but a responsible acceptance of it.

We have moved steadily toward the language of the great Christian thinkers for describing the nature and destiny of man. The significance of the existentialist revolt against Freud as it has been stimulated by Heidegger has been to insist that our understanding of man is vastly different from the reductionist version offered by Freud. We are not "nothing but" unconscious, instinctual drives wrapped in conflict with reality. We are human existences: unique and responsible; finite and free; in the world and not of the world; nature and spirit; creature and transcending our creatureliness; participants in a world of meanings as well as the world of things. *We are anxious beings,* not simply because of instinctual conflicts but because of the compound nature of our being. As finite creatures who know their finitude, who can contemplate their *finis* in death, we know the "dizziness of freedom." We know the anxiety of being precarious in our existence by virtue of being both thrown and projected at all times. We inherit a past and invade a future in every present moment. We have no set resting place but the resting place of non-being. To live is to move toward death, steadily, unavoidably, irrevocably.

This much of the Heideggerian analysis of *dasein* as taken over by the existential psychotherapists can be readily applauded by the Christian, even though it leaves unsaid the final Word of our being which is proclaimed in Christ. The Christian can thank the existential philosopher and psychotherapist who rescue human existence from the confines of biological determinism into which it had fallen under

[2] Ludwig Binswanger, *Being-in-the-World,* tr. by Jacob Needleman, New York: Basic Books, 1963, p. 218.

Freud's management. Even though the final Word of salvation from beyond ourselves is left unsaid, the existentialists depict with accuracy two matters which are preparatory for this Word: (1) the fact of human existence as precarious and ambiguous, as compounded of nature and spirit, and (2) the essential rather than accidental nature of man's spirit by which he reaches toward the meaning of his precarious existence. To this we, as Christians, need only add that the Word of salvation is not a fabrication of precarious, ambiguous man, but it is given by God in his self-disclosure in Jesus Christ.

The existentialist psychoanalysts and psychotherapists have begun to take seriously the meaning-questing aspect of man as central to man rather than epiphenomenonal. In this glimpse of man as the meaning-seeking animal, they embrace a framework which has room for the Christian interpretation of man, of history, of meaning itself. As such they open a new horizon of possibilities for discussion with Christians which offers the possibility of respect for the essence of the Christian stance in the world even though they may not themselves go so far as to be believers in the Christian evangel.

# 12

# The Significance of Meaning for Health

*Viktor E. Frankl*

EVER more frequently, a psychiatrist today is confronted with a new type of neurosis which is mainly characterized by loss of interest and lack of initiative. Psychoanalysts complain that in such cases conventional psychoanalysis is no longer effective. Indeed we psychiatrists are more and more consulted by patients who doubt that their life, or life altogether, has any meaning. They speak of a lacking worthwhileness and complete futility of life, of the experience of an inner void and emptiness which I have termed "existential vacuum," an emptiness referring to the complete lack of an ultimate and higher meaning to one's existence.

When I inquired of my students at Vienna University whether or not they knew, from their own experience, this

---

VIKTOR E. FRANKL, M.D., Ph.D., is Professor of Psychiatry and Neurology, University of Vienna; Head, Neurological Department, Poliklinik Hospital, Vienna; and President of the Austrian Medical Society of Psychotherapy.

inner condition, my students—from Germany, Switzerland, and Austria—gave an affirmative answer of 40 per cent. However, my students who attend those lectures which I conduct in English—American students—answered in the affirmative to an extent of 81 per cent!

How should psychotherapy and psychiatry cope with this state of affairs? I think, first of all, it would be dangerous and, above all, useless to still stick to a statement which Sigmund Freud once made in a letter to Princess Bonaparte that the moment a man questions the meaning and value of life, he is sick. I rather think that such a man proves only that he truly is a human being, because only a human being is capable of raising the question of whether or not his own existence is meaningful. An ant or a bee would certainly not question the meaning of its life. Quest for meaning is nothing pathological, and even doubting and questioning the meaning of one's personal life is not yet a neurotic symptom.

Along with this phenomenon which I call "existential vacuum" or "existential frustration"—that is to say, the frustration of the innermost motivational force operating in man, what I call his "will to meaning," his longing and groping for a higher and ultimate meaning to his existence—we may find another phenomenon which seems to play an even greater role: the widespread apathy which particularly seems to spread among the academic youth of the United States. People, especially educators, are puzzled, astonished, surprised about this symptom of a collective neurosis. I think they should not be astonished about it if they teach and preach in American colleges that man in the final analysis is nothing but a set of mechanisms, nothing but the product and outcome of various forms of conditioning processes, be they biological or psychological or sociological in nature; because this way man's freedom for decision making has been neglected and omitted. It has been erased out of our picture of man. Behavioral scientists have taught an understanding (better to say misinterpretation) of the human being along the lines of what Gordon W. Allport of Harvard University called the "machine model," or the "rat model." And only recently, and fully justifiably, an American minister, in an article on this logotherapeutic concept of a will to meaning, has said that there is no chasm between religion and psychiatry but only a chasm between psychiatrists and religionists who, on the one hand, interpret man in a wholly mechanistic way and those others who know that man is a being reaching out for some meaning to fulfill.

Is it not a paradox that as long as man was used to interpreting his own existence, his own humanness, in terms of a creature, he understood himself after the image of God? But once he started to interpret himself as a creator, he understood himself after the model of his own creation: the machine—*l'homme machine,* as the French materialists proclaimed. Man is not free from conditions. This would be an illusion. But man is always free to take a stand toward whatever conditions might confront him.

There is another symptom of the collective neurosis of our days: hedonism; that is, preaching that ultimately and basically man's psychological life is dominated by what is called in psychoanalysis the pleasure principle. Of course I am aware that there is also something like the reality principle, but, according to Sigmund Freud,[1] the reality principle only serves the purposes of the pleasure principle, is nothing but its extension.

But the pleasure principle, I venture to say, is self-defeating, because we may observe time and again that the more a man sets out to gain pleasure, the less he is able to obtain it. From my clinical experience and practice, I venture to state that about 95 per cent of sexual neuroses are due to this fact. Pursuit of happiness is, in a sense, a contradiction of itself. Man is thwarted in his very pursuit of happiness, in his very "will to pleasure," because pleasure establishes itself once a man has fulfilled a meaning, has fulfilled a task. Then he gains pleasure because he had not aimed at it. It is the same, for instance, with sleep. The more a man tries, the less able he is to fall asleep, because sleep presupposes a relaxed state, and this cramped and forcible striving for sleep is contradictory to relaxation. It is the same with health. Health also belongs to a certain class of human phenomena which can only be obtained by not caring for them, by not aiming at them, by not being concerned with them; because once a man makes health his main goal he has already fallen sick—he has become a hypochondriac. A man

[1] Sigmund Freud, *A General Introduction to Psychoanalysis,* tr. by Joan Riviere, Garden City, N.Y.: Garden City Publishing Company, Inc., 1943, p. 312.

who sets out to actualize his will to power, along the lines of the Adlerian "status drive" for instance, would also be thwarted in his very pursuit of power, because people would notice that this is a status seeker and would ignore him.

Nowhere will you find a more illustrative presentation of this intrinsic fact of human existence than in the Bible where Solomon is reported to have been invited by God to utter his deepest wish (*I Kings* 3:5–14). Solomon pondered for a while; then he said, "Lord, I would like to become a wise judge for my people." Thereupon the Lord answered, "Solomon, you have wished to become a wise judge for your people, yet not wished for wealth and health, for long life, for happiness, for jewelry, for richness. So I will make you the wisest judge who ever existed, but at the same time I also will make you a wealthy and healthy and famous and long-living man." By not aiming at it, by not intending it, Solomon was granted all these gifts.

It is somewhat similar with such typical American slogans as self-actualization, self-realization, struggle for identity; you can only actualize and realize yourself to the extent to which you are fulfilling the meaning of your life. Then you are actualizing yourself in terms of a by-product, of a side effect; but if you are concerned with actualizing yourself, you are missing this target. There is a wise word which has been published by the great German philosopher, Karl Jaspers, who said that what man is he ultimately becomes through the cause to which he has committed himself. I would say identity is not found by aiming at it but by reaching out for something other than one's self, by committing one's self to something rather than being concerned with one's self.

Once when I had lectured at Melbourne University in Australia, I was given as a souvenir a real Australian boomerang. After contemplating it for a while, I realized this is the very symbol of human existence. Everybody thinks that a boomerang has the task of returning to the hunter. This, they told me in Australia, is not at all the truth, because only that boomerang returns to the hunter which has failed to strike the prey, its target. It is the same with man. Only that type of man is so much concerned with himself—with his own self-actualization and self-realization, with his own identity—who has neglected to care for that meaning which, out there in the world, is waiting to be fulfilled by him and, what is even more, exclusively by him.

People are also much concerned with peace of mind and peace of soul, with homeostasis and inner equilibrium. Psychoanalysis is depicting man in terms of a being concerned with restoring or maintaining his inner equilibrium, and for this purpose satisfying drives and instincts, gratifying needs, materializing archetypes, and so forth. This is not right, because man is never primarily concerned with anything within himself but with other beings to encounter and meanings to fulfill. And we should not adhere to what I regard to be a misconception of mental health—namely, the assumption that mental health depends on a tensionless state. My contention is that a sound amount of tension is even indispensable for mental well-being and, even more, for human being—the kind of tension which is established in a polar field of which one pole is represented by a man who is groping for a meaning to fulfill while the other pole is represented by that unique meaning which is waiting for each and every individual to be exclusively fulfilled by him. This tension between the actual state of affairs on the one hand and the ideal state of affairs which is still to be materialized: this is a necessary tension. All those people who preach and proclaim that everything is all right, that what one needs is just to develop one's inner potentiality, are going astray and leading others astray. They preach: Why reach out for the stars, i.e., the ideals to fulfill? Why reach out for the stars to bring them down to the earth? This is completely unnecessary. Behold, the earth itself is a star; that is to say, everything is already present and man just should live out his potentialities.

But the meaning, the ideal, the values, the purpose, must never coincide with the actual state of being, because this could destroy the intrinsic self-transcendent quality of human existence. Meaning must set the pace for being; therefore it must always be ahead of being. You will certainly understand it at once if I resort again to a story told in the Bible, and I hope you will forgive my transcending the boundaries of psychiatry. There is the following story: When the people of Israel went through the wilderness for forty years, it has been said that a cloud preceded them; that is to say that this cloud symbolized the presence of God, preceding Israel and thereby guiding it. Imagine what would have happened if this cloud had not preceded Israel but dwelt in the midst of Israel. Rather than being able to guide them, this cloud would have darkened everything, and Israel would have gone astray.

The pacemakers in history are known to us all. The great genius of religiosity, Moses, was a pacemaker. He did not spare his people from being confronted with the Ten Commandments which he brought down from Sinai. And he even confronted the people of Israel with their own lagging behind those ideals, because he anticipated the wisdom of Goethe, who said, "If we take man just as he is, we make him worse. But if we take man as he ought to be, we help him become it."

Therefore, one should not speak of ideals and values disparagingly. Meaning orientation is so basic in human life that even empirical evidence could be brought to the fore. For instance, an American psychologist has found that the logotherapeutic concept of meaning orientation is the best criterion of mental health. Three other American authors have found, in the frame of their experiments with what is called sensory deprivation, that when people are deprived of any sensory data, then hallucinations and artificial psychoses occur. But these hallucinations cannot at all, as the authors found out, be obviated by simply providing the subjects with sensory data but only by restoring a meaningful contact with the world; and these authors conclude that what the brain needs is meaning.

There is another trait specifically in the culture of this country which makes itself more and more noticeable in terms of a collective neurotic symptom, and this is escapism from the necessity to suffer. The stand of logotherapy is thoroughly optimistic, although it points out that suffering is an indispensable and inescapable constitutive factor in human existence, because we teach that suffering—unavoidable suffering—can be turned into a heroic achievement and accomplishment. And after all, this is optimism, while escapism teaches that scientific progress will do away with suffering, that there is no guilt in the world but just neurotic guilt feelings, and preaches: Don't speak of dying but just forget about it, because science will even abolish this.

Escapism is both illusional and delusional. Recognizing man's finiteness, that is to say, recognizing that man has failed, that he is suffering and will die: this means doing justice to *la condition humaine,* the human condition.

Let me quote the story of an old general practitioner who came to me because he could not overcome the loss of his wife two years before. I just asked him, in a Socratic manner as it were, "What would have happened if you had died first, Doctor, and if your wife would have had to survive you?" He answered, "Oh, that would have been terrible for her. How much she would have suffered!" Thereupon I said, "See, Doctor, such a suffering has been spared your wife, and it was you who spared her this suffering. But now you have to pay for it by surviving and mourning her." At that moment there took place something like a Copernican revolution, a reversal of his attitude toward the same fate, which of course could not be changed; now he could see a meaning in his suffering. Man is longing for a meaning rather than just for pleasure or the avoidance of pain.

I am recalling this story because I would like to make you acquainted with the comment which an American psychoanalyst gave to this story some months ago in New Jersey. He said, "Well, Dr. Frankl, I understand your point. But if we start from the fact that this gentleman had suffered so deeply from the loss of his wife only due to the fact that, obviously, in his unconscious he had hated her all along . . ." I answered, "I admit, Doctor, that after having this patient lie down on your analytical couch for 500 hours you would have succeeded in indoctrinating and brainwashing him to the extent that, like the Communists behind the Iron Curtain—at least in former times—, he would accuse and criticize himself and tell you, 'Yes, Doctor, you are right. I have hated my wife. I never loved her.' But then you would have succeeded also in depriving this man of the last treasure he still cherished after having rescued it and preserved it in his past: the unique marital life, the unique love he could succeed in building up; while I, by a mere happenstance, was happy enough to bring to this man some consolation." I know that psychiatrists are often too proud to bring consolation to people, but may I remind you that in the constitution of the American Medical Association exists a paragraph wherein a doctor is reminded of his responsibility, in cases in which he can no longer bring help, to bring consolation.

Let me conclude these remarks by pointing out that

alongside suffering there is also the problem of guilt involved in what I call the tragic triad of human existence. But after all, only in the face of guilt does it make sense to improve, and only in the face of death is it meaningful to act; otherwise there would be no need, no necessity to make the best use of the limited time which is at our disposal.

I know that the ultimate meaning of life is not a matter of prescription on the part of the doctor or the psychiatrist or even a logotherapist. Each one has to find out the meaning of his own life, and the ultimate meaning of life is no longer a matter of intellectual cognition but rather a matter of existential commitment, of a decision. The intellectual capacities of man are so finite that they resemble the situation of an ape which is being punctured day by day in order to produce anti-polio vaccine. Such an ape never could guess what the meaning of its suffering is because this meaning dwells in a higher dimension: the world of man. But now let me ask: Is man a terminal in the development of the cosmos? Is it not conceivable that there is a higher dimension in which man can reach out only through phenomena which are called "belief" and "faith"?

I am also fully aware that interpreting the ultimate meaning of life involves and implies a personal decision. Let me recall the following experience. Shortly before the United States entered World War II, I received a visa to immigrate into this country; in fact, my old parents did not expect anything but that, of course, I would make use of this visa immediately. But at the last moment I hesitated and asked myself whether I could just leave Vienna and my old parents, knowing that they would be sent within one or two weeks to a concentration camp or an extermination camp where they would be gassed. While pondering the question of my responsibility in this situation, I came home one day and noticed a small piece of marblestone on a table. I asked my father about it and he explained that he had found it at the site where the largest Viennese synagogue had stood until the day the Nazis burned it down. He discovered that this small piece of marblestone formerly had belonged to the two tables containing the Ten Commandments. Then he said, "And if you are curious, Viktor, I could even tell you more, because this Hebrew letter, gilded and engraved, is the abbreviation only for one of the Ten Commandments." Eagerly I asked him, "For which one?" And he quoted, "Honor thy father and mother, and you will dwell in the land." Thereupon I decided not to make use of my visa but to stay with Father and Mother in the country and let the visa lapse. You might answer that this is a projective test. The actual decision had been made in my unconscious all along, and I only projected the outcome of this decision into this piece of marblestone. But if I had seen nothing but $CaCO_3$, calcium carbonate, in this piece of marblestone, this also would have been the outcome of a projective test, that is to say, the expression of an existential vacuum.

Another danger to the value of the individual is what you call—this is an American term—reductionism: that is to say that people are taught that values are nothing but defense mechanisms and reaction formations. My response to this interpretation has been that I would not be ready to live for the sake of my reaction formations, or even to die for the sake of my defense mechanisms. What might be necessary is to complement, to supplement—not to substitute, but to supplement—so-called depth psychology by what might be called height psychology; not only to care for aggressiveness and sexuality, not only to care for the instinctual depth, not only to care for the subhuman strata, but also to care for the humanness of man.

May I quote in conclusion two "height psychologists." One has said that what is needed is a basis of convictions and beliefs so strong that they lift individuals clear out of themselves and cause them to live and die for some aim nobler and better than themselves, and one should teach students that ideals are the very stuff of survival. Do you know the "height" psychologist who uttered these sentences? Indeed it was a "height" psychologist: the astronaut John Glenn.

The second height psychologist whose interpretation I would like to present to you has said—and to this I can subscribe after three years spent in concentration camps—that men are strong as long as they represent a strong idea. This height psychologist was Sigmund Freud, and we should take his advice that reverence before the greatness of a great spirit is a good thing, but reverence before facts should even surpass and exceed it. I think it is time to recognize the fact that man is more than just a mechanism or the outcome of conditioning processes, to recognize the humanness of man, to recognize that man is a being in steady search of meaning, and that his heart is restless until he finds meaning in his life.

# 13

# The Spiritual Dimension of Man's Health in Today's World

*Howard S. Hoyman*

HEALTH is as complex and hard to define as human life itself. Our modern concept of health has deep historical taproots. It is an outgrowth of Western Civilization, but it also has been nourished by other ages and cultures. In final analysis, our health model rests upon underlying, often conflicting, theories of man in the universe. It has been influenced by scientific, philosophic, and religious assumptions related to fundamental issues such as: divine vs. natural creation; the natural vs. the supernatural; absolute vs. relative values; the mind vs. the body; good vs. evil; sin vs. sickness; and the spirit vs. the flesh.

HOWARD S. HOYMAN, Ed.D., F.A.P.H.A., is Professor of Health Education, University of Illinois, Urbana, Illinois.

### HEALTH INVOLVES THE WHOLE MAN

The problems and challenges of the Space Age necessitate a more comprehensive health model in terms of the whole man and his style of life, including his spiritual nature. Does man's health really have a spiritual dimension?[1] It does if health involves the whole man; because man is the religious animal. Up to a certain point, both in man and apes, health is based upon physical, mental, and social well-being. But of all living things—including apes—only man's health has a spiritual dimension that is inextricably related to, but goes beyond, the physical, mental, and social. Health is wholeness. It is rooted in man's flesh, grows and develops in his heart and mind, and flowers in his spiritual life. The four pathways to optimum health are: a sound body, an alert mind, a warm, compassionate heart, and a creative spirit.

But we must be careful: the terms "spirit," "spiritual," and "spiritual faith" can easily become weasel words. I use the words "spirit" and "spiritual" to mean the highest and finest part of man's nature that is related to but transcends his body and mind. In this sense "spiritual" refers to the central focal point of man's humanness; but it does not imply that man has a spiritual entity separate from his mind and body that survives after death. And I am using "spiritual faith" in the sense of a set of *essentially* religious feelings, beliefs, actions, and values related to ultimate concerns and commitments and to ultimate reality. In this sense the "religious" or "spiritual" may or may not be based upon any given religion. It is assumed that the moral, ethical, and spiritual are all enmeshed in man's endless struggle for the good life, expressed through a *living faith* that is satisfying, credible, and morally responsible.[2]

### WHY BE HEALTHY?

Why does a man want to be healthy? Certainly not as an end in itself—unless he is a health crank or hypochondriac. A man wants health as a means of living the kind of life and striving toward the kind of goals that he sets for himself and

[1] Halbert L. Dunn, "High-Level Wellness for Man and Society," *American Journal of Public Health,* 49, 6:786–92, June, 1959.

[2] Paul Tillich, *Morality and Beyond* (Religious Perspectives, Vol. 9), New York: Harper and Row, 1963.

by means of which he, and others, measure the success or failure of his life. A healthy person seeks to transform and transcend himself; and to give purpose and meaning to his life—and to the lives of others—through spiritual aspiration and religious faith that link up the brute facts of his worldly existence with ideal ends. A truly healthy person will sacrifice his physical health and, if need be, his life for values that he considers greater than himself. For us to ignore man's spiritual nature in developing our current model of health would be to deal with a caricature of man—with modern man dehumanized.

Health as a goal does not imply an overly cautious, timid, health-and-safety-at-any-cost approach to life. There is no easy road to mental and spiritual health. The way is strewn with blood, sweat, tears, toil, and suffering, with death constantly lurking ahead in the shadows. At its best a healthy human life is an adventurous search and a courageous struggle for ideals and values. Healthful living involves risks and commitments in meeting dangers and challenges facing us in the world today. Thousands upon thousands of examples of people from all races, colors, and creeds and from all walks of life bear witness to the spiritual spark in the minds and hearts of men that needs to be fanned into flame. For example: an Einstein or Julian Huxley seeking truth; an Eleanor Roosevelt seeking goodness;[3] a Renoir, Marion Anderson, or Grandma Moses seeking beauty; a Martin Luther King and courageous Negroes and whites seeking racial justice; a Mahatma Gandhi seeking freedom; a Jacqueline Kennedy facing a shattering experience with courage and dignity; a Bertrand Russell seeking peace; a Winston Churchill fighting tyranny; a Helen Keller[4] overcoming great handicaps; an astronaut, John Glenn, exploding into unknown space; an Albert Schweitzer[5] and a Paul Carlson[6] extending compassion and medical aid to the Negroes in Africa—all testify that man can escape from an endless round

[3] Joseph P. Lash, *Eleanor Roosevelt: A Friend's Memoir,* Garden City, N.Y.: Doubleday and Company, Inc., 1964.

[4] Helen Keller, *The Story of My Life,* Garden City, N.Y.: Doubleday and Company, Inc., 1954.

[5] Werner Picht, *The Life and Thought of Albert Schweitzer,* tr. by Edward Fitzgerald, New York: Harper and Row, 1964.

[6] Editorial Staff, "The Congo Massacre," *Time,* 84, 23:28–32, Dec., 1964.

of servitude to that insatiable tyrant, self, and devote himself to higher ends based on love, hope, and faith.

We are coming to see that man's health is more than physical fitness, social well-being, and mental-emotional adjustment—important as these are. In the modern sense: *health is personal fitness for survival and self-renewal, creative social adjustment, and self-fulfillment.* The most exacting test of one's health is to stay alive and to retain the capacity for self-repair and self-renewal.[7] Creative social adjustment is based upon a two-way interrelationship between a person and his socioculture, not on blind conformity. And self-fulfillment is expressed in terms of actualizing desirable, unique human potentialities as related to ideals and values.[8] As an ultimate goal: optimum health is an exciting challenge for modern man to become more fully human, using acceptable means to achieve noble ends.

But man is fallible; and he has potentialities for both good and evil.[9] In striving for physical fitness, creative social adjustment, and self-fulfillment: he needs to guide himself by ideals, values, and spiritual goals related not only to short-range objectives but also to more ultimate concerns and commitments.[10] Since there is no human certainty—either scientific or religious—man must proceed in part on the basis of faith. His faith should rest upon intuitive religious insights and beliefs as well as upon scientific facts and theories, philosophic assumptions, and common experience.[11] In this sense his health has a spiritual dimension based partly on faith.

However, this position does *not* imply that a man has to believe in a personal God, divine revelation, the supernatural, any particular religion—including Christianity, the divine authority of the Bible, personal immortality, original sin, or the virgin birth, divinity, or resurrection of Jesus

[7] John W. Gardner, *Self-Renewal: The Individual and the Innovative Society,* New York: Harper and Row, 1963.

[8] Gardner Murphy, *Human Potentialities,* New York: Basic Books, Inc., 1958; Abraham H. Maslow, ed., *New Knowledge in Human Values,* New York: Harper and Brothers, 1959.

[9] Erich Fromm, *The Heart of Man: Its Genius for Good and Evil* (Religious Perspectives, Vol. 12), New York: Harper and Row, 1964.

[10] Loren Eiseley, *The Firmament of Time,* New York: Atheneum Publishers, 1960.

[11] J. Bronowski, *Science and Human Values,* New York: Julian Messner, Inc., 1956.

Christ—to be healthy. He may or may not believe in any or all of these and still be healthy. Nor does it imply that he should violate his personal integrity and accept some form of dogmatic finality or commit intellectual suicide as the price of faith, personal salvation, and health.[12]

It does imply that a truly healthy person continues to ask the big questions about life; and that he sees his life in part as a spiritual odyssey in which he seeks and strives to relate himself and his life meaningfully to his neighbor, his society, the world, the universe, and to *his* God.[13] It assumes that atheism and skepticism are not final answers, in the sense that an atheist or a skeptic is still faced with the problem of how and why to live a healthful fully human life.[14]

## HEALTH AN EVOLVING TARGET

Our evolving health model has been shaped by many movements and forces: the rise of Christianity and the message and example of Jesus; the rise of modern science and technology; the Enlightenment with its assumption of historical progress and human perfectability;[15] the Romantic movement with its conflict between the claims of reason and the irrational in man;[16] the impact of Copernicus, Galileo, Darwin, Einstein, Marx, and Freud on modern man's image of himself and the world, as related to materialism, mechanism, and determinism; the war between science and religion; the rise of modern medicine and public health; the current impact of human ecology, existentialism, and evolutionary humanism; and our current theories of personality development and mental health and mental illness. All these forces and movements, and many others, have shaped, and will continue to shape, our evolving model of health in the twentieth century.[17]

[12] Arnold Toynbee, *An Historian's Approach to Religion,* New York: Oxford University Press, 1956.

[13] Huston Smith, *The Religion of Man,* New York: Harper and Brothers, 1958.

[14] Reinhold Niebuhr, *The Nature and Destiny of Man* (Gifford Lectures), New York: Charles Scribner's Sons, 1941; Martin E. Marty, *Varieties of Unbelief,* New York: Holt, Rinehart and Winston, Inc., 1964.

[15] Albert W. Levi, *Philosophy and the Modern World,* Bloomington: Indiana University Press, 1959.

[16] J. B. Priestley, *Literature and Western Man,* New York: Harper and Brothers, 1960.

[17] Richard Thruelsen and John Kobler, ed., *Adventures of the Mind* (from the Saturday Evening Post), New York: Alfred A. Knopf, 1960 and 1961.

### *Evolutionary Humanism*

For example, according to the theory of evolutionary humanism: the whole of reality, including man, is one gigantic evolving process, with three interacting phases—the physical, the biological, and the human or sociocultural phase—each with its own ways of working, its own rates of change, and its own kind of results, as Julian Huxley has pointed out.[18] Evolution is assumed to be directional in time and therefore irreversible, and without any cosmic purpose or goal, and without supernatural design or guidance.[19] In scientific man, nature became conscious of herself and the embarrassing lack of cosmic design in the universe; and evolutionary humanism is struggling manfully to supply at least a limited answer to the riddle of life here on earth.

According to humanists such as Simpson[20] and Huxley, in the human phase, evolution becomes concerned with much more than survival and reproduction. They, and others like Gardner Murphy,[21] believe that man seeks and needs to find a deeper meaning for his life through personal fulfillment of his human potentialities.[22] Man cannot live for himself alone, for his destiny is enmeshed with nature's destiny, as Marston Bates points out.[23] If he decimates his fellow man and devastates the earth, he has signed his own death warrant.

According to evolutionary humanism: realistic models of health, disease, and aging must be based upon man's evolutionary nature in a world that has evolved and is still evolving.[24] Health and disease are viewed in terms of organismic adaptive capacity, emerging from the interaction of heredity and environment; and the physical, mental, and even spiritual dimensions of man are seen as organs for coping with his physical, biological, and sociocultural environment. Health, disease, aging, and death are considered to be natural phenomena due to natural forces, not to divine

[18] Julian Huxley, *Evolution in Action,* New York: Harper and Brothers, 1953.

[19] George G. Simpson, *The Meaning of Evolution,* New York: The New American Library of World Literature (Mentor Book), 1951.

[20] George C. Simpson, *This View of Life: The World of an Evolutionist,* New York: Harcourt, Brace and World, Inc., 1964.

[21] *Ibid.*

[22] Julian Huxley, ed., *The Humanist Frame: The Modern Humanist Vision of Life,* New York: Harper and Brothers, 1961.

[23] Marston Bates, *The Forest and the Sea,* New York: Random House, 1960.

[24] T. Dobzhansky, *Mankind Evolving: The Evolution of the Human Species,* New Haven, Conn.: Yale University Press, 1962.

agencies.[25] And it is assumed by evolutionary humanists that man's future role in controlling some of the natural factors related to mutation and natural selection in biological evolution, and to other factors operating in his sociocultural evolution, will have important effects on his health, disease, aging, and longevity and upon future models of these phenomena in medicine and public health.[26]

### *Existentialism*

Our evolving concept of health has also been influenced by existentialists, with their insistent focus on the "human predicament," with its inescapable lot of suffering, disease, and despair, from which there is no exit except death.[27] And their stress upon the crucial importance of becoming an *authentic* person capable of moral choice, decision, and action has influenced our views about mental and spiritual health. The existentialists have pointed to the depersonalization of man in industrialized, urbanized mass culture. They have stressed the loss of meaning at the center of human existence, the drift toward nihilistic despair and existential anxiety with the breakdown of traditional religious beliefs and faith, and the need for modern man to reorient himself in the world today.

Some atheistic existentialists, such as Sartre, see man as standing completely alone in an indifferent, if not hostile, world, and therefore totally responsible for what he makes of himself and society. It is up to man alone whether he makes a Heaven or Hell on earth. But human existence is contingent on death and therefore finally absurd in a world from which God and personal immortality have been banished. Yet, according to Sartre, despite man's lonely estrangement and his temptation to despair and suicide because of life's absurdity, modern man must fight back at life and do the best he can on earth.[28]

[25] R. W. Hepburn, "The Religious Humanist's Predicament," *The Listener,* LXXXI, 1835:869–71, May 28, 1964; Hepburn, "Possible Approaches to Humanist Religion," *The Listener,* LXXI, 1836:924–25, June 4, 1964.

[26] Hermann J. Muller, "The Guidance of Human Evolution," *Perspectives in Biology and Medicine,* 3, 1:1–43, Autumn, 1959; Rene Dubos, *Mirage of Health* (World Perspectives Series, Vol. 22), New York: Harper and Brothers, 1959.

[27] William Barrett, *Irrational Man: A Study in Existential Philosophy,* Garden City, N.Y.: Doubleday and Company, Inc., 1959.

[28] Frank Kappler, "Sartre and Existentialism," *Life,* 57, 19:86–110, Nov. 6, 1964.

Religious existentialists such as Marcel, Buber, and Tillich have somewhat different views of man in the universe. But in general they see modern man in terms of a more religious humanism, with less nihilistic despair over man's existential anxiety, and with greater optimism for the future of mankind in his earthly odyssey.[29]

### *Human Ecology*

To cite a final example: our evolving model of health is also being decisively shaped by the current movements in human ecology[30] and epidemiology. Human ecology utilizes holistic models based on a *unitive* view of man as an *open system* engaged in reciprocal dynamic transactions with his total environment. Man is viewed as a self-regulating, self-renewing, self-actualizing organism, capable of inhibiting his impulses in satisfying his needs as related to his ideals, values, and goals.

Health is a multidimensional unity—with physical, mental, and spiritual dimensions—determined by interacting hereditary, environmental, and personal factors.[31] Health, disease, aging, and longevity are ecologic outcomes—as well as operational factors—determined by multiple interacting variables, not by single factors operating alone. According to the ecologic view: the health-disease spectrum ranges from zero health (death) at one end, through various levels of disease and wellness, to optimum health at the other end. Unfavorable ecologic variables push one down into the zones of disease and death; favorable ecologic factors push one up into the zones of wellness and health.[32]

Human ecology, evolutionary humanism, and existentialism, along with changing notions in modern science and mathematics, all point to new ways of looking at cause-and-effect relationships, not only in physics but also in biology—including human biology.[33] A specific example is the trend

[29] Maurice Friedman, ed., *The Worlds of Existentialism: A Critical Reader,* New York: Random House, Inc., 1964.

[30] Edward S. Rogers, *Human Ecology and Health,* Part III, New York: The Macmillan Company, 1960.

[31] H. S. Hoyman, "Our Modern Concept of Health," *Journal of School Health,* 32, 7:253–64, Sep., 1962.

[32] H. S. Hoyman, "An Ecologic View of Health and Health Education," *Journal of School Health,* 35, 3:110–23, Mar., 1965.

[33] E. Mayr, "Cause and Effect in Biology," *Science,* 134, 10:1501–6, Nov., 1961.

toward developing stochastic models based upon the mathematics of probability. Thus for the older notion of a causal chain we now have the related concept of a stochastic process—a chain with uncertainty at every link.[34] All of these movements underscore the fact that science has no final answers, and that man cannot now see, and may never be able to see, clearly the end of the road in his long quest for certainty.

### MAN'S SPIRITUAL DILEMMA

The modern age increasingly views man as a natural phenomenon in a natural world that has evolved, and is still evolving. But toward what, if anything, the world is evolving nobody really knows. So modern man tends to see himself as a natural, integral part of a vast universe, without, as yet, any scientifically discernible beginning or end, and without any objectively verifiable grand design or cosmic purposes or goals.[35]

Yet, despite his growing religious skepticism and secularization of life, man still finds the universe mysterious, at times awe-inspiring and a source of reverent humility, and, so far, incomprehensible in its vast wholeness.[36] He finds himself deeply confused and sorely tormented in trying to tie up his life on the tiny planet earth with the gigantic universe of which he is a part.[37]

This has created a crisis of meaning for man in the twentieth century that eats away like a worm at the core of his mental and spiritual health.[38] He is uncertain as to what his life is all about, despite his aggressive individualism; his deeply ingrained tyranny of self; his Faustian need to conquer nature for his own ends; his secularized, skeptical approach to life with its endless struggle for material things.

[34] E. R. Hilgard, *Theories of Learning,* 2nd ed., New York: Appleton-Century-Crofts, Inc., 1956, Chap. 11.

[35] Editorial Staff, "Life and Death of the Universe," *Newsweek,* LXIII, 21:63–67, May 25, 1964.

[36] Aldous Huxley, *The Perennial Philosophy,* London, England: Chatto and Windus (Fontana Books), 1958.

[37] H. Shapley, *Of Stars and Men: Human Response to an Expanding Universe,* Boston: Beacon Press, 1958.

[38] R. C. Zaehner, *Matter and Spirit* (Religious Perspectives, Vol. 8), New York: Harper and Row, 1963.

As Emerson put it, modern man finds: "Things are in the saddle, and ride mankind."[39]

He is faced with a spiritual dilemma. He believes strongly in science and material things, and views himself in evolutionary terms, but modern man cannot fully accept himself as *nothing but* a machine or the latest model ape.[40] He has a deep-seated need for a more spiritual outlook on and approach to modern life. He has spiritual longings and aspirations that make him crave a more intimate feeling of belonging in the universe.[41] He is more deeply disturbed, in his meditative moments, than he likes to admit by the current view of man as an outsider in a blind purposeless universe, utterly indifferent to the things that he holds near and dear.[42] He is faced with many fundamental questions: What is modern man for? What is his life all about? What is the good life, here and now, as well as in the future? Which way should he turn for help: to himself alone? to Martin Buber's "I and Thou" relationship? or to God?

### MAN'S SPIRITUAL ICE AGE

What is God for us today? Is God dead or dethroned, or did he ever really exist? Is modern man already in the "Spiritual Ice Age," as Koestler puts it in his essay "The Trail of the Dinosaur."[43] Have all gods silently withdrawn from the modern world, as Camus portrays in his writings such as *The Plague*?[44] Or were all gods, including the Christian God, an illusion, a figment of man's imagination, based on wishful thinking, as assumed by Freud and Sartre? Or was Friedrich Nietzche really speaking for our age when, in the parable of the madman in *The Joyful Wisdom* (1882),

[39] Quoted in: Ralph L. Rusk, *The Life of Ralph Waldo Emerson,* New York: Charles Scribner's Sons, 1949, p. 388.

[40] Joseph W. Krutch, *The Measure of Man,* New York: The Bobbs-Merrill Company, Inc., 1953.

[41] Franklin L. Baumer, *Religion and the Rise of Scepticism,* New York: Harcourt, Brace and Company, 1960.

[42] Helmut Thielicke, *Nihilism* (Religious Perspectives Series, Vol. 4), New York: Harper and Row, 1961; Rudolf Otto, *The Ideas of the Holy,* tr. by John W. Harvey, New York: Oxford University Press, 1958.

[43] Arthur Koestler, *The Trail of the Dinosaur and Other Essays,* New York: The Macmillan Company, 1955.

[44] Albert Camus, *The Plague,* New York: The Modern Library: Random House, Inc., 1947.

the madman rushes into the marketplace and cries out: "God is dead!"

Should modern man discard the God hypothesis as obsolete today and try manfully to cope with his problems alone, as Julian Huxley[45] and Sartre advocate? Should we accept a view of godless man living in a secularized society and a godless world as the final answer? Is religious renewal possible today? Is Christian renewal possible? Or have we finally reached the point of no return after twenty centuries of Christianity? Only time will tell.[46]

New signs of life are stirring within the Christian church itself, both Catholic[47] and Protestant. The spiritual challenge of a new reformation is in the air. The ecumenical breakthrough in Catholicism and Protestantism is heartening. The contemporary spirit of Christian renewal is questioning, critical, searching, and challenging.[48]

Germany's Rudolf Bultmann insists that Christian mythology is finished in our scientific age and that Christianity must demythologize and translate the essential elements into terms that relate to man's existential predicament and problems in today's world.[49] The American, Bishop Pike of San Francisco, in his *A Time for Christian Candor,* takes the position that it is now time to do away with past distinctions between the secular and the sacred.[50] Paul Tillich views God not as a separate being but as the ground of being itself, or ultimate reality. And the Englishman, John Robinson, Bishop of Woolwich, in his best-selling *Honest to God,* proposes that Christianity substitute a new image of God for the old notion of a personal deity "out there."[51] Various proposals such as these underscore the deep truth that no one

[45] Julian Huxley, *Religion Without Revelation,* revised ed., New York: Harper and Brothers, 1957.

[46] Editorial Staff, "Christian Renewal: Christianity—The Servant Church," *Time,* 84, 26:45–49, Dec. 25, 1964.

[47] Pierre Teilhard de Chardin, *The Phenomenon of Man,* New York: Harper and Brothers, 1959.

[48] Maurice N. Eisendrath, *Can Faith Survive?* New York: McGraw-Hill Book Co., 1965.

[49] John A. T. Robinson, *Honest to God,* Philadelphia: The Westminster Press, 1963, pp. 24–28, 32–36.

[50] James Pike, *A Time for Christian Candor,* New York: Harper and Row, 1964.

[51] Robinson, Chaps. 1, 2, 3.

vision of God or religion will satisfy everyone's spiritual needs and aspirations.[52]

### SPIRITUAL FAITH: HEALTH AND MODERN LIFE

As Tillich points out, faith is not a matter of the spiritual side of man in isolation; it is the centered movement of the whole person toward something that has ultimate meaning and significance for him.[53] Spiritual and ethical values are central to human personality development and mental health, because religious faith helps one to create a more fully integrated and meaningful life.[54]

But spiritual faith alone will not make a man more fully human or healthy. In fact, faith held and expressed in the wrong way, or faith and belief in the wrong things, may make a man sick and less than human. At times faith may be blind, or even vicious or evil in its effect on a person or group. Man's spiritual life cannot feed upon itself alone and stay healthy; it must be nourished by all the things that give life meaning and value here and now, as well as in the future.[55]

Religions come and go, but man's religious nature and his need for spiritual faith in something greater than himself alone remain.[56] But action as well as faith is needed. As

[52] Tanneguy De Quentain, "How the French See God," *Realities,* 165:38–43, Aug., 1964; Aldous Huxley, "Shakespeare and Religion," *Show,* IV, 2:58, 99–101, Feb., 1964.

[53] Paul Tillich, *Dynamics of Faith* (World Perspectives, Vol. 10), New York: Harper and Brothers, 1957; C. H. Waddington, *The Ethical Animal,* London: George Allen and Unwin, Ltd., 1960.

[54] James C. Coleman, *Abnormal Psychology and Modern Life,* 3rd ed., Chicago: Scott, Foresman and Company, 1964; Marie Jahoda, *Current Concepts of Positive Mental Health,* New York: Basic Books, Inc. (Joint Commission on Mental Illness and Health, Monograph Series, No. 1), 1958; George L. Engel, *Psychological Development in Health and Disease,* Philadelphia: W. B. Saunders Co., 1962.

[55] Aldous Huxley (Introduction), *Bhagavad-Gita: The Song of God,* tr. by Swami Prabhavananda and Christopher Isherwood, Hollywood, Calif.: The Marcel Rodd Co., 1944; *The Way of Life According to Lao Tzu,* an American version by Witter Bynner, New York: The John Day Co., 1944; Alan W. Watts, *The Way of Zen,* London, England: Penguin Books, Ltd., 1962.

[56] Robert Bretall, ed., *A Kierkegaard Anthology,* Princeton, N.J.: Princeton University Press, 1951; Ludwig Curtius (Selections), *Goethe: Wisdom and Experience,* tr. with an Introduction by Hermann J. Weigand, New York: Frederick Ungar Publishing Co., 1964; Leo Tolstoy, *A Confession: The Gospel in Brief: What I Believe,* tr. with an Introduction by Aylmer Maude, London, England: Oxford University Press, The World's Classics, 1961; F. Dostoyevski, *The Brothers Karamazov,* New York: Random House, 1929.

Dewey puts it in discussing the religious: "Any activity pursued in behalf of an ideal and against obstacles and in spite of threats of personal loss because of conviction of its general and enduring value is religious in quality."[57]

The world is full of things for man *to fight against:* war, ignorance, tyranny, injustice, self-seeking, racial discrimination, the population explosion, destruction of natural resources, man's inhumanity to man, and many other forms of suffering and evil in the modern world. Fortunately, the world is also full of things *to fight for:* truth, goodness, beauty, freedom, justice, peace, joy and delight, social well-being, human dignity, and man's humanity to man.

What pathway should man take to the good life? Julian Huxley and others have outlined the humanist approach.[58] Hamilton has suggested a pathway that can be taken by the "secular saint," the man struggling for a Christian style of life in the world today.[59] Bonhoeffer, an original and profound modern theologian who was active in the German resistance movement against Hitler and the Nazis, imprisoned by the Gestapo, and finally hanged by Himmler at the age of 39, said: "Man is challenged to participate in the sufferings of God at the hands of a Godless world."[60]

Whatever pathway we take, we must honestly admit that faith includes doubt and uncertainty. But a truly healthy person strives to lead a good life, based partly upon spiritual faith, *in spite* of doubt and uncertainty, the mystery of the universe, the enigma of human existence, and the tragic sense of life.[61]

## HEALTH EDUCATION FOR TODAY AND TOMORROW

What does all this have to do with health education? Ralph Tyler has pointed out some of the implications of

[57] John Dewey, *A Common Faith,* New Haven, Conn.: Yale University Press, 1960, p. 27. (Quoted by permission of the Yale University Press.)

[58] Julian Huxley, *The Humanist Frame, op. cit.*

[59] William Hamilton, *The New Essence of Christianity,* New York: Association Press, 1961.

[60] Quoted in: W. Hamilton, *The New Essence of Christianity,* New York: Association Press, 1961, pp. 109, 158. Also see John D. Godsey, *The Theology of Dietrich Bonhoeffer,* Philadelphia: The Westminster Press, 1963.

[61] Aleksander I. Oparin, *Life, Its Nature, Origin and Development,* tr. by Ann Synge, New York: Academic Press, 1961; G. G. Simpson and Ann Roe, eds., *Behavior and Evolution,* New Haven, Conn.: Yale University Press, 1958.

behavioral studies for health education in today's world.[62] He has stressed that recent research indicates that biologic drives represent only a small part of human motivation; that personal purposes, values, and goals are very important human motivators; and that long-range goals are of great importance in achieving healthy maturity. He has also pointed out the health educator's responsibility (1) in constructively utilizing the kinds of motivations that young people already have, and (2) in helping them to develop additional long-range values and goals. Allport has outlined a new theory of conscience; and he has discussed the role of religious sentiment and faith in healthy personality and character development.[63]

Health is partly innate and partly acquired; and in a very real sense one has to learn to be healthy. This is especially true in developing and maintaining mental and spiritual health in our increasingly mobile, rootless, urbanized, industrialized, automated, secularized world of today that has been cut loose from its moorings. A man's personality, character, and behavior may make him sick, or even help to kill him. Or they may serve as vital health resources expressed in full, fruitful, enjoyable living.[64]

### *School Health Education*

What can we do about this in our schools? We can teach children and youth that health—*their* health—has qualitative as well as quantitative dimensions. We can develop and use models of health and healthful living that include the moral and ethical needs and spiritual dimension of man.[65] We can work cooperatively with the home, the church, and the community to help young people develop a

[62] Ralph W. Tyler, "Implications of Behavioral Studies for Health Education," *Journal of School Health,* 33, 1:9–15, Jan., 1963

[63] Gordon W. Allport, *Becoming: Basic Considerations for a Psychology of Personality,* New Haven, Conn.: Yale University Press, 1955, pp. 68–78, 88, 101.

[64] Calvin S. Hall, and Gardner Lindzey, *Theories of Personality,* New York: John Wiley and Sons, Inc., 1957; Orville S. Walters, "Metaphysics, Religion, and Psychotherapy," *Journal of Counseling Psychology,* 5, 4:243–52, Mar., 1958; Morton M. Hunt, "The Remarkable Self-Healing Powers of the Mind," *Family Weekly,* Jan. 12, 1964.

[65] T. Brameld, and S. Elam, "Values in American Education," *Phi Delta Kappan,* Bloomington, Ind., 1964; S. Elam, and Nancy Gayer, eds., "The School's Responsibility for Moral Education," *Phi Delta Kappan:* Special Issue, XLVI, Bloomington, Ind. 2:41–89, Oct., 1964.

philosophy of life, geared to today's world but oriented toward *their* future. In dealing with health topics such as personality and character development and mental health and illness, we can help our students to develop long-range as well as short-range goals. This will help them to give purpose, meaning, dedication, and a sense of direction to *their* lives. And, although the teaching of religion has been banned from our public schools, we can still use the Bible as a *health reference book* in teaching about personality, character, and mental health.[66] Whatever else it may be, the Bible is one of the greatest psychology and mental hygiene books ever written. For example, we should not overlook the deep human wisdom contained in statements such as: "Man does not live by bread alone."[67]

We can teach by example as well as by precept. We can dramatize and personalize our health teaching by bringing life into the health classroom: for example, we can use current health events, with moral, ethical, and spiritual implications, and give more consideration to current health heroes, as "stars to steer by," to use Sally Lucas Jean's inspiring words.

We can keep these criteria in mind in health curriculum construction as related to needs and objectives, scope and sequence, methods and materials, and evaluation of pupil progress. Young people need to see "health" and "healthful living" as something more than brushing their teeth, washing their hands, eating the Basic 4 Diet, and exercising daily—important as these are. We can revise our health textbooks and courses of study with these points in mind, so that there is less emphasis on fragmented "blood-and-bones hygiene" and greater emphasis on health as involving the whole person[68] and his style of life.[69] This would give us a more solid foundation to work from in helping the students to make intelligent decisions and moral choices about health matters such as: drinking, smoking, exercising, and sex conduct; and

[66] Clarence W. Hall, "Is Religion Banned From Our Schools?" *Reader's Digest,* 86, 5114:49–54, Feb., 1965.

[67] *The Holy Bible,* Revised Standard Version, New York: Thomas Nelson and Sons, 1953, Deuteronomy 8:3, p. 143.

[68] T. Dobzhansky, "Evolutionary and Population Genetics," *Science,* 142, 3596:1131–35, Nov. 29, 1963.

[69] Marjorie L. Craig, and Francis U. Everett, *Developing Health Potentialities,* New York: Metropolitan Life Insurance Company, School Health Bureau. (Reprinted from Teachers College Record, 61:8, May, 1960.)

also in relation to personality development and mental health and mental illness.

Perhaps we have focused too much on what is wrong with modern youth and too little on what is right with them. Youth is a time of great potentiality for idealism—and modern youth is no exception. Perhaps we need to capitalize more on this golden opportunity in the health education of the future. Since about 45 per cent of our total population in the United States is under 24 years of age, this is a great challenge to health educators.

### *Public Health Education*

We have pinpointed the great killers in the United States such as heart disease, cancer, and stroke, and the major disablers such as accidents and the arthritic-rheumatic diseases. And we are now focusing on better ways to diagnose, treat, prevent, and delay the onset of these master killers and disablers. Fortunately, we also see more clearly that staying alive in the modern world is only half the battle. Human beings need something to live *for* and to live *by*, since life is a marathon race, not a hundred-yard dash. Most people want to live only so long as they can carry on an active, useful, and meaningful life; they are not interested in living in the deep-freeze or simply in existing as human vegetables. Living a spiritual, healthful life may not necessarily mean that a man will live longer, but he will certainly lead a more meaningful, fully human life.

What can we do about this in public health education? We can develop and use models of "health" and "healthful living" that include a spiritual dimension. We can develop public health education films, pamphlets, posters, and charts that include all the major dimensions of health, not just the physical, social, and mental. We can prepare exhibits and displays in health museums based upon holistic-ecologic concepts of health, including the spiritual dimension; and we can include discussions of these matters in health-lecture series for the adult public, to live audiences as well as by radio and television programs. We can stress the multiple-factor (including moral, ethical, and spiritual factors) etiology of health, disease, aging, and longevity instead of single-factor causation; so that modern man may become less susceptible to searching for panaceas, or of trying to live like human guinea pigs on the frontiers of medical science. We can deal with health, disease, and aging as phenomena of the whole man and his life style, in ways that will make him less susceptible to poor consumer health attitudes and practices and to quackery. We can work cooperatively with other institutions in relating public health education to poverty, social class, work, recreation and leisure, citizenship, esthetic experiences—including those with nature and home and family life. We can work with other groups in pointing to love, hope, and faith as more healthful than nihilistic absurdity and despair. We can cooperate in working toward the development of communities with a physical, social, cultural, and spiritual environment in which human beings can live healthier, more enjoyable, meaningful, and creative lives.[70]

## HEALTH EDUCATION FOR CREATIVE LIVING

Health education has an important role in education for creative living.[71] It has been too self-centered and narcissistic in the past. Modern health education should take us out of ourselves, by helping us to establish stronger links with nature and life, including man, and with the spiritual dimensions of ourselves and the universe.

Man's restless energy, adventuring nature, and creative spirit will be expressed either *constructively* or *destructively,* since he has great potentialities for both good and evil. Human perfectability and progress are not inevitable. We need to help nourish the creative spirit of man to improve his health, and to help save him from self-destruction and annihilation through a *living faith* that guides his daily life.

This is an exciting challenge for young and old alike, because healthful creative living involves far more than blind obedience to "thou shalt nots." Our goal cannot be reached by escaping into a grim, ascetic, other-worldly approach to life. A man's first responsibility is to become a real man among men. And we must remember that Hell is still paved with good intentions, self-righteousness, and cant.

[70] Jean Rostand, *Can Man Be Modified?* tr. by Jonathan Griffin, New York: Basic Books, Inc., 1959.

[71] Edgar Dale, "Education for Creativity," *The Newsletter,* 30:3, Dec., 1964.

Life and health are for living, here and now. At its finest, human life is grounded in love and mutual service. Meeting the challenge of healthful, creative living involves choices, decisions, risks, adventures, toil, sacrifice, and suffering.

But life is not all grimness and suffering. A healthy, creative person loves life and experiences the deep joys of living. Just to live and experience the truth, goodness, and beauty of the world should be a source of endless delight. An old Chinese proverb points the way: "Do the best you can in this world, and the next one will take care of itself."

# 4

# VALUES, GUILT, *and* ILLNESS

# 14

## Patient or Penitent

*David Belgum*

THE ROLE in which a person perceives himself will greatly influence how he reacts to his situation in life. For example, two roommates in a hospital are incapacitated by a physical or mental illness. One considers himself the victim of an impersonal disease over which he has little or no control; the other views himself as a sinner who is receiving just reward for his evil life. Such a basic difference in viewpoint has profound implications for diagnosis of the disease, responsibility for the cure, type of therapy to be used, the locus of the problem, as well as for the question of one's philosophy of life.

### SYMPTOMS—THE AMPLIFIED AND DISTORTED VOICE OF CONSCIENCE

It is now a commonplace that negative and antisocial emotions or actions can be the cause or precipitating factor in a wide variety of physical and mental symptoms. There have been many estimates as to the percentage of an average physician's patients who have functional rather than primarily organic difficulties.

In *Psychiatry in the Medical Specialties,* Dunbar says:

> It has been found that at least 65 per cent of patients are suffering from illness syndromes initiated or seriously complicated by psychological problems.[1]

The Joint Commission on Mental Illness and Health has found that:

> Nearly all doctors reported a considerable number of mentally ill or emotionally disturbed patients. Several doctors estimated that as many as 75 per cent of their patients were emotionally disturbed.[2]

With careful definition of terms and the statistical tabulation of sufficient case data, it should be possible to be more exact concerning the nature and extent of the psychosomatic problem in both private medical practice and in the general medical-surgical hospital. The hospital chaplain would be the logical one to be involved in such research.

There have been many attempts to correlate the moral and religious factors in a patient's life with the nature and meaning of his symptoms.[3] No one claims that 100 per cent of illnesses are functional, but the tendency in recent years is to look suspiciously at an increasing number. Guilt-producing behavior, negative emotions, etc. tend to throw the body into a precarious position, to disturb necessary homeostasis, and to make the person more susceptible to the ravages of germs and bacteria, which up to this time have been kept

[1] Flanders Dunbar, *Psychiatry in the Medical Specialties,* New York: McGraw-Hill Book Co., Inc., 1959, p. v. (Used by permission of McGraw-Hill Book Company.) See also Chap. 1, "Changing Concept of Disease"; cf. O. Spurgeon English, and Gerald H. J. Pearson, *Emotional Problems of Living,* rev. ed., New York: W. W. Norton & Company, 1955, "Psychophysiologic Disorders," pp. 490–92.

[2] Reginald Robinson, David F. Demarche, and Mildred K. Wagle, *Community Resources in Mental Health,* New York: Basic Books, Inc., 1960, "The Nonpsychiatric Physician," pp. 301–3.

[3] See David Belgum, *Why Did It Happen to Me?* Minneapolis: Augsburg Publishing House, 1960, Chap. 1, in which are discussed the insights into stress. See also Hans Selye, *The Stress of Life,* New York: McGraw-Hill Book Company, Inc., 1956, "General Adaptation Syndrome." See also Granger E. Westberg, *Minister and Doctor Meet,* New York: Harper and Row, 1961, Chap. 6. Aarne Siirala goes further and states that mental illness, in particular, says something about the morality and conscience of the community. It is a symptom of a sick society. "The Meaning of Illness,' *Journal of Religion and Health,* 1, 2:153–64, Jan., 1962.

under control by various natural barriers. Thus Dunbar even includes accidents in the "three illness groups" together with cardiovascular disease and cancer.[4] When an "accident prone" patient has a need to punish himself for his past life, the question of morals and values comes urgently to the fore.

Simmons raises the question of the psychosomatic aspects of cancer.[5] When an excessive amount of certain hormones is produced, they bombard body tissue with carcinogenic elements, according to him. He would like to see more research into the etiology of cancer from a functional point of view. Cancerous deaths are 75 per cent higher in heavy smokers than among nonsmokers. He raises the question whether excessive smoking may not be a crude gauge of the amount of emotional stress under which the person is trying to live. Perhaps that is the variable rather than the specific noxious agents in the tobacco itself. Anger and fear, according to Simmons, also flood the body with hormones containing carcinogenic elements.

It is, however, in the enormous field of mental illness that some of the sharpest distinctions may have to be drawn between patient and penitent. Can it be that many neurotic and psychotic symptoms are also the amplified and distorted voice of conscience? An increasing number of reputable psychotherapists are becoming discouraged about the psychoanalytic interpretation of mental illness and its various modifications in psychiatric practice—Eysenck, Szasz, and Mowrer, to mention a few.[6] Eysenck finds no scientific or statistical evidence for the efficacy of psychotherapy as it is generally practiced today. Szasz denies the term "mental illness" calling it a "myth." And Mowrer believes that neurotics and psychotics (barring any organic involvement) are not "sick," but "sinners" caught and condemned by their own consciences.

Mowrer's theory has already been tested on a small scale by Peterson[7] of the University of Illinois and Swensen[8] of

[4] Dunbar, *loc. cit.*

[5] Harold E. Simmons, *The Psychosomatic Aspects of Cancer,* Washington, D.C.: Peabody Press, 1956.

[6] H. J. Eysenck, ed., *Handbook of Abnormal Psychology,* New York: Basic Books, Inc., 1961, Chap. 18; Thomas S. Szasz, *The Myth of Mental Illness,* New York: Harper and Row, 1961; O. Hobart Mowrer, *The Crisis in Psychiatry and Religion,* New York: D. Van Nostrand Co., Inc., 1961.

[7] Donald R. Peterson, "The Insecure Child: Over-Socialized or Under-Socialized?" A mimeographed paper issued at the University of Illinois, 1961.

[8] Clifford H. Swensen, Jr., "Sexual Behavior and Psychopathology: A Test of Mowrer's Hypothesis." A mimeographed paper issued at the University of Tennessee, Jan. 12, 1962.

the University of Tennessee. As it turns out, Mowrer's hypothesis is easily tested, as Swensen indicates:

If Mowrer's contention is correct, one would expect people who seek psychotherapy for neurotic complaints to have violated moral laws more frequently than normal people coming from the same socio-economic background. . . . A group of 25 co-eds who had entered psychotherapy were compared with a control group of 25 co-eds who were matched with them according to age and school class. It was found that the group needing psychotherapy had engaged in significantly less social activity but had had more extensive sexual experience than the control group. Within the control group itself, it was found that the girls who had had sexual intercourse had significantly more psychosomatic problems than the girls who had not engaged in sexual intercourse.[9]

Surely this is a question for research and should be studied on a large scale in various settings. The results could help answer the question: Should the incapacitated person play the role of the patient or the penitent? If his symptoms are the amplified and distorted voice of conscience, the answer is quite obvious.

### GUILT AND RESPONSIBILITY

Our generation may well be characterized as an age of *irresponsibility*. Rather than accepting our guilt for misdeeds, we rationalize our way out, blaming "conditioned" causes; we attribute our behavior to our environment or heredity, or to our faulty training or lack of need-gratification. A nationwide survey conducted by the Joint Commission on Mental Illness and Health discovered the following:

Despite the fact that it seems to take an unusual degree of insight for an individual to admit that he needs help with a mental or emotional problem, only about one-fourth of those who sought assistance traced their problems back to their own inadequacies with any clarity . . . few were prepared to be told that they must accept at least a share of the responsibility for their problems and that they must change themselves accordingly.[10]

A man nearing middle age had been the private patient of a psychiatrist and had also been treated by a clinical

[9] *Ibid.*, pp. 1, 6.

[10] Joint Commission on Mental Illness and Health, *Action for Mental Health,* New York: Basic Books, Inc., 1961, p. 103.

psychologist. He had been told that the reason he felt a compulsive need to abuse his wife verbally and physically was that he was expressing symbolically his hatred for a hostile and unloving stepmother. The pastor-counselor to whom he came for help despaired of going through the long catharsis which would have brought the two of them once again to the "insight" that the stepmother was the *cause* of his problem. So against his better judgment, he decided to confront him simply with the question of responsibility.

The minister asked, "On the last occasion when you beat your wife, if she had called the sheriff, what would the charges have been, if any?"

The client replied, "I don't think she ever would—as a matter of fact it never occurred to me. But I guess she would have a case; the charge would be assault and battery."

The next question was supremely naive, and only because there was a good relationship between them, no one laughed. The counselor simply asked, "And who would be tried and sent to the workhouse for thirty days? You or your stepmother?"

The interview moved rapidly onward and centered around the matter of guilt and its ensuing responsibility. It turned out that there was much to feel guilty about, much of it for which he acknowledged responsibility. It became increasingly less realistic or useful for him to use his dead stepmother for a scapegoat.

Since Freud we have assumed that "insight" into the forces that have molded our personalities is a good and health-producing experience. The goal has been the age-old proverb: "Know thyself." However, the irony of it has been that many times it has led to the "insight" that it is someone else's fault that we have turned out as we have and that we act or feel as bad as we do. The longer we have talked in therapy the longer has grown the list of those culprits who are *responsible* for our disordered lives.

One of the clichés in the mental-health field has been that mental illness is nothing to be ashamed of because it is simply an illness like any physical illness. But psychosomatic medicine has taken the comfort out of that reassurance, for, if the message is clear, ulcers, arthritis, some cardiovascular diseases, etc. may very well be matters about which to be ashamed (excluding obvious organicity). Neurotic and psychotic breakdown may be an involuntary confession of guilt, just as many somatic symptoms are the amplified and distorted voice of conscience. The appropriate action for one so stricken would be penitence in the face of guilt, rather than a plea of irresponsible illness.

The opposite of acceptance of responsibility for one's life is paranoid projection—attributing blame and responsibility to others or to the outside environment. In this sense, the paranoid patient is sicker than the one who is sunk into a deep depression. The latter at least knows he has a problem and that it is *his* problem.

During Professor Mowrer's Seminar at the University of Illinois (Spring Semester, 1962), the following operational definition was evolved: "If a person has done something that he is afraid to have known, he is guilty." This brings us to the clear-cut division between those who are publicly declared to be guilty and those who are surreptitiously guilty, but camouflaging it under the guise of mental or psychosomatic illness.

### THE HOSPITAL PATIENT AND THE PENITENTIARY INMATE

Everyone agrees that the penitentiary inmate should be penitent. Public disgrace is a great aid in this spiritual exercise, although some hardened criminals are not penitent because they have an underdeveloped, squelched, or atrophied conscience. In psychological parlance, they are psychopathic because they lack an adequate Super Ego; they have not been adequately socialized.

But what of those who have done wrong, who have violated their own conscience and the demands of society, but have not been caught? Some inexorable sense of moral homeostasis, some built-in sense of justice seems to take over, and they punish themselves with a six- to twelve-month sentence of psychotic depression, frightening hallucinations, or other morbid mental states. Or they may choose one of a dozen or more psychosomatic symptoms.

Those who use the cliché referred to above, that mental illness is nothing to be ashamed of, will chide me for being harsh and judgmental toward patients who have suffered enough already. But I should like someday to see the mental-hospital patients and the psychosomatic patients compared with penitentiary inmates, case history by case history, for I suspect that their behavior and their characters are quite similar. My own experience has not been broad enough to give a reliable answer; but it has been varied enough to raise some questions.

Why is it that in clinical-pastoral training in hospital ministry so much effort is directed toward helping the student chaplains to overcome their shock, their amazement and surprise, at what they hear from the patient's record, or, in mental hospitals, what is revealed at staff meetings? At present some of us are working at a state mental research hospital with a group of psychotic women. In more than 20 that have passed through the group or remain in it, there is represented theft, adultery, homosexuality, incest, masturbation and assorted perversions, beating and strangling of children (short of murder), criminal abortion, alcoholism, lying and other forms of dishonesty, rejection of responsibility concerning familial or vocational duties, temper tantrums as well as physical violence—just to mention a few things from memory. The question is: Would case histories from the penitentiary sound much different? These are persons who were not apprehended by an officer of the law, but who were caught by their own consciences and who punished themselves by various forms of psychic and social misery.

The differences between the hospital and penitentiary groups have recently been made to appear less distinct, the contrast less great. In many ways the increased use of psychological and psychiatric services in penal institutions has been based on the assumption that the criminal offender is suffering from some form of mental illness. His crime is a symptom and should be treated more or less medically. Juvenile delinquency appears to some to be more of a sickness than a sin. According to this trend, it is less and less likely that one would come across a bona fide penitent, but increasingly likely that one would discover patients, whether suffering from physical, mental, or social diseases. Criminals would be "hospitalized" for their antisocial sickness.

It is the contention of the line of argument outlined above that there may indeed be less difference between the hospital and penitentiary groups, but for exactly the opposite reason. Namely, the psychosomatic patients and the mentally ill have as much to be penitent about as the penitentiary or criminal group. All three groups have violated the moral demands of society, and have alienated themselves from society; the social accident of having been publicly apprehended turns out to be psychologically as well as ethically incidental. They all suffer one way or another as long as this condition of disobedience and alienation remains unresolved.

In medieval times it was not uncommon to speak quite openly about the consequences of sins. The "Penitential Handbooks" were in some ways crude, but in other ways more perceptive than are we in our abnegation of personal responsibility.[11] If man is in any genuine sense responsible for his behavior, we will have to reverse some of our attitudes about his misconduct. Men will have to face more realistically and more humanly the consequences of their sins. If a man burns with hatred for his boss for ten years, covets his wife, and plots against him at the office, it may turn out to be scientifically unsophisticated to say with surprise, "I can't imagine what hit me," when he becomes incapacitated with arthritis or sinks into a deep psychotic depression. Therapy which gives him a combination of hormones and tranquilizers will not be thorough enough; nor will the hospital chaplain have fulfilled his function when he has counseled him to the point where he has "insight" into the combination of interpersonal influences in his personality development that *made* him do it, say it, or wish it.

## ROLE OF THE MINISTER OF RELIGION

In proportion as it becomes scientifically demonstrable that symptoms are often the amplified voice of conscience, it should become logically inescapable that the religious agencies which *inform* conscience have the function of restoring those persons who have run afoul of their consciences. The church has called this many things: "binding up the brokenhearted," "the ministry of reconciliation," and "the cure of souls."

Such a ministry may well have as its function helping many afflicted people to discover, or rather acknowledge,

[11] John T. McNeill and Helena M. Gamer, *Medieval Handbooks of Penance,* New York: Columbia University Press, 1938. See also Thomas Pollock Oakley, *English Penitential Discipline and Anglo-Saxon Law in Their Joint Influence,* New York: Columbia University Ph.D. dissertation, 1923.

that they are not victims of an impersonal and amoral disease, but that their illness has a moral and theological perspective that is of vital importance to them. Many people have not suffered from illness, per se, but they are sick (some sick unto death) of the kind of life they have lived and the interpersonal relationships they have destroyed.

Acknowledging psychosomatic and mental illnesses as a chastisement for guilt can have a positive aspect. It means that one still has conscience and character enough to be bothered by wrong-doing and is sensitive to the moral demands of one's fellow men. One has not passed beyond the pale into that total lack of moral concern, which is dangerously close to, if indeed not, the "sin against the Holy Spirit."

Who else can operate competently in this vital ministry if not the clergy of the Church and the chaplains that minister in our hospitals? What other point of view can handle this issue if not a theology which is aware of the problem of sin and which stands ready to deal effectively with the ravages of guilt? And the test of such a ministry of reconciliation may well be whether persons dodging responsibility under the guise of psychosomatic or mental illness will exchange their role of patient for penitent.

# 15

# The Problem of Guilt

*Gordon E. Jackson*

### THE SENSE OF GUILT

"THE SENSE OF GUILT is the most important problem in the development of civilization. . ."[1] We can go further by saying that it is a mode, like dread in the thought of Heidegger, of man's being-in-the-world. At the simplest level guilt is situational; that is, it refers to a concrete, remembered episode. In its complexity and profundity guilt has neurotic and primal dimensions. In this chapter we shall trace these dimensions, point out their relationships, and suggest some meanings for the ministry of the church.

Freud's studies led him to conclude that the sense of guilt originates in the oedipal complex. The son wishes his father dead. This hatred of the father is due to his being a

GORDON W. JACKSON, Ph.D., is Dean and Professor of Pastoral Theology, Pittsburgh Theological Seminary, Pittsburgh, Pennsylvania.

[1] Sigmund Freud, *Civilization and Its Discontents*, tr. by James Strachey, New York: W. W. Norton & Company, 1961, p. 81.

rival for the mother. The death-wish toward the father or the actual killing of the father is the "principal and primal crime of humanity as well as of the individual."[2] Yet any attempt to remove the father would result in castration. So the son gives up the wish to kill the father and possess the mother, but he does not actually give it up for it remains in the unconscious. Fear of the father, that is, castration-fear, forces this repression. The repressed desire to kill the father is the basis for the sense of guilt.

In *Totem and Taboo* Freud urges that there need have been no actual killing of the primal father of the horde by the sons. As with neurotics whose psychic realities, e.g., impulses and feelings, are sufficient to produce neurotic guilt, so with primitives: the mere impulse of hostility towards the father and the existence of the wish fantasy to kill and devour him and take his place with the women would be enough. Wishes and impulses have the full value of fact for neurotics and primitive man as well.[3]

Over against the hatred of the father is the tender love for him, love that fills the son with remorse. A primordial ambivalence of hatred and love brought remorse. Out of hatred the son wished to kill the father; out of love he was filled with remorse. Love sets up the superego by which the son identifies with the father, the superego being the power of punishment for the deed done and restriction to prevent a repetition.[4] The superego is the father internalized and is the father's power against a repetition of the deed. Because the impulse of aggression is repeated in successive generations and because ambivalence continues, the sense of guilt has persisted. ". . . the sense of guilt is an expression of the conflict due to ambivalence, of the eternal struggle between Eros and the instinct of destruction or death."[5] Civilization actually heightens the sense of guilt by replacing the father with the group which reconfirms, strengthens, and intensifies

[2] Sigmund Freud, "Dostoevsky and Parricide," tr. by James Strachey, in *Collected Papers,* New York: Basic Books, 1959, 5:229.

[3] However, Freud did conclude in *Totem and Taboo* that the deed was probably done. (*Totem and Taboo,* tr. by A. A. Brill, New York: Vintage Books, Random House, 1946, pp. 206 ff.) In *Civilization and Its Discontents,* written 17 years later, Freud also held that the aggression against the primal father was not suppressed but was carried out (pp. 78 ff.).

[4] Freud, *Civilization and Its Discontents,* p. 79 (cf. Freud, "Dostoevsky and Parricide," p. 231).

[5] *Ibid.*

the need to keep hostility repressed while obeying the erotic impulse to concrescence.[6]

The unconscious sense of guilt is identical with the need for punishment.[7] The instinct of aggression in the form of a death-wish against the father is taken over by part of the ego and used against the ego. This is the development of the superego. The reason for the aggression's being turned in in the first place is the fear of a loss of love. The child is dependent and he is exposed to dangers of abandoment. The hostile impulse itself, apart from a deed, is bad; that is, it is felt dangerously as the loss of love. Therefore, the superego which has taken over the aggressiveness felt toward the object (e.g., father) turns against the self as the aggressive impulse in the form of punishment. What was first felt as a sense of guilt in the presence of external authority (e.g., father) is now internalized and the nagging conscience continues.[8] The tension between the superego and the ego is the sense of guilt and expresses itself as need for punishment. The sense of guilt is a form of anxiety: in its earlier stage before the all-powerful father, in its later stage before the superego.[9]

It will be helpful now to turn to Erik Erikson, a neo-Freudian, who has plotted eight stages of human development of which the first three concern us here. It is in the third stage, the oedipal period, that Erikson locates guilt *per se*. However, his deepening and expanding of Freud are due to his study of the prior two stages.

The first stage is the oral period which lasts about the first twelve months of life. The oral period centers in the intake of food. Along with this is the intake of pleasurable experience, the pleasurable feeling of being played with, wanted, loved. The infant "takes in" with his eyes, his hands, his ears, his skin, as well as his mouth. Through sucking, seeing, feeling, hearing, the infant incorporates his "world." Thus the oral stage is the incorporative stage, the first half more passive and the latter half more active. Passive

[6] *Ibid.*, p. 80.

[7] Sigmund Freud, "The Economic Problem in Masochism," tr. by Joan Riviere, in *Collected Papers,* New York: Basic Books, 1959, 2:263.

[8] Freud interprets Dostoevsky's epileptic seizures as self-punishment for a death-wish against his father. He had wished his father were dead, and the epilepsy satisfied his need of punishment for this evil wish. Freud believed that religious feelings are built on this filial guilt and the need for punishment. See Freud, "Dostoevsky and Parricide," pp. 229, 234.

[9] Freud, *Civilization and Its Discontents,* p. 82.

incorporation emphasizes the mode of getting in the sense of receiving and accepting, while active incorporation is the mode of taking and holding on. The quality of the "world" received and accepted or not accepted and rejected ("spitting up") is the matrix for the first psychosocial crisis. During this period the infant develops basic trust or basic mistrust.[10]

By "trust" Erikson means trustfulness toward the outside and trustworthiness toward the self.[11] By "basic" he means pervasive. The infant comes to have a sense of goodness or well-being, a generally good feeling of warmth and mutuality. "This forms the basis in the child for a sense of identity which will later combine a sense of being 'all right,' of being oneself, and of becoming what other people trust one will become."[12] Mistrust is primarily a sense of badness in which "outside providers" are not trustful and the self is not trustworthy. Basic mistrust derives from the feeling of being deprived, divided, abandoned. A negative oral character may develop which is pessimistic and has the forms of "being empty" and of "being no good."[13] A sense of badness develops which is the loss of all that is good because the person's own badness destroyed it within and destroyed or drove it away outside. Erikson offers the case study of Jean, whom he describes as an early ego failure, which is the study of maternal estrangement due to illness and its effect upon the infant. The separation, because of tuberculosis of the mother, came when Jean was nine months old and continued for four months. Jean communicated to Erikson that she had "hurt" the mother and for this reason she had been banished from her mother's room. She talked of "throwing away a chest," meaning that she should be thrown away. Later she became outspoken and asked to be "thrown away."[14] This is basic mistrust with its obvious incipient guilt.

The second stage is the anal period which lasts approxi-

[10] For material in this paragraph see Erik H. Erikson, *Childhood and Society,* New York: W. W. Norton & Company, 1950, pp. 67 ff., 219 ff.; Erik H. Erikson, "Identity and the Life Cycle," *Psychological Issues,* New York: International Universities Press, 1959, pp. 55 ff.; O. Spurgeon English and Gerald H. J. Pearson, *Emotional Problems of Living,* rev. ed., New York: W. W. Norton & Company, 1955, Chaps. 1 and 2.

[11] Erikson, "Identity and Life Cycle," p. 56.

[12] Erikson, *Childhood and Society,* p. 221.

[13] *Ibid.,* p. 61.

[14] *Ibid.,* Chap. 5.

mately 18 months. This is the time of toilet training when the child is confronted with the realities of mother's wishes and demands concerning the time and place of elimination. During this period the emphasis is on *holding on* and *letting go,* on retention and elimination. Of course there is overlapping with the oral period. "The emotional life of the child centers in interest in both nutrition and excretion, and his eroticism follows a similar path."[15] And: "It is noteworthy that drastic interference with the child's oral gratifications encourages anal retentive attitudes which compensate for the inhibited oral gratification."[16]

The psychological crisis of stage two is Autonomy vs. Shame and Doubt. This is a period of decision-making when the child learns bowel and bladder control, learns to accept regulations, learns to become responsible for holding in and letting go. Thus a sense of autonomy begins—the "ability to do without anybody to lean on."[17] Shame is the sense of being exposed and looked at; shaming increases the sense of being small. Shame is a feeling about the body: shameful, disgusting, nasty. This feeling easily reaches over into genitality because of the association of sex organs with excretion. "Doubt is the brother of shame."[18] It is the consciousness of having a "behind," unseen by the child but dominated by others; and thus one's autonomy is lessened. Doubt leads to self-doubting and to paranoic fears.[19] Shame and doubt are related to the sense of mistrust or badness of stage one as autonomy is related to the sense of trust or goodness.[20] Erikson says, "Shame is early expressed in an impulse to bury one's face, or to sink, right then and there, into the ground."[21] The shamed self may turn against himself, develop a precocious conscience, and begin the process of a compulsive character development. In the light of Freud's discovery that obsessive compulsive sufferers are dominated

[15] Franz Alexander, *Fundamentals of Psychoanalysis,* New York: W. W. Norton & Company, 1948, p. 51.

[16] *Ibid.*

[17] Erickson, *Childhood and Society,* p. 78.

[18] *Ibid.,* p. 224.

[19] *Ibid.*

[20] *Ibid.,* p. 80.

[21] *Ibid.,* p. 223.

[22] Sigmund Freud, "Obsessive Acts and Religious Practices," tr. by R. C. McWalters, in *Collected Papers,* New York: Basic Books, 1959, Chap. 2.

by a sense of guilt,[22] we can pin some guilt down to a very early and very deep level in the child's life. Furthermore, if hostility and guilt are correlated, as Freud thought, and if this hostility is not instinctual but at least in part an outgrowth of anal frustration,[23] the anal period for the locus of early guilt becomes all the more significant. Behind this, of course, is the incipient stage of guilt in the oral period.

The third stage is the oedipal period, roughly from three years to six. As we have seen, Freud locates the beginnings of a sense of guilt in this stage. The psychosocial crisis is Initiative vs. Guilt. Initiative is the movement of the self toward a favored position with the parent of the opposite sex, which movement is doomed to failure (this is the meaning of the incest taboo and the castration complex). The sense of guilt develops due to this inevitable failure.[24] It is guilt over something never done nor possible of being done,[25] the phallic fantasies of vague murder and rape.

The oedipal period is a marked time for superego development. The conscience actually becomes rather well established during this period. It is the self turned against itself (superego vs. ego) in an accusatory, condemnatory, and punishing way. The parents, and especially the parent of the same sex, are introjected into the interior of the self and continue to peer over the shoulder of the self into all of its secret impulses and thoughts. For the very thoughts and impulses the child feels guilt.[26] This guilt leaves a substratum effect of badness in the child. The need for punishment, then, gets its impetus here. Although masochism begins earlier,[27] it is confirmed and deepened into the substratum of the personality during this stage.

Assuming Freud's position on guilt development during the oedipal stage, which is supported by Erikson, and undergirding that with Erickson's stages one and two, we have this line of schematic development:

[23] Alexander, p. 52.

[24] Erikson, *Childhood and Society*, p. 225.

[25] *Ibid.*, p. 86. Erickson does not hold to a primal deed of murder done by the sons against the horde father.

[26] *Ibid.*, p. 80.

[27] Freud locates it in the aggressive instinct itself; English and Pearson, pp. 50, 68, and Erikson, *Childhood and Society*, pp. 63 ff., locate it in the anal stage; although its precursor is in the biting rage of the oral stage: *ibid.*, p. 220.

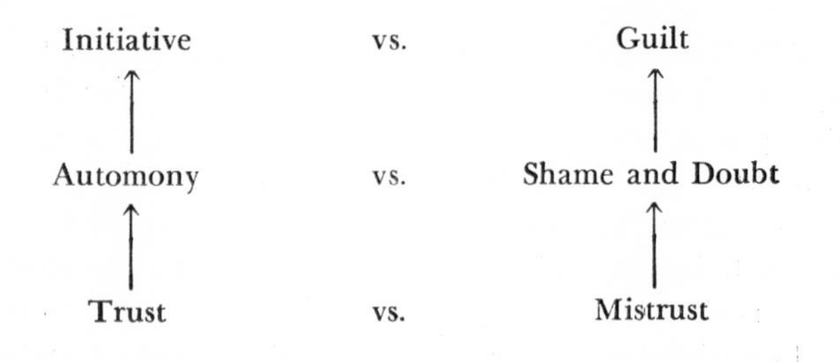


This schema does not mean to suggest a white-and-black set of differences as though trust-autonomy-initiative were without guilt and mistrust-shame-doubt-guilt were nothing but guilt. The ambiguity of the human development would preclude this as would the universality of the oedipal experience and its concomitant, guilt. On the other hand, the sense of guilt would seem to vary from very little to deep pathology. This is accounted for partly by a markedly successful or unsuccessful repression but largely, it would seem, by the quality of relationships forming the milieu of the child's development. We shall return to this more fully.

### A THEOLOGICAL PERSPECTIVE

When we turn to a theological perspective on guilt, we are confronted by two sets of facts agreed to by biblical scholars no matter how diverse their points of view may be. The first of these facts is that the Hebrews attached little importance to the distinction among sin, guilt, punishment, and need for forgiveness. These words are inextricably bound together. Whether it is the technical, ritualistic root *'shm* or the richer, dynamic expression *'awon,* not only guilt but sin or mistake, iniquity, burden, forgiveness are involved. Gottfried Quell, discussing this circle of ideas, uses Psalm 32:1, 2 to illustrate the point.

> Blessed is he whose transgression is forgiven *(nesuy pesha'),* whose sin is covered *(kesuy hata'ah).* Blessed is the man unto whom the Lord imputeth not iniquity *('awon).*

The emphasis on guilt is unmistakable.[28] Quell cites Genesis 4:13 to illustrate punishment and suffering felt by Cain but

[28] Gottfried Quell, "Sin," tr. from Gerhard Kittel's *Theologisches Worterbuch zum Neuen Testament* by J. R. Coates in *Bible Key Words,* New York: Harper and Brothers, 1951, 3:22.

also his awareness of a standard contradicted: "My *'awon* is greater than I can bear."[29] The complex of ideas centering around sin, guilt, judgment, burden, need for forgiveness is one of the richest in biblical literature.

This introduces us to the second fact of Hebrew thought with reference to guilt. Not only are sin, guilt, punishment, and the need for forgiveness inextricably bound together, but what binds them together is that they are always human experience *before God* or in the presence of God. The religious concept of guilt derives from a numinous root.[30] As Walter Grundmann observes, sin is godlessness and is "responsible guilt" before God.[31] Guilt is part of man's reality as he stands before God. Thus "every individual sin committed by and against men acquires its significance before God and has before Him the character of guilt."[32] Von Rad, interpreting the serpent-man relationship in the story of the Fall, views it in terms of "fate," universal tragedy, suggesting the enigmatic destiny in which man is involved. It is the destiny of "fallen" man, estranged man, a destiny wider than personal guilt forming the universal context for that guilt. This "fate" or universal tragedy he finds the Yahwist tracing to the *one* trouble of man's relation to God.[33] Eichrodt, employing the conceptual framework of covenant, sees the covenant God creating but also judging and abrogating covenant. It is this judging and abrogating work of God which developed in Israel a corporate national guilt. Eichrodt says:

The Yahwist account of the dawn of man's history, with its heart-breaking lament for the curse laid on human existence as a result of a deliberate primal decision against God and the consequent hostile effect of

[29] *Ibid.*

[30] *Ibid.*, p. 23.

[31] Walter Grundmann, "Sin in the New Testament," tr. from Gerhard Kittel's *Theologisches Worterbuch zum Neuen Testament* by Geoffrey W. Bromiley, in *Theological Dictionary of the New Testament*, Grand Rapids: Wm. B. Eerdmans Publishing Co., 1964, 1:303. Hobart Mowrer, arguing that sin is etiologically related to neurosis and psychosis, does not once define sin in terms of man's relation to God. He is quite content to see sin as "whatever causes one to go to Hell," and by Hell he means neurosis and psychosis. Anything that carries man toward these "forms of perdition" is sin. He lumps together irresponsibility, wrong-doing, immorality, and sin. His approach to sin is a new-old moralism and has little or nothing to do wth sin theologically understood. See O. Hobart Mowrer, *The Crisis in Psychiatry and Religion*, Princeton, N.J.: D. Van Nostrand Co., Inc., 1961, Chaps. 3, 4, 11.

[32] *Ibid.*, p. 311.

[33] Gerhard Von Rad, *Genesis*, tr. by John H. Marks, Philadelphia: Westminster Press, 1961, pp. 90 ff., esp. p. 98.

divine judgment, survives as testimony of undeniable significance, for the religious feeling of ancient Israel.[34]

Guilt is part of this religious feeling. And Bultmann, who denies a universality of sin attributable to something in human nature or to a "fateful event" out of a hoary past but who finds its origin in experience, argues for a proto-sin of apostasy as "factual sin," the "sin of sins," "real guilt," before God.[35] The "proto-sin of apostasy . . . repeats itself in every Now in the fact of that possibility of knowing God which is open to every Now."[36]

Possibly the *locus classicus* for the feeling of guilt is in Genesis 3. Bodily shame is the phenomenology of guilt, the "most elementary emotion of guilt feeling at the deepest root of human existence, the sign of a breach that reaches to the lowest levels of our physical being."[37] Guilt is the sense of disturbance. A disunity of body and spirit is felt as shame and is depicted as nakedness. Isolation defended against in the displacement of blame to the woman, God, the serpent, betrays the anxiety of guilt. Fear of God which eventuates in hiding shows the anxiety of guilt. Punishment experienced as the judgment by God on the woman, the man, the serpent, is the counterpart of guilt. The sense of fateful tragedy hangs over human existence. But there is also the profound sense of the need for, and experiences of, forgiveness marked by God's clothing the pair in garments of skins although they had made for themselves aprons of leaves.

The fundamental theological point in the idea of guilt is that guilt is vis-à-vis God. Guilt is existence in the wrath of God. It is not only or merely a sense of badness or wrongness; it is the gulf between us and God. Sin is the happening creating the obstacle of guilt. Something has happened; the past cannot be changed by us. Guilt binds us to this past, identifying us with what has happened and cannot be undone. Guilt is the bad conscience about this happening as well as the gulf created by it.[38] In Barth's way of putting it,

[34] Walter Eichrodt, *Theology of the Old Testament,* tr. by J. A. Baker, Philadelphia: Westminster Press, 1961, 1:464.

[35] Rudolf Bultman, *Theology of the New Testament,* tr. by Kendrick Grobel, New York: Charles Scribner's Sons, 1951, 1:250.

[36] *Ibid.,* pp. 250–51.

[37] Von Rad, p. 88.

[38] Emil Brunner, *Man in Revolt,* Philadelphia: Westminster Press, 1947, pp. 134 ff.

guilt is man's responsibility for his repudiation of God, for his being in enmity toward God, for his defiance of God. It is his "failure to keep a promise" and his "repudiation of an obligation."[39] Guilt continues because man responds to the grace of God, "not with a corresponding thankfulness, but in one or many forms of his wretched pride."[40] Guilt is the name of the relationship of the sinner before God. It is God who holds man in the relationship of guilt; that is, God's love for man is his wrath and judgment against man who refuses God, refuses to be himself, refuses the neighbor. Since man is not absolutely or ontologically godless, standing as he does before the God who stands before him in Jesus, man continues his shamed and guilty existence.[41] This is primal guilt. That all men do not seem to have a sense of this guilt is no argument against it, for the testimony derives not from a sense of guilt but from God's declaration in and through Jesus Christ. As Reinhold Niebuhr has said, "It is only by an ultimate analysis from beyond all human standards that the particular guilt of the great and the good men of history is revealed."[42]

While we do not have the tools for sorting out two senses of guilt, one developmental and the other primal or theological, if there are two, the Christian who works with guilt, whether his own or another's, must always bear in mind that there are two dimensions of guilt, each born out of a malignant relationship, as Lewis Sherrill has said.[43] From the Christian perspective the deeper guilt is theological; yet undoubtedly it and developmental guilt so interlace and reinforce each other that theology and psychiatry have a common task around this mode of man's being-in-the-world.

## OEDIPUS AND CHRIST: A CASE ILLUSTRATION

Guilt, both in the form of pronouncement (e.g., from God) and as "a sense of," derives from a relationship that is faulty. For Freud it is the erotic and murderous impulses of

[39] Barth, *Dogmatics,* IV/1, 484, Edinburgh: T. & T. Clark, 1956.
[40] *Ibid.,* p. 489.
[41] *Ibid.,* pp. 480 ff.
[42] Reinhold Niebuhr, *The Nature and Destiny of Man,* New York: Charles Scribner's Sons, 1943, 1:227.
[43] Lewis Joseph Sherrill, *Guilt and Redemption,* Richmond: John Knox Press, 1945, pp. 130, 173, 180.

the oedipal period which bring to the child a sense of guilt before the hated-loved father. For Erikson and other neo-Freudians it is also the early relationships within the home, and especially between the child and the mother, which are the matrix of guilt feelings. Sin is the word describing the faulted relationship between man and God which evokes the wrath of God, the objective side of guilt, as well as the sense of guilt, the subjective side. Some relationships are supportive and redemptive but may be viewed as threatening and destructive. This is the way God's affirming Yes is felt by the sinner. Other relationships are destructive and are so perceived. This is the way an overdemanding or an over-indulging mother might be experienced by her infant or the way an uninvolved father might be taken by his four-year-old daughter. The welter of relationships in which a child develops, whether accurately or inaccurately perceived by the child, are crucial in their production of guilt. A case summary will illustrate this point.

G. is 35, a Spanish-speaking woman quite articulate in English. She is married to a man 25 years her senior and has one child, a boy 7 years of age. She was born in South America. She has five sisters and one brother, the brother younger than herself. She could remember exceedingly little about her mother except that she loved to dance and play the guitar, and her father disapproved of both. She could not remember her mother's showing much interest in the children. But she recalled a great deal about her father. He was a fierce, stern man who frightened her and the other children because he became angry so easily. He was very demanding of the children as far as home responsibilities were concerned. Even when she played she had an uneasy feeling. Yet she could also remember his gentleness and affection. He would often lie down with her and her sisters until they were asleep. Many times he would sleep with them. It was he who tucked them into bed at night. She never saw any demonstration of physical love between her father and her mother. G. remembered vividly visiting a girl friend's home when she was nine and being shown around the house. The girl friend pointed out her father and mother's room. G. asked if they slept together. When the reply was yes, G. thought this was very vulgar. When I asked G. what was vulgar, she replied, "For a man and a woman to sleep together. My father and mother never did. I never saw my father kiss my mother." But your father slept with you and the other girls, I reminded her. "But we were girls! For a woman and a man to sleep together. . . . He wouldn't even let us see boys, or date; and he got mad when we talked about boys. Only three of us are married out of seven. When I wrote my dad I was going to get married, he was mad at first. He always told us men might do bad things." Instilled into G. from early childhood was guilt about maleness and femaleness.

Not long after G. had come to the United States, she married a man 25 years her senior. This would be a "safe" marriage because it would continue the father-daughter relationship. Very soon after their marriage G. became pregnant which angered her husband. Two weeks before the baby was due, he left for work one morning but did not return. A few days later she got a wire from him that he was in Miami and would not be home until after the baby was born. Almost a stranger in the city, she was frightened and lonely. After delivery and during the first three months of the boy's life G. was in and out of the hospital because of hemorrhages, headaches, weakness, dizziness, and a nervous breakdown. At about three months the baby was discovered to be a "blue baby." Shortly after this the mother was institutionalized with a psychoneurosis of a depression type.

During the time of her hospitalization the baby was placed in a foster home. (Also during this period he had a successful heart operation.) When the baby was about two years old, the mother was released from the hospital, really against her wishes. She felt secure in the hospital, more secure than she had ever felt before. When she was released, she was afraid that she would not be able to measure up to the responsibility of taking care of her baby. So the baby remained in the foster home. Between the time she left the hospital and three years later when she began to care for her child, she was constantly afraid: afraid to be home alone, afraid to go up in the apartment elevator if there was a strange man on it, afraid she would be robbed or attacked.

When she did begin to care for her child, he was five years old. Yet she considered him her baby and treated him accordingly. She fed him baby food. She would talk baby talk to him (as well as to her husband), sleep with her child, constantly watch his health because he had been a "blue baby," intercede for him at school, protect him both from play and at play, hover over him almost constantly. She said in one interview, "You know, I didn't have him for five years." Yet she would get very impatient with him, expressing her impatience in anger over his not eating, or wanting only baby food, or his back talk, etc. Some of her real feelings toward her child had gotten across to him. One day when she was sick, he said to her, "I make you sick. I make you angry. Maybe I should kill myself." On another occasion he said to her that maybe he and his father should go away for a visit so that "you wouldn't have a bad little boy to make you angry." (Another generation of neurotic guilt was in the making.)

Her husband's being 25 years her senior occupied our attention from the beginning. As the interviews moved along, her feelings toward her husband became more openly hostile. Much of her anger centered in their sexual relationship. She talked of herself as being frigid. Yet she had much curiosity about sexuality. A major break came when she began an interview, "My father—I mean, my husband." From here on she began to evidence increasing concern about her father. She was afraid he was not being cared for. She wanted to see him. She reminded me that he was quite old, not very able to take care of himself, and that she was not sure he was getting the right care. She often expressed the wish that she could return to her paternal home to see him; and yet when I suggested that this might be a very good thing for her to do, she found all kinds of reasons why she could not do this.

What were G.'s real problems? Undoubtedly she had not moved satisfactorily through the oedipal relationship. Her father's stern restrictions about sexuality and her almost total repression of memories about her mother made the working through of the family relationships most difficult. In some real but unconscious sense she had become fixated at the level of a little girl. Her treating of her own child in babyish ways was an identification with him at an infantile level, expressing her need to be cared for. She married a man 25 years her senior, who was quite obviously a father-figure to her. The baby born of this union was unconsciously the baby of her father. This she could not tolerate and a postpartum psychosis developed. She resented the baby and so at times could not control her anger toward him. Her guilt feelings were intensified when her husband abandoned her around the time of the birth, when the baby was a "blue baby," when she could not care for him in his first five years of life. She tried to expiate these guilt feelings by overindulging her child, rationalizing this in a number of ways. A part of her very primitive guilt was her feelings of having been motherless, together with a probable underlying fantasy that she was responsible for estrangement between her mother and father.

Here was a woman who knew primal guilt to begin with simply by being part of this estranged human existence. Guilt through the development process became so unbearable to her that she had a psychotic break; and when that was somewhat healed, she approached reality neurotically. A love relationship with other human beings and with God she either had not known or could not trust. When it was suggested to her that she might find help through her priest, she became visibly frightened. Too many overtones of maleness were implicit in that relationship. She enumerated some of them: the priest is a man; he is called Father; God is conceived of in terms of maleness (e.g., Jesus Christ, He, Him, Father). (For the first time I came to understand the psychological power and meaning of the role of the Virgin Mary in Roman Catholic thought.) The counselor's role became primarily that of a mother-figure until, strengthened through that relationship, G. could begin to face and handle her problem with maleness. Only with some confidence in the human relationship could she move ever so gingerly toward the divine-human. She essentially had to go back to her unfinished business of childhood and deal with that within a love relationship. Only then could more ultimate relationships become at all meaningful. As faulted relationships are the matrix of guilt, so warm, embracing, affirming relationships are the matrix for resolving the destructiveness of guilt. Paradoxically, God's affirming "Yes" is taken as a "No" by the guilt-ridden until there is insinuated into the guilt-ridden a human experience of love. To this we shall return at the close of this chapter.

### GUILT AND HOSTILITY

Guilt and hostility are causally related. Freud, as we have seen, locates guilt in the aggressive instinctual drive, or more precisely within the ambivalence between that instinct and eros. A modified Freudian view will locate guilt in infantile rages turned in on the self as well as in oedipal hate, fear, remorse. The biblical position, not sorting out guilt from the complex of sin and punishment, sees man as hostile toward God and then guilty for his defiant hostility. Guilt derives from a deed done or the impulse to do the deed, from punishment or its threat, from introjection of the "world" around, etc. But this only increases the hostility, either toward the "world" or toward the self, which in turn intensifies the guilt. Guilt and hostility interact in a vicious circle. This is seen clearly in the criminality syndrome where the need for punishment, a vicious deed, and confession, whether of actual or neurotic guilt, often go hand in hand. It is not only of importance theoretically to see this causal relationship but it is of prime importance for a healing or saving ministry when either hostility or guilt is the problem. Its companion is nearby.

### GUILT AND RESPONSIBILITY

A fundamental problem related to guilt is that of responsibility. The question of responsibility is usually located in the realm of morality. The question then is: How much is man responsible for his guilt? The question so put has legal significance and some moral value. Yet it appears to be asked with a predilection for judgment, with a bent for ascertaining moral culpability, with a slant toward seeking out and pinpointing fault or blame. In psychological language much of this is projection and displacement. Responsibility so often means departure from an established norm, in which case it has a teleological reference to what should be or ought to be. This way of viewing responsibility degenerates into moralistic considerations on the basis of goals rationalistically and abstractly conceived or culturally produced. A peering attitude develops as the habit of assessing departure from norms or goals becomes increasingly fixed. Responsibility then becomes the matter of fixing or attributing guilt on the basis of a severely limited edition of reality. It does not say much about guilt in its concrete, existential form. Dynamically, this way of dealing with guilt and responsibility is not very helpful.

Alfred North Whitehead provides a way of seeing responsibility ontologically and the meaning of guilt in the actual becoming of a self.[44] His doctrine of prehension has to do with the self's perceiving its "world." By "perceiving" he means not merely visual or auditory perception but perception in the mode of "causal efficacy." The past is the datum for each present. The present feels the past viscerally; that is, the feeling-tone of the past carries (its vector quality) into the present and the present prehends or "feels" or responds to the feeling-tone so presented to it. The self in the present also responds to the possibilities looming before it as it stands between the past and the future. Thus, the self in essence is a self in relationship, a self which is always responding—negatively, positively, gladly, angrily, etc. This is not simply a reactive self though it can be that. It is not simply a conforming self or there would be no novelty. It is a self with the ability to respond and its response is its own unique way of taking its world. Profoundly this is its *response-ability* which is ontologically prior to *responsibilty* in any moral or evaluative sense. All moral or evaluative judgments must be made outside of this prehending self. This is why all such judgments are abstractions. In Whitehead's own thought, only God is with the percipient being in any immanent sense. Therefore, all our judgments must veer toward legalism and moralism; they must measure departures from objective standards, and they must do so almost exclusively in terms of appearances only. Making judgments about behavior is necessary for protecting the self or society when the self cannot handle its responses, as in criminality or insanity; but this is not for the sake of punitive retribution. Evaluation of behavior is necessary for making new, whether healing medically or saving theologically; but this is not for the sake of condemnation. The Christian insists that judgment belongs to God who in Jesus Christ has both judged the world and brought to the world forgiveness. Furthermore, it is the Holy Spirit who is the indefatigable Worker throughout the history of every self, bringing judg-

[44] See Alfred North Whitehead, *Process and Reality*, New York: The Macmillan Company, 1929, pp. 184 ff., 255 ff., 334 ff.

ment to bear and reconciliation. Guilt and responsibility in the ontological structure proposed by Whitehead mean that God's judgment of guilt is made possible because He is *with* the percipient being in the context of his decision-making and He alone knows the interior nature of the responses made by the self.

The problem of inherited guilt and responsibility is one with which the Augustinian-Calvinistic interpretation wrestled. For Augustine man's nature is faulted, and this faulted nature is passed on through concupiscence in marriage. Humanity is condemned and bound "in the fetters of inherited guilt. . . ."[45] The infant belonging to the "ruined mass" is guilty.[46] Because God constituted Adam the representative of the race, his fall is also our undoing. This formulation, while extremely vulnerable,[47] takes most seriously the problem of the past. Hobart Mowrer does not give any weight to this problem, the bondage of the will, or a psychic past, and consequently he can write glibly of the "absurdity of the Reformation doctrine of human guilt and divine grace."[48] Freud, on the other hand, assumed a "psyche of the mass in which psychic processes occur as in the psychic life of the individual. Moreover, we let the sense of guilt for a deed survive for thousands of years, remaining effective in generations which could not have known anything of this deed."[49]

Whitehead's way of seeing the self emerging with reference to its past, what he calls causal efficacy, provides a new tool for dealing with inherited guilt and responsibility. The self responds to a past that is laden with guilt[50] and it is inconceivable that a self could avoid guilt-type reactions in response to such a past which moves into the ever new present. The ontological structure of response-ability assures this. The form of the response, e.g., guilt, conforms to the past but still maintains its own discrete configuration. Inherited guilt and responsibility are together at an ontological depth, guilt being one way this self responds to his "world."

[45] *Augustine: Confessions and Enchiridion,* tr. and ed. by Albert C. Outler, Philadelphia: Westminster Press, 1955, p. 354.

[46] *Ibid.,* p. 365 ff.

[47] Cf. Brunner, pp. 119 ff., 142 ff., 145 ff.; E. LaB. Cherbonnier, *Hardness of Heart,* Garden City: Doubleday & Company, Inc., 1955, Chap. 8 and *passim.*

[48] Mowrer, p. 175.

[49] Freud, *Totem and Taboo,* p. 203.

[50] What constitutes the past guilty is dealt with *supra,* pp. 250–60.

This means profoundly that a sense of guilt inbedded in the becoming self *is* the self's responsibility: the feeling-tone of the self is guilt, for that is how it has embraced its world. The feeling-tone of the past has elicited a correspondence that accords or agrees with *(respondeō),* that is compatible with, its own nucleus of feeling.

## GUILT AND THE MINISTRY OF THE CHURCH

If guilt derives from a faulty relationship, whether that be with God or within the human family, the Church is on the wrong track when it deals with guilt as though it were simply a deviation from a prescribed norm, law, or ritual. Lewis Sherrill notes that the Jews, as a protection against the sense of guilt before God, barricaded themselves with the Torah, which expanded through the centuries from the Law of the Pentateuch through the minute Mishnah to the vastly expanded Talmud.[51] Moralism, legalism, and ritualism conspire against the healing of guilt. First, they misunderstand guilt, for they suppose that guilt is primarily deviation, whereas guilt is fundamentally located in a malignant relationship. Second, they continue guilt by providing counteracting rituals of obedience to external laws, regulations, forms, etc. These counteracting rituals may be obsessive acts, and therefore unconscious, which begin as defensive measures. (It was in this context that Freud once called religion a "universal obsessional neurosis."[52]) Or they may be the dull habit of religion. In any case they actually defend against the pain of guilt feelings but bring no healing. Third, they prevent the self from dealing with guilt, as well as the sense of guilt, through healing relationships and thus keep the self from its true humanity before God, toward its fellows, in itself. Moralism, paradoxically, prevents the self from becoming moral; for morality, as Tillich has shown, is the process of centering the self, of constituting the self as a person. Morality is the "totality of those acts in which a potentially personal life process becomes an actual person."[53]

[51] Sherrill, p. 195.

[52] Freud, "Obsessive Acts," p. 34.

[53] Paul Tillich, *Systematic Theology,* Chicago: University of Chicago Press, 1963, 3:38; cf. his *Theology of Culture,* New York: Oxford University Press, 1959, Chap. 10; Nels F. S. Ferre, *The Sun and the Umbrella,* New York: Harper and Brothers, 1953, *passim.*

I believe one of the Church's most basic problems is how to have its theological and moral structures without their getting in the way of a person's development or his relationship with God and his fellows. Theological formulations and moral imperatives are means to the end of a new humanity. But they are not the end. They may be channels of communication, means of insight, boundaries of relationship. When they become more, they are usurpers exercising the heavy hand of tyranny over the self in its relationships. The Church's temptation is idolatry. Whether it is idolatry of the high places or the low, guilt is fastened on in wrong places, in wrong terms, under wrong conditions. The idol may be sobriety, or industry, or chastity, or honesty, or tithing, or Sabbath observance, or any other of the innumerable virtues, none of which is much more than doodling when compared with the weightier matters of love of God and neighbor. Fetishes such as these keep primal, phylogenetic, or developmental guilt from being faced. If guilt is *before God,* idolatry points away from God. If guilt is derived from childhood, then idols bar the way against the arrival of help by encouraging the wrong focus of the self's problems. Laziness is illustrative. The dictionary definition is: "Averse to labour, indolent; idle; inactive, slothful." This simply describes behavior, with the implied judgment that this is not good behavior. Western middle-class society in general and the Church in particular would eschew laziness as at least a moral defect. I am wondering, however, if laziness has any meaning at all except as a popular judgment and condemnation. The word slothful is used to describe laziness, but it also describes the "man of sin" for Barth. Sin is a profound defiance, hostility, guilt. But the mere castigation of laziness ignores the deeper source of indolence. For the mistrusting, shamed, guilty little boy whose developmental history has taught him that inaction (another description of laziness) is the only safe way to live, the charge of laziness is not only misplaced but is actually cruel. Yet that little boy, identified as lazy, will live up to that identification. He will be averse to labor. And because industry is a good, he will always be judged guilty. From beginning to end, this kind of judgment, these kinds of criteria, this way of dealing with guilt are false. The Church contributes to this falseness in misrepresenting the issues, continuing the wrong criteria, getting in the way of redemptive and healing processes.

The second consideration is that guilt, like hostility, needs a community of acceptance. English and English define acceptance as "an attitude or a relationship that recognizes the worth of a person without implying personal affection."[54] This definition stands naked. It needs to be clothed. To clothe it in psychological dress will not be sufficient for the Church precisely because what theology brings to acceptance makes a fundamental difference to the concept itself. Tillich would replace the terminology of justification with acceptance.[55] This suggests something of the word's depth, for it is God who justifies, God who accepts. While we are unacceptable before the law, while we are sinners, God accepts us. Our sin is forgiven, our distance from God overcome, our guilt borne by Him. His acceptance of us has come at awe-ful cost. Thus His judgment is involved in acceptance. Christian acceptance, therefore, is compounded of a dynamic, a model, and a mission. The dynamic is God's forgiveness of us, accepting us as we are, which conceptually can free us from the need to judge since we have been judged and are accepted. Thus the dynamic of Christian acceptance is not humanistic love, however valuable that is, but is the divine forgiveness itself. The model for Christian acceptance is God's way with us in Jesus Christ. The counseling room may give us great insight into acceptance, but the primary model is Jesus Christ. The mission of Christian acceptance is to be the neighbor to whoever happens to be in need, be he outcast or enemy. For he, too, is the creation of God, the object of God's forgiveness and acceptance, and his worth derives precisely from this relationship. This puts the "worth of a person" in an inviolable context, and keeps it from being so vulnerable to the caprice of human pretension and cynicism.[56] Guilt—primal, psychological, situational—needs a climate of acceptance so that confession[57] can be made, the sense of guilt be expressed without fear of further guilt feelings, forgiveness—divine and human—be found, and continuing support be experienced through acts expressing the relationship of forgiveness.

[54] Horace B. English and Ava Champney English, *A Comprehensive Dictionary of Psychological and Psychoanalytical Terms,* New York: Longmans, Green, 1958, *ad loc.*

[55] Tillich, *Systematic Theology,* p. 224.

[56] One needs only to remember the decades of 1930 and 1940 in Germany to be reminded how slippery is the phrase "worth of a person."

[57] By "confession" I mean private (as in prayer), one-to-one, liturgical, sharing as part of a group experience (as in a class), etc.

# 16

## Sin, Illness, and Guilt

*Russell J. Becker*

O. H. MOWRER's recent quasi-religious turn in his writing calls for an analysis which would be given by one who holds both theological and psychotherapeutic concerns. Mowrer has set forth a strong set of attacks upon the use of the term "illness" in relation to mental and emotional conflicts in persons. He has adopted the term "sin," much to the horror of the scientific community. What he may not appreciate is that his use of the term "sin" is equally appalling to the theologian. It is important to sift through Mowrer to find what his contribution really is.

Leaving aside the polemics against psychoanalysis to which Mowrer is drawn, we find the central concern of Mowrer is that we recover an awareness of the ineradicable element of responsibility which attaches to human behavior. When we view neurotic behavior as an exception to the horizon of responsibility in the human situation we have made an exemption which cancels the very substance of life.

On this basis Mowrer attacks classical psychoanalytic

views. He believes they treat the neurotic individual as ill or sick rather than in error or sin. Unconscious forces or the inadequacies of infant years are believed to account for present neuroticisms rather than the conscious person. The overwhelming forces of the id are assumed to have asserted themselves. The task of psychoanalysis is strengthening the ego so that "where id is, there shall ego be." The neurotic has *guilt feelings* induced by the superior pressures of the id but not *guilt.*

Mowrer takes issue with this line of classical psychoanalytic thought. His assertion is that there is real guilt, not just guilt feelings, *even in the neurotic.* The guilty stance of the neurotic is that he utilizes his rational-cognitive faculties to ward off and evade the glimpse of himself as less than his self-ideal. The superego here is seen as being the bearer of a positive and not merely a punitive force upon the ego. When the person evades the dismal contrast between present reality and the sought-after ideal of the ego, he enters upon his guilt. Let me illustrate: When Adam and Eve, facing the Lord God in the cool of the evening, excuse their behavior with "she made me do it" (or the serpent), they are guilty at that moment of evading their previous disobedience in eating of the forbidden fruit. Quite apart from the primal disobedience they are now engaged in the sin of the neurotic. They are bent upon avoiding the unpleasant picture of their primal disobedience. What is their need? Several hundred hours on the analytic couch so they will see that their guilt feelings were a bit overdrawn? "No!" says Mowrer. Their need is to confess their guilt, the neurotically avoided guilt, by acknowledging responsibility for the avoidance of the unpleasant picture of disobedience. Once they make open confession, then they need to be restored to essential human fellowship by some action penance.

There are two elements of Mowrer which bother the religious interpreter. His understanding of sin is what I have been calling in this illustration "neurotic sin." This is a secondary usage of the term sin so far as the Christian is concerned. The first and primary usage is the *primal* act of disobedience. Man is a sinner in relation to God. There are secondary elaborations of the life of sin such as the Genesis story holds; but the primary sin is the breaking of our fellowship with God. Eating the apple is our sin. Mowrer locates the sin of the neurotic in something less. Mowrer identifies as sin behavior which is found at the level of the statements "She made me do it." and "He made me do it." He sees the neurotic engaged in the sin of deception, evasion, and dissimilitude after he has broken the primary bonds of fellowship. The neurotic's sin is that of compounding the already sinful state of man. The "already sinful state of man," man as sinner before God, man as the adversary of God, is not in Mowrer's purview as he speaks of sin. He uses the term sin without any reference whatsoever to original sin or to our fractured relation to God.

The second element of Mowrer which bothers the Christian pastor is his strong suggestion of justification by works. If penance is a necessary accompaniment of confession, as he insists, then man restores the broken relationships of his life by what he does in his penitential acts. However worthy this thought is in human relationships, it is a denial of the free grace of God which restores man to fellowship with God. Because Mowrer adopts the word "sin" for speaking about the neurotic's responsibility in his neuroticism, he blurs the distinction between the sins which men may ameliorate and the sin whose damage only God can repair because the damage is to the relationship with God himself.

We will be helped in our encounter with this topic of sin to keep a distinction between "original sin" and "neurotic sins." Mowrer misleads and confuses because he does not make this distinction. But can we adopt the term sin for what the neurotic does? Is not the neurotic better seen and helped if we call him sick or emotionally disturbed or mentally ill rather than sinner?

The contemporary scientific mind thinks so. Mowrer thinks not. Phenomenologically and existentially oriented psychotherapists agree with Mowrer in principle even if they shy away from the religiously loaded term sin. Mowrer, as we have just noted, is not concerned in the least about the religious loadings of the term sin. It is a religiously and theologically neutral concept for him. But it is a significant term for alluding to the fact of responsibility in human behavior even when speaking of neurotic behavior. What makes neurotic behavior neurotic is the fact that the person is using his cognitive and affective powers to avoid and evade a less than pleasing judgment which comes from his ego-ideal.

Neurotic action remains responsible action. It is an action of response by a person. It is evasive action which must be "owned up to" or there is no release from the binding and blinding effects of neurotic reactions.

It is interesting to note that Mowrer's contention regarding responsibility in neurotics is well believed across the length and breadth of the psychiatric world. In so orthodox a document as the *American Psychiatric Association Diagnostic and Statistical Manual,* virtually every abnormal behavior pattern is termed a "reaction" in order to denote precisely this element of nonreligious responsibility and responsiveness at the heart of all behavior, whether adaptive or maladaptive.

The whole trend of psychotherapy since Freud bears the marks of this note of accountability in behavior even for the neurotic and psychotic in spite of using terms of moral neutrality such as neurosis, mental illness, and the like.

Beyond this we may additionally note that permissive forms of psychotherapy take on the tinting of a confessional disclosure. They permit the client to open up the unpleasant picture of self which he has wanted no one including himself to see. Once this disturbing picture is seen the individual is able to restructure his living with greater realism and less appearance, less facade, less personage, more person.

The question is still before us. Is sin the term which is to be preferred to "illness"? Mowrer, who advocates its use, is in fact advocating nothing new except for a questionable penitential system. He is urging an awareness of the note of responsibility in all human behavior, including neurotic behavior. Basically, psychotherapists of the permissive, acceptant, and client-centered varieties have been stressing the same matter for years without speaking either of sin or of illness but rather of persons facing difficulties in living who have a capacity to face their difficulties responsibly.

There is one important danger which the continued use of the term illness has in the field of emotional-personal behavior. Rather than jump to the theologically significant term sin for mental illness, I would prefer to note the one real shortcoming of the term illness as it is used. If persons *have* mental and emotional illnesses, then they no longer need see that they *are* their illnesses. The illness becomes an impersonal thing, merely a something "at-hand," which has settled itself upon the person. The person searches for *causes* rather than for his lost self. He thus is encouraged in the deception which already is his burden. Instead of forsaking the term illness and substituting the theological concept of sin with its transcendent overtones, we would do well to continue the use of the word illness—noting its weaknesses—until some new word comes along.

But, it may be asked, is there not an unconscious control of behavior occurring in compulsive acts which lies outside the usual realm of awareness, responsiveness, and responsibility? Here we encounter the questions of responsibility in relation to identifiable acts of wrong-doing. Can we attribute responsibility as a factor in all forms of emotional "illness"? Ontologically we can and we must. Juridically it is a little less certain matter.

What we must first recognize is that guilt may be experienced in three levels: ontologically, realistically (objectively, socially), and fantastically (neurotically or privately). All three levels can be and usually are present at the same time. The sensitive pastoral counselor has to listen to the echoes which sound from each of these levels.

1. *Ontological* guilt is the guilt which we experience in the ground of our being—as beings before the Creator God who calls us into being—yet as beings who are not God. We live in the realm of creature possibility and creaturely limitation. Whatever we do we are responsible agents, but we never fulfill the whole of the possibilities which a fecund Creator sets before us. The classical Christian belief in original sin points toward this primal condition of our being as creative creatures standing always in the limits of possibility imposed by our finitude. We are at once free to sin and bound to sin. We are simultaneously responsible and yet unavoidably caught in ambiguities of existence which leave no escape from sinning. Guilt and sin of this order are rooted in the ambiguities of our finite-free nature. They are not contained in any specific incident nor are they ever seen apart from some specific act.
2. *Realistic,* objective, or social guilt is the guilt which is the appropriate condition of a man whose actions are blameworthy in his social environment. Set as we are in the context of life with others, realistic social guilt is the

state of the individual who has fallen short of the requirements of life-with-others. Here cultural differences can and do define entirely different behaviors about which one will feel and be guilty. Cultural differences can even shape the issue of whether shame in relation to loss of face will be a more predominant response than guilt in the internal reaction pattern of the individual.

3. *Fantastic* or neurotic guilt is the guilt of guilt feelings. It is the guilt felt for a private reason which does not interfere with the claim to life which others make. It is the inward compounding of a judgment which may be socially initiated but is privately elaborated. Preoccupation with private elaborations of our blameworthiness is the burden of the depressed individual. The sensitive and skillful psychotherapist is able to be helpful with such conditions. What he does not usually see and distinguish are the other two levels of guilt as these may be present in a given person. The pastor needs to be sensitive to all three levels of guilt and to the feelings which bear all three forms of guilt in the life of parishoners. Let me be specific by reference to a counseling situation.

Recently a minister and his wife came to me to talk about the burden of feelings they were experiencing over the loss of their 14-year-old son. They sensed that the grief they felt had not been worked through though six months had passed since the death. As I listened to the story of a tragic loss, multiple levels of guilt were clearly presented. The son had died by hanging one evening. The death had been officially declared accidental rather than deliberate suicide. The father and mother, in spite of wanting to believe this desperately, were deeply torn with doubts and questions as to whether this was accidental.

At the level of the private fantastic, they each had elaborated all sorts of guilt which they punishingly administered to themselves. Though he was a bright, sunny, well-liked lad with a remarkable sense of curiosity, and though they had discovered school notes in a hygiene course dealing with the autonomic functions of which the boy had written these words of the teacher, "Try to stop breathing voluntarily and you will discover that you cannot," and though the actual hanging involved two straps drawn around the abdomen as though to put this theory to test, they found all manner of failure within themselves to excoriate. The boy had persisted in thumb-sucking to the age of eight; he had occasional problems of bed-wetting. These, they felt, must be taken as signs of some unmet insecurity. The boy had disassembled a radio set, leaving the parts strewn around in his room. After several weeks had passed the father admonished him to clean up the mess. All manner of fragments were taken as evidence of their failure. They held themselves guilty of pushing the boy to suicide as a deliberate act. In the absence of a suicide note or any sign of futility in the boy, they yet felt guilt feelings and were in the midst of many elaborations of these. At this level one could help only through patient reflective listening to let them sift and sort among the fantasies and elaborations until they had brought these hidden condemnations into the light of day. Unexamined, these fantastic images were dragging both parents down into feelings of being worthy of nought but death themselves.

At a second level they found guilt feelings present which were due to identifiable acts and omissions of their lives. They might have listened to him more. They loved him but they knew the parsonage was a place which crowded children to the edge of the family on evenings when entertaining took place and when guests were in the home. There was a younger son and an older daughter, and the lost child suffered inevitable comparisons with them. These things happened, they were not simply imagined. At this level, there were both guilt *feelings* and *real* guilt. There was no reason to believe the reality of guilt which life with others nurtures. But neither is there reason to consign oneself to die in the midst of these realities.

The third level of guilt which was present was the guilt before God. The guilt of broken faith crept in. The Resurrection faith was outdistanced by thoughts of a body decaying in the ground. The faith stance maintained before a congregation crumbled into hollowness when they doubted the wisdom and love of God. At this level the word which they needed to hear as the Word of God addressing them was: "Blessed are those who mourn." Here they heard their acceptance before God as grieving, faith-shaken children enduring great loss, hurt, and real (social, objective) guilt. Here the ontological guilt of their lives was seen in the frailty and finitude of their own faith and belief. Here they could see that believing in God and His promises did not exempt them from disbelief, doubt, and rebellious reaction to God. At this level all of us stand before God, awe-struck, and fearful, the frail creatures who cannot comprehend the holy majesty of God. At this level only God Himself heals the fracture of our ambiguous finite freedom. In His Son on a Cross we confront the God who Himself suffers our tragic circumstance. The one word which bridges the chasm is the Word of God given to us sinners and present in the assurance that we may be beatified even while we mourn.

The three-leveled way in which we experience and meet guilt cannot be neatly separated into compartments as this analysis has just done. It would be wonderful if this were possible. But as pastors we confront people who will be touched by all three levels of guilt in the brief compass of a pastoral conference. We cannot and need not separate off the private, fantastic elaborations of guilt and assign them to the psychiatrist even if we could find a quick and ready referral available. When the private elaborations of guilt become predominant and "seemingly" exclusive, then this division of labor makes sense. But even so, we should remember that the word of absolution which pertains to realistic guilt and to ontological guilt is also one which we should be prepared to join with the secular absolution the person may receive from his private elaborations of guilt as unfolded and aerated with the psychotherapist. The multiple levels of guilt may require multiple counselors if the person is already seeing a secular psychotherapist.

The problem of team functioning with secular psychotherapists is raised at this point. It involves a complex issue which is theological as well as the issue of how one professional can have knowledge of another's professional competence. Unless the secular psychotherapist shares the understanding of man as a creature before God whom God justifies and saves, he will not be able to see any meaningful place for the Christian priest and pastor who does. At this point pessimism overwhelms me, for the acids of skepticism and doubt have etched more deeply into the lives of most children of our culture than I care to think about. The possibility of finding theologically sophisticated and believing psychotherapists is not great. The answer is not to bemoan this state of affairs so much as to recognize it and return more eagerly to the work of elemental evangelism.

Do we ourselves believe the preposterous assertion that God Himself was present in the human situation in the life of Jesus of Nazareth? If we do, then we must share this belief, proclaim this truth, and continually refer our own lives to its saving reality. Perhaps the "team" issue in the mental health field which we as clergymen feel so strongly will settle down into its true dimensions—an issue of whether intelligent, scientific minds in the twentieth century can any longer find meaning in the singular and elemental Christian claim of Emmanuel, God with us, and whether we ourselves truly celebrate this mystery.

Whether persons facing the complexities of guilt we have noted are helped in the several dimensions may depend more upon the sustained communication of the theological-ontological issue of guilt by religious leaders to writers such as Mowrer than upon the hope that separate counselors might work with open confidence in each other. The meeting of multiple-level issues of guilt as they exist in persons may depend upon the increase of multiple-level understandings of the human situation. Mowrer could make an important contribution to interdisciplinary understanding if he were to appreciate the ontological and theological depths of the term sin which are present in the lives of the emotionally disturbed. With such recognition he might well elect to leave the term sin for the guilt of man which is both ontological and realistic. He then might prefer to seek another term than illness for the guilt which is private-fantastic. What I have suggested is that three *kinds* of guilt could more adequately cover the distinctions and hold the note of responsibility in each instance.

17

# Objective Guilt and Neurosis

*Gunter Elsasser*

"WHATEVER MAN TOUCHES is loaded with guilt, as fire is with smoke," states the 18th Canto of the Bhagavadgita. Even if, from our Western-Christian perspective, we have to reject such a generalization that every human act is guilty by definition; nevertheless, we have to admit the monstrous implications of the guilt problem in daily life. While animals inevitably and without any feeling of sin follow their impulses and instincts, we men are again and again confronted with the possibility and the necessity of making decisions which often lead us into guilt-ridden entanglements. To learn how to live rightly with such guilt is a task which is set before each of us—a task in which even the so-called healthy people are able to become uncomfortably lost. Among neurotics, who suffer from inner conflicts mainly stemming from childhood, the mastery of this task is generally difficult. More

GÜNTER ELSÄSSER, M.D., is Psychiatrist, Institute für analytische Psychotherapie im Reinland, Bonn, West Germany.

often than not we find here the conditions which contribute to the appearance of a full-blown neurosis.

As a superficial opinion it is usually considered that in order to overcome the problem of guilt, man need only find the right way by listening to the "voice of his conscience." This corresponds neither to the discoveries of depth psychology nor to the moral-theological teachings of the Christian church. To be sure, conscience is obviously a psychic function within us which is changeable and subjective since it depends upon environmental and educational influences which have affected the individual since childhood. At the same time conscience also depends upon its particular hereditary disposition and eventually on ethical self-decisions of the older and more mature man. Thus conscience is a psychic function that changes in life and therefore cannot be an absolute yardstick of values.

Etymologically "conscience" derives from "to know" just as do the German word *Gewissen,* the Greek word *syneidesis,* and the Latin word *conscientia.* "Conscience," then, means the subjective consciousness of the moral worthiness and unworthiness of one's own behavior. However, the act of conscience does not consist, in the main, of a clearly conscious intellectual process; rather it is precisely the dark, emotional, primarily warning and apprehensive inner voice that tries to direct us. It is the confidant (conscientia) in us, that part of our personality which calls our attention to any deviation from the norm. The subjective individual conscience is not the norm itself but rather—as the Evangelical moral theologians express it—an organ for the examination of the moral code or—as a Catholic point of view would maintain—an organ which qualifies the judgment according to the objective divine norms.

Hence the individual subjective conscience is by no means suitable as a plumb line for the practical behavior of society, and is equally ill-suited as a norm of conduct for the particular individual. There is, however, an objective appraisal of value that is able to show a direction to man: the ethical (eventually religious) norm set in every cultural sphere. However, even this norm is not a firm and unalterable pattern. One must, first of all, differentiate between an average norm (one which is considered right by the majority of contemporaries) and an ideal norm. Not only is the average norm alterable but so is the ideal norm. It can undergo considerable change within the historical duration of a culture, as we painfully experience it in our time. On the other hand, the norm often differs tremendously from one culture circle to another. In spite of this, a valid set of values (ideal norm) for each cultural circle is the only possibility of giving man a guideline, even if he as sinning man will constantly remain more or less distant from this ideal norm. Guidelines of behavior, as defined and set off, are also essential for the man who seeks to make his own particular ethical decisions on the basis of personal responsibility. But in order to experience such an ideal value system as a challenge directed to us we need the "voice of conscience," that is, the affective capacity to react to prohibitions and commands.[1]

Doubtlessly, the act of conscience does not correspond to a clear, rational judgment, but represents a highly complex psychic process which also speaks to modern man on a magical level[2] of knowledge (for example, in the superstitious fear that punishment must be released through the repression of guilt) and constantly reechoes in his deepest affective and instinctive experiences. Thus the act of conscience is necessary for each individual man, and so also is the particular experience of guilt which begins during or after the transgression of the norms. Generally speaking, the robust, naive, average man feels himself completely innocent before the law and, if it occurs to him, seeks the fault in his neighbor or in external situations. This unembarrassed assignment of blame to a fellowman is so frequent because the great majority of all guilty actions spring from the fact that men live

[1] Robert Scholl, in his book *Das Gewissen des Kindes* (Stuttgart: Hippokrates-Verlag, 1956), shows particularly impressively out of experiences with his own children how this capacity is carefully awakened among little children by good parents and educators, while they cautiously build upon previous predispositions. Only if one equates conscience with entelechy can one say with T. Brocher, "Conscience is not an entity that first has to be impressed, or that first has to be formed, but rather it exists *a priori*." This is an inappropriate shift of concept and one-sidedness. However, we have to see clearly the fact that "conscience" is a rather complex psychic entity that contains the unassimilated or insufficiently assimilated unfamiliar suggestions of the infantile world (that is, Freud's "Super-ego") as well as the possibilities for ethical decisions that in favorable cases correspond to the momentary entelechy. It should not be overlooked that precisely among neurotics both sides of the conscience exist side by side, often in a disturbing manner.

[2] Cf. Hans Gebser, *Ursprung und Gegenwart,* Stuttgart: Deutsche Verlag-Astalt, 1949.

together; in other words it is sociologically conditioned. A guilty behavior which has not been admitted publicly and thus has not brought a loss of reputation to the culprit generally does not disturb a strong, robust person, or at least not for very long. This is true even when we are not dealing with indifferent scoundrels. To be sure, it is different with those particularly worthwhile persons who (with various inner motivations) feel a burning guilt after the realization of a full picture of themselves. They feel a realization of the death of that which they know as right and proper in the world by their personal relaxation of the ideals. This experience of the "shadow" in one's own soul (in C. G. Jung's sense) is certainly not an experience limited to neurotic or neurotically oriented persons, but rather it is part of the general human experience, inasmuch as only a certain degree of spiritual development and differentiation is achieved with the capacity for self-responsibility.

Neurotic, and thereby pathological, resolutions of guilt experiences are much greater than would be expected, provided fixed characteristics of neurosis are demonstrable. Zulliger expressed the "failure reaction of the conscience" particularly well in his book *Umgang mit dem kindlichen Gewissen.*[3] If we here show not the individual neurotic species but rather the large composite, it presents the one possibility that objectively unimportant lapses or omissions, exaggerated and with heavy guilt feelings, will always be resurrected and also communicated so that it handles as real that which is harmless; be it to awaken consideration and compassion or to enforce ratification. As is known, in such cases there is often an apparently harmless guilt in the foreground, while in reality the guilt feeling is being caused by another much heavier guilt, whose meaning is not known or not permitted to enter into consciousness. It is now clear that overly fearful people of this kind make themselves guilty out of fear and cannot impartially experience things and act unaffectedly. We therefore have a group of people before us who, in their activity and contribution to the world about them, are seriously restricted. Such restraint—somewhat as a reaction to the guilt-fixing action—can increase despondency and despair more and more.

[3] H. Zulliger, *Umgang mit dem kindlichen Gewissen,* Stuttgart, 1954.

People who exaggerate the value of their own guilt of this kind appear to us, without further examination, to be pathological. Also a repression contrary thereto can be labeled as being neurotic; namely when an objective, present, and important guilt is carried with apparent calm and unconcern. That this behavior in a thin-skinned, sensitive person could cause a repressive process is evident. Such people, with their particularly unbalanced feeling of self-evaluation, evidently find it impossible to discern in themselves any greater fault, to admit it, to repent, and through a good action (or at least through a firm purpose to do good) to compensate for it—that is, to enter upon the only road that can really free them from a committed offense.

Also it is known that if a well-adjusted child commits an "outrageous deed," he expects a punishment to follow and with that the incident will be forgotten and the guilt discharged. The adult is supposed to have become sufficiently competent to undertake such a discharge by himself, insofar as he himself is split to some extent into prosecutor, judge, defender, and defendant—that is, he confronts himself in a matter-of-fact and conscious way. It is understandable that this is precisely what the neurotic patient can accomplish but with the utmost difficulty. He is tossed by his changing feelings and instincts; moreover, he often finds himself under the influence of fantasy images and daydreams. One could say that his conscience does not function properly, and, in spite of a greater effort of the will and a good intelligence, it *cannot* actually function properly without psychotherapeutic help. Just as the neurotic patient first has to learn how properly to sleep, eat, drink, love, work, defend himself, and so on, so he has to learn in the psychotherapeutic treatment how to get along with his fragmentary human nature and with the guilt entanglements that spring from it.

Man ought to learn to get along with his "shadow." I would like, however, to point to the fact that the guilt experience as used here is taken in a narrower sense than Jung's "shadow." It contains the objectively guilty impulse, but is not limited to those that are painful, disconcerting, and of inferior value. In therapy it is naturally neither possible nor necessary to distinguish between both types.

Both previously mentioned ways of reacting to consciously experienced feelings of guilt (namely, on the one hand, a way of taking it too seriously and, on the other hand, a way of taking it too lightly) certainly do occur also among healthy people. When they appear in an extremely pronounced manner or in a repetitive pattern or in connection with neurotic symptoms, then usually we have to deal with neurotic guilt reactions. The knowledge of these reactions is particularly important for the treatment of the patient. It is more frequent and hence better known that a person takes his guilt too seriously. This is manifest in tendencies of self-punishment, in compulsory neurotic symptoms, as well as in some hysteric and pseudo-depressive symptoms. The second sort of reaction is less known, taking it too lightly due to repression. Both types of reactions should be made somewhat clearer through some examples.

Taking one's guilt too seriously appears most frequently with symptoms of masturbation. If one relies on the Kinsey Report,[4] one can indeed ask whether we have here anything in the frame of guilt at all. Since, according to these statistics, practically all men and 62 per cent of women somehow have practiced masturbation, one could in reality consider such behavior as normal and average.[5] This view, on the other hand, is contradicted by the fact that—aside from the demands of the Church—so many people experience feelings of guilt concerning it. These guilt feelings however are not always to be evaluated only as neurotic. The Kinsey Report gives us the computation of the average norm but, understandably enough, it gives us no hint as to the ideal norm that still actively exists.

But it is precisely this ideal norm that operates in feelings of guilt following masturbation. It may and it should be said to the patient that masturbation if not practiced in excess is harmless, and that it occurs frequently among other people. This news alone, however, does not satisfy the patient and often causes an aggressive attitude toward the attending physician, as if he did not possess sufficient understanding. Hence it should be further articulated that masturbation is not a mature form of sexuality, and that its real

[4] A. C. Kinsey, *et al., Sexual Behavior in the Human Male,* Philadelphia: W. B. Saunders, 1948.

[5] An experienced sport-physician maintained the opinion that feelings of guilt because of masturbation seldom occur among healthy people of the younger generation, approximately only among 5 per cent. Its real frequency, however, escapes our present knowledge.

fault lies in the fact that it renders more difficult a loving approach to other people or even—because of the isolation created through the feelings of guilt—that it makes this approach impossible.

Another hint of fundamental significance is that the guilt feeling due to masturbation often does not originate because of the physical occurrence itself but rather because of a much greater difficulty: the simultaneous and often astonishingly dissolute sexual fantasy. Sins of the thought, too, have in the inner space of the psyche a character of reality. Also these fantasies must be expressed in order that the unbearable and guilty feeling of the patient can be re-experienced as something utterable, as something in the realm of "human possibility," as something that belongs to man. Both the guilt experiences taken too seriously as well as those taken too lightly ought to be relocated during therapy into a balanced and matter-of-fact mean, and so they ought to be experienced.

This process occurs in severe experiences of guilt completely by itself, since the patient himself feels the urge for self-expression. It is more difficult when a guilt is "assimilated" lightly and superficially, that is, repressed. In such cases the physician must lay a finger on the wound, because for certain people there is considerable danger that such unsettled conflicts of guilt might call forth neurotic symptoms.

Because of the importance of these connections for therapy, two case studies are given here:

A 34-year-old nice, scrupulously clean and neat woman came for treatment because of extreme conditions of fear. She had to be brought first in a car, later she was accompanied by her 12-year-old daughter. The anxiety set in six months before in connection with an abortion and expressed itself chiefly in palpitation of the heart, a pressure upon the chest, and the fear whenever she saw a knife that she would harm both her children with it.

There were already numerous previous medical treatments: an intensive chlorpromazine-cure, cardiasolshocks!, "psychotherapeutic" conversation, and vitamin shots. In the psychotherapy she was told that she was unconsciously aggressive against her children, of whom she wishes to get rid, in order to develop a flirtation with a business friend of her husband. This hasty and obviously false interpretation caused a storm of indignation since the patient particularly loved both children, while the flirtation that occurred lasted but a short time and was a matter of no consequence.

I myself asked for a detailed description of the beginnings of the symptoms and learned to my surprise that the abortion, though therapeutically performed, was preceded by her taking 60 tablets of a prescription upon the advice of a girl friend. What particularly struck me was the naive unaffectedness with which the attempted self-induced abortion had been admitted. Her girl friend had already taken the prescription more than once; though she would like to have a child, she was about to move to a new house, and so on.

I did not give any interpretation and did not express any moral valuation, but rather I tried to learn more about her. Her biography showed that the patient, the youngest of five daughters of a particularly conscientious and upright public officer, had herself always led a scrupulously precise and proper life. For her overly conscientious pattern of personality that tended toward the compulsive neurotic, the guilt feeling of an abortion was simply unbearable; moreover, this guilt feeling became minimized—in other words, it became repressed. The insight into these connections was carefully interpreted; nevertheless it effected a strong emotional reaction upon which the acute anxiety symptoms quickly faded away. She feared that she would be punished for her behavior, i.e., the loss of both of her sons, and even that she herself would execute this punishment. Her fear was increased in the moment when the patient had destroyed the fetus within herself.

Another instance of a minimized guilt experience:

A 24-year-old foreign student experienced violent emotions of fear while looking at a cultural film about psychotherapy; he himself had undergone such a psychotherapeutic treatment, and since then he could hardly ever leave the house. The background of the case was that he had for a long time neglected his studies in an irresponsible manner, and rather than psychotherapy he needed to amend his way of life. Nor had this patient admitted his obvious offense and acted accordingly. On the contrary, he was in the meantime entangled in quite a serious neurosis which only served as an excuse for his not studying. This neurosis cannot be cured as long as the irresponsible activity is not made up for or—in case this is impossible—as long as a new plan of life is not found for the patient.[6]

One could think that such cases in reality have little to do with the psychotherapist. Actually the first step, namely the nonadmission and even the rejection of guilt, is quite a frequent phenomenon for a healthy man too. The danger, however, is by no means slight that with corresponding preliminary psychic conditions some neurotic symptoms may set in. Hence one can only advise devoting particular attention in the treatment of neurotic patients to such unsettled experiences of guilt.

As long as the patient still has the capacity—even if with some effort—to admit his guilt, the corresponding treatment process is relatively simple. New and particularly conditioned difficulties arise, however, when a guilt experience cannot be understood as such at all because its road to conscious judgment is barred. This is the case in child therapy: the child may be aggressive against his parents whom he also loves. The same applies to some other conflicts of guilt, particularly those that originate in infancy and which were never conscious.

An eleven-year-old boy is brought in because of his stuttering which started when he was three, at which time his father, who had lived in seclusion, suddenly came back to the family in a very nervous condition. The father was always very critical and demanding of both of his children, the patient and a daughter three years older. The little patient, who at first had rejected the father violently but was at the same time full of anxiety, now solicits his approval in a touching manner.

At present the father is no longer a nervous and overstrained man. In this case the father himself should have been treated long ago.

In the therapy of a child it is, understandably, completely impossible to make conscious the deeply concealed aggression, because it would be felt precisely as much too sinful. In this case one cannot and one may not hint anything. Rather the tendency should be to introduce carefully

[6] The guilty neglect of studies is in this case only a motivation (at any rate, particularly important) for the beginning of the neurosis.

in the play therapy a loosening of the aggression and at the same time an encouragement of the child; as a matter of course, a correction of the behavior of the father and of the other persons involved should simultaneously be achieved.

This completely commonplace child neurosis shows us to our astonishment that to bring things to the conscious level is by no means a preliminary condition of the cure. The original Freudian maxim for the treatment, "Where Id was, Ego shoud be," is not so simple to interpret. The point cannot be simply to make all unconscious material conscious, because the unconscious embraces very different psychic categories and by no means only the repressed material from the personal previous history. It is particularly essential that with neurotic patients some "healthy," salutary psychic functions do remain in the unconscious depth of the soul. That these salutary psychic functions unfold themselves self-activated and self-aided, with assistance of a suitable stimulus or deliverance, is by far the most meaningful assertion in the doctrine of C. G. Jung.

On the other hand, reasonable insight is quite important and contributes substantially to the analytic therapy, but it is never the only assisting factor. This insight will even fail, generally speaking, in cases of neurotic negligence—a fact that should at least be mentioned. Such patients have no insight whatsoever into their failure and obstinately decline any guilt feeling. To be sure, such an attitude is practiced not only by neurotics but also by many other people (for instance by a great many criminals) without the question of neurosis being brought at all into consideration. Without doubt, neurotic basic dispositions have a part in the process: this is a problem which would require a separate discussion.

To summarize, then, each person must face again and again the fact of objective guilt. Even the healthy person does not always experience his guilt in a thoroughly factual and sensible way. Pathological manifestations, however, appear only when certain types of reaction are extremely pronounced or perhaps are even associated with neurotic symptoms. If we disregard such single symptoms, then the following modes of reaction result for the neurotic patient: his own guilt is experienced either in a most difficult and disheartening way or, on the contrary, in a most obviously superficial and apparently harmless way. (This second reaction corresponds in most of the cases to a process of repression and ought to be attended to particularly during the therapy.) The original experience of guilt, however, can be completely removed from the conscious judgment, insofar as it corresponds to experiences of early childhood. (Hence there are some difficulties and particularities peculiar to child therapy.) Finally, it happens frequently (indeed chiefly in the neurotic negligence phenomenon) that the guilt feeling is obstinately denied. The knowledge of these various reactions is important for treatment since a new way has to be found in each case in order to balance, compensate for, and redress the pathological manifestations of the experience of guilt.

# 18

## Values in Sickness and Health

*William W. Zeller*

VALUES are everybody's business; yet they are very personal. They emerge at all levels of life and enter into all that we think, feel, and do. In a sense, personal values are ideals or standards that give meaning to our existence. They serve as guides for our behavior and give direction to our strivings. Thus they are of great concern to those interested in human motivation and behavior. Usually associated with moral and spiritual matters, values are considered to be in the province of the philosopher or the clergyman, but since they are closely associated also with psychological matters, they are of major importance to psychiatrists whose task it is to understand man and the way he functions in sickness and health.

In the past few decades the specialty of psychiatry has made greater advances in the understanding of human relationships than in all its preceding history, and its involve-

WILLIAM W. ZELLER, M.D., is Director of Psychiatric Education, Institute of Living, Hartford, Connecticut.

ment has extended to many areas of human activity. Nowadays the psychiatrist is called upon not only by the individual in distress but also by social, educational, and business associations and agencies that seek professional guidance concerning the problems of human relationships in groups ranging from the small family up to the large industrial plant or government organization.

The increasing demands on psychiatry, of course, have paralleled the increasing complexity of human activity. Modern living in a world whose standards are changing drastically has created perplexities for man, whose own basic nature meanwhile remains essentially unchanged. He is therefore confronted with the problem of adapting his life and his ways and his standards to the new circumstances in which he finds himself.

### FOREBEARS' FIRM BELIEFS

Our forebears had problems too, of course, but their world was in some ways simpler than ours, and it was a world geared largely to humanistic rather than materialistic values. Man was more sure of his personal identity fifty years ago than he is today. He knew where he belonged in the scheme of things. His roles in relation to his fellow human beings, to his work, to his society, and to his God were more clearly defined. Guided by a set of values that was reasonably stable, he lived within a framework that gave him a sense of security and self-assurance.

Increasingly for greater numbers of men one of these values was progress. Because man valued progress and because he had the curiosity, the intelligence, and the ingenuity to achieve a large measure of it, the scientific, industrial, and social advances made in the last few decades have been truly enormous. Standards of living have been raised; comfort, ease, and leisure have increased; production of goods has exceeded all expectations; the health of the nation has improved; the human life span has lengthened; and unbelievable developments have occurred in the field of technology.

But these accomplishments have been attended by anxiety and unrest. Modern man now finds it difficult to keep pace with the changes he has set in motion. After struggling for the advantages that progress brings, he discovers that something else, something equally important, has gone out of his life. He regrets the passing of the old security and the emotional strength he derived from adhering to tested traditions and values. The changes in his environment and in his way of life leave him feeling threatened, frightened, and anxious. In a state of transition from the old ways to the new, he vacillates between them. He is confused and disturbed by what seems like a moralistic decline in society, a lack of ideals, a lowering of standards of behavior; and he may feel powerless to stop the trend which he does not find acceptable. He finds too that all the technological progress in the world does not solve his personal problems, and that modern computers and proposed trips to the moon, although they bespeak technological progress, do not bring him personal fulfillment and peace of mind.

And so he asks himself whether all sense of values has been lost in the social change and upheaval that accompanies progress. The rules he used to live by no longer seem adequate to meet present-day crises and no firm new standards have been set to supplant them. Wondering whether the world has gained anything, he frequently tends to succumb to hopelessness and helplessness.

## MUST REMOLD VALUES

Although this pessimistic outlook may be partially justified, the situation is not hopeless, nor is it uncorrectable. Mankind will survive the crises of this age as he has survived others and will move toward a higher level of social and personal adaptation. Using our old standards as a base, we can replace those values that are no longer valid in modern society; we can modify and adapt others to present circumstances; and we can hold firm to those basic values that have not changed at all and are just as applicable in any situation. They can continue to guide us as they guided our forebears. To benefit from them requires an unfrenzied approach to our problems; it requires that we pause to assess the meaning of our values in terms of current realities, to take stock of our goals, and to chart our directions accordingly.

With this in mind, we shall try first to define values and then, since the establishment of values is an integral part of human development, we shall examine how we acquire them and how they function in our lives. Finally we shall look into what happens to values when emotional illness occurs. Clarification of the role of values in our lives is an important part of psychiatry's effort to help human beings understand themselves.

How then can we define values? Very simply, a value is our personal estimate of what is desirable; it is our judgment of the worth of an endeavor. Many factors determine and influence this idea of what is desirable, so that we make our judgments of worth on various levels in the order of relative importance. We are free to choose from among many alternatives those things that hold the greatest value for us. We thus establish a hierarchy or scale of values with respect to personal, intellectual, artistic, political, economic, social, and ethical matters. So it is that some value artistic achievement above economic gain; others put power or money before ethics; while still others place spiritual or moral values above everything else. On our personal scale of values there is always the choice of what is good or what is not good for us.

Values are handed down from generation to generation, in family, society, and culture. We acquire our personal values from those of the society and culture in which we live. In society, values have definite functions, one of which, for example, is to insure our survival. Chaos would result if men were free to live and behave according to completely personal whims without regard for the effects of their behavior on others. Society's code of values places limitations on conduct and enables men to live peaceably with each other. Thus ethical values protect us against our own tendency toward antisocial behavior, mediating between our destructive inner impulses and society's demand that we control them. They are not necessarily rigid, negative restrictions but are rules and standards for the purpose of maintaining order. Because of the acceptance of the values we have derived from these social standards, we surrender a certain amount of personal freedom of action for the general good. Such sacrifice is in accord with our own ideals in addition to being necessary for the benefit of the larger society. No matter how independent we may pretend or profess to be we are social creatures who need other people, and normally we find that our own welfare is served when we give up our selfish interests to conform to social standards.

## MOST ENDURING STANDARDS

Now how do we make this choice—the choice between yielding to selfish motivation and exercising mature responsibility? We are forced to make the choice during our development by a process of learning—learning through experience, through the influence of others, and through identification with others, particularly with those we love.

The first and most enduring values, therefore, are acquired in the home. These are the values that guide behavior and set attitudes for the future. The infant behaves at first with complete selfishness. He wants only his physical comfort and the pleasures he derives therefrom, and he makes his demands for satisfaction without regard for or awareness of the rights and welfare of others. When he wants food the young child is not concerned with his mother's needs and duties; he does not know that she has to do the laundry, vacuum rugs, answer doorbells, feed other members of the family, and act as wife and companion to her husband.

As we know, this complete self-interest does not last long. The infant soon finds out that he must defer some of his demands and give up some of his pleasures, and he discovers that a real world exists outside himself which now begins to make some demands on him. Although he is at first completely dependent on his mother for all his needs and pleasures, he gradually finds it expedient to give up some of his selfish behavior to gain her approval and love. He does not always submit readily to his mother's wish to train and control him—that is, not without struggle and conflict—but he can resolve his conflict in a normal way if he feels loved and secure. He conforms not because he is forced to but because he wants to maintain a good and necessary relationship. He thus discovers that obedience and conformity to rules have greater value to him than having his own way. The feeling that comes from mother's smiling approval when he eats his vegetables becomes more important than the feeling of power that comes from refusing to eat what is put before him. He gives up a little part of himself to gain something outside himself that has greater worth for him. Unconsciously he makes his choices in sequence, according to their relative importance, thus establishing his hierarchy of values according to his age and stage of development. He is ready, in other words, to give up something, to pay the price to get the things that represent the greatest value to him.

This learning process is subtly—and perhaps not so subtly—influenced first by the mother and later by the father in accordance with their personal and cultural standards. The child, identifying with his parents, tries to do what they do and be what they are, and he is anxious to behave properly in order to earn their love. He readily senses their disapproval when he has done the wrong thing, and is well aware of their approval when his behavior is acceptable. He learns that in order to *be liked* he has to *be like* the grownups in the world around him. Thus an idea of the difference between right and wrong begins to form, and gradually the child accepts this idea as his own. He internalizes or incorporates the "dos and don'ts" of his parents; literally they become part of his boy's mind and whole substance. The child feels guilty and ashamed when he departs from the code; he is proud when he lives up to it. He acquires a functioning conscience of his own, a "silent policeman at the elbow," or superego as we call it, that enables him to control his own behavior even when his parents are not present to express approval or disapproval. The superego develops slowly, of course, and goes through many stages before it becomes fully effective and mature, that is, before the individual becomes fully responsible for his own actions and behavior.

### PARENTS SHOULDER TASK

Meanwhile a proper amount of discipline is needed to make the code of behavior clear to the child and to impress on him the importance of maintaining it. For parents it is far more difficult to restrict a child than to allow him to do what he pleases. Discipline requires taking the trouble and the time to teach the child what is expected of him. Its ultimate purpose, of course, is to teach him that discipline stems from love and understanding, and it contains a combination of authoritativeness and permissiveness, of firmness and flexibility. Properly administered and appropriately applied according to circumstances, discipline does not intimidate the child, nor is it so lacking in assurance that it fosters conflict in him; but it does instruct the child in the need for self-control and demonstrates the rewards of a reasonable degree of conformity. "Let your yes be yes and your no be no," captures the essence of consistent discipline, and this is part of the process of conscience formation.

From this process develop the child's feelings for moral and ethical principles and his attitudes toward other people. The integration of a stable system of values in a normal and healthy home helps a child through life's crises. This system, reinforced in school and in church or synagogue, will be modified and extended with the passage of time and as life adds new experiences and brings new exigencies with which he must cope.

A child learns what his parents transmit to him and absorbs those values they adhere to themselves. The basic standards of any family group, however, are derived from a much larger social system. Though the parents are not alone in setting the values within the home, their interpretation of them is theirs alone. In our heterogeneous culture, therefore, there are great variations in the way social values are interpreted. Each cultural segment has its own particular subset of values, and each segment influences other segments in many ways. Inevitably there are conflicts in values between groups and between home and community, but usually there is enough overlap of interest to allow workable compromises on fundamental matters. The adult members of the family themselves seek approval in the larger social system; their acceptance in the community depends in large measure on how they conform to its standards. They usually make the effort to do so in their general behavior and in the way they rear their children.

## SOME ELASTICITY NEEDED

This means that there must be a certain amount of flexibility in the family value system. Flexibility does not imply thoughtless abandonment of values or wavering about universal verities, but it does mean that family standards may be altered for appropriate reasons without causing a revolution in the basic value system of the home. Outside pressures or internal problems may upset this system at any time, and emotional and psychological adjustments may have to be made under special circumstances.

Suppose, for instance, that a father's illness has decreased the family income. Such a situation requires a distinct change in the accustomed standards of living in the household and affects many other family standards. A growing daughter may be called upon to give up fashionable clothes and entertainment that she has always taken for granted; an adolescent son may have to abandon his plans for college or find ways to finance his education without family help. Confronted with these realistic problems, the members of the family have to reassess their values concerning money. Decisions will have to be made to retain those things that are essential to their self-respect, happiness, integrity, and the satisfaction of basic needs, and to give up or to compromise concerning those things which have only relatively superficial importance. The welfare of the family as a whole then becomes the highest value in the hierarchy, and each member makes personal sacrifices for the common good. Intelligent thought and mature judgment help them make their choices with a minimum of conflict. This selection calls for self-sacrifice and self-knowledge, both of which are in themselves valuable. The increased capacity for self-sacrifice and the greater self-knowledge gained from this experience may very well aid in the emotional growth and health of the family members in the long run.

## WHEN GUIDES ARE INCONSISTENT

Not all families, however, can make choices in a mature way. During the developmental process, many things may interfere with proper emotional growth. Distortions and misconceptions may result from family standards that are inconsistent or arbitrary. When the demands made upon the child fluctuate, he does not know which choice to make among several alternatives for action. Parents may say one thing and mean or do another—"One way they look, another way they steer." Then the child has no yardstick, no sure value to go by, and he senses contradictions he cannot understand. When he finds himself in such a conflict, he does not know instinctively which value takes precedence over the other, which ranks as most important.

If a child has been taught to be honest, for example, and if this precept has been adhered to consistently at home, he will have little difficulty in deciding in favor of honesty in most situations. But when he is told by his parents that he must be honest and then observes them in acts of deceit and falsehood, he will not know where he stands. Father may tell him that laws are made to be obeyed, but when the family is out for a drive and father passes through a stop signal, he gives the child the idea that sometimes, particularly if you do not get caught, it is acceptable to disobey the law. The mother who lies about a child's age in order to obtain a reduced admission to a theater has given a lesson in dishonesty and deception. How then is the child to know what is right? Honesty and all other values are learned only by consistent examples in actual practice. If the child finds they are not practiced, he may lose faith in adults, and this may not augur well for his future emotional health; meanwhile it certainly creates disorder in family relationships.

Often the effects of the conflicts engendered in the child by inconsistent, vacillating, immature parents have to be resolved in later years. The difficulties that can arise out of such experiences can often be lessened through sound education and guidance.

Education concerning mental health is indeed needed. Throughout history there has been a great deal of misunderstanding about mental and emotional illness. Ignorance and superstition reigned centuries ago. In the past the mentally ill often were considered witches or were judged as criminals—relegated to inferior asylums, placed in chains, and punished for what was at that time deemed sinful behavior.

## ON PASSING JUDGMENT

Sickness was equated with sin in those days, and this idea has persisted in peoples' minds through the years. The basis for this notion can be seen in the evolution of the meaning of the words "sin" and "disease" which are related to each other etymologically. "Sin" comes from the Latin word *sons,* meaning guilty, and *morbus sonticus* means a dangerous illness or disease. "Health," on the other hand, is derived from the word "whole," which in turn is derived from the Old Saxon "hale" as it has come down to us in the phrase "hale and hearty." Akin to "whole and health" are words that mean to become well and also to make well, hence to heal. To be healthy, therefore, is to be whole or complete.

The word "integrity" also enters the picture; this word, which has moral and religious connotations, means to be untouched, hence unbroken or whole. The word "holiness," incidentally, also derives from the word "whole." Thus we see that historically there is a close interrelationship of the words health, integrity, and holiness. In similar fashion, the antonyms or opposites of these words—sickness, incompleteness, and sin—are also conceptually interrelated.

The derivations of these words reveal the origin of the notion that health is related to integrity as sickness is to sin. The significance of the historical derivation of these words is that in centuries past the sick were looked upon as sinners and therefore people believed themselves justified in passing judgment on them. Actually they were reacting in fear and ignorance to their own prejudices rather than to the facts. Prejudice, of course, disregards the principle of "judge not lest ye be judged." Dr. Earl Bond's remark that "emotionally sick people are just like us only more so" bears repeating; it is to this point that this chapter is directed. There is no justification for passing moral judgment on the sick person. As human beings, we are no different than the patient and we are just as subject to emotional problems and just as vulnerable to emotional disease.

Thus far we have discussed what values are, how we acquire them, and how they function under normal circumstances. Now let us examine the effect of emotional illness on the value systems of individuals.

Emotional illness is the result of a combination of environmental forces acting upon the total psychological and physical entity of the individual. Certain circumstances may upset the balance of these forces, giving rise to what is described as stress. Some persons are able to take this stress in stride, adjusting to it satisfactorily; others may be overwhelmed by it, depending in part on the severity of the stress. Thus stress is the main factor responsible for the appearance of psychiatric symptoms.

A crisis in our lives, perhaps a severe personal loss, represents extreme stress and sometimes sets the stage for emotional illness. The Chinese use two characters in writing the word "crisis"; one means danger and the other means opportunity. The wisdom underlying these conceptualizations is apparent, since crisis carries with it both the danger of emotional upset and the promise of new opportunity for growth through suffering and increased insight.

It may be pointed out that in time of physical and psychological stress, the individual may have to test the validity of parts of his value system. Sometimes a person may hold particular beliefs which have little basis in fact. When the realities of life bring him into sharp conflict with these beliefs, psychiatric symptoms may occur as a result of the stress. But even if psychiatric illness does ensue and even if there are apparent changes in behavior, thought, and feeling, nevertheless the value system which is deeply rooted in the personality remains intact. Contrary to common belief nothing really drastic happens to it. A well-established system of values continues to exist within the personality. Despite the notion, for example, that a hypnotist can influence an individual to do things he really does not want to do, the fact remains that a moral person cannot be persuaded to commit immoral acts under hypnosis. So also does an essentially good and moral person remain so even when ill. The socially unacceptable behavior of the mentally ill person has little to do with morals. A defect in moral sense does not cause mental illness, nor does a high moral sense prevent it.

## NONE CAN BE EXEMPTED

No one is exempt from emotional upsets, which include the severe forms of emotional illness. In illness the power of the value system may be overcome by the strength of innate impulses. Part of the role of the normal value system is to control unacceptable or antisocial impulses. These impulses do break through occasionally during the acute phase of some severe emotional disorders, and when they do the patient may do or say things that he would be ashamed of if he were well. When he does recover, he may be more condemnatory of his own behavior than those who witnessed it when he was sick. As a matter of fact, most persons can recall at least some occasions when, during an emotional upset, they did or said something which was not in keeping with their usual system of values. Later they wonder how on earth they came to do or say such inappropriate things.

To look at it another way, when a person is emotionally ill the value system may be visualized as being partially paralyzed, just as the muscles of the patient who has suffered a stroke are paralyzed. But just as the muscles can be returned to normal operation, so can the value system be restored to useful function by treatment.

When a person is sick his energy to think, feel, and behave is not available for normal use. In severe emotional illnesses this psychic energy, as we call it, may be dissipated in what to the outside observer may seem to be purposeless thought and activity. On a comparable but minor level, the same phenomenon is seen when an individual appears to the observer to be fruitlessly and unduly worried about unimportant things. Also, in a state of illness a person may not be able to use his value system to make appropriate decisions and choices.

The severely depressed person, for example, although he may want to get well, is unable to do anything to help himself. This incapacity is part of his illness. Even the decision to seek help may be too much for him, and the decision to place him under medical care may have to be made by relatives. During the crisis, even though he knows the criteria by which he should be guided, he is unable to act on his own behalf. It is the psychiatrist's task to restore this patient to health. Physical measures, such as electroshock therapy and the administration of antidepressant drugs, help to put his body back into physical balance, to lift or remove the depression, and thus to restore normal function. His normal psychic energy then becomes available to the patient for use in his own rehabilitation. In the early stages of therapy, physical measures make it possible for the individual to be restored to a state in which he can examine and deal with any preexisting emotional problems. The doctor may for a while have to interpret reality for him until the patient himself can judge his problems realistically, work them out with the doctor's help, reassess his values, and finally reorganize his goals.

A common example of moral condemnation mistakenly directed at the psychiatrically ill person is well demonstrated by the common attitudes held in respect to the person with alcoholism. There is almost universal moral condemnation of individuals so afflicted. Yet in actual fact the use of alcohol is but a symptom of turbulent emotions, of anxiety, of severe depression, and not infrequently of overwhelming guilt.

Thus in a treatment situation the psychiatrist must be understanding and not condemnatory. To lecture the patient only increases the problem. It is not the function of the psychiatrist to pass moral judgment. The therapist discusses with the patient the deleterious effects of the unrestrained use of alcohol on physical health and the harm his drinking can bring to others. These are realities the patient must face, just as he must ultimately come to face the fact that for him there can be no alcohol.

## ROLE OF THE PSYCHIATRIST

What about behavior disorders in young patients? The psychiatrist's role here is different. The young patient usually is brought to the psychiatrist at a time of life when his value system is not yet firmly established. He may be moving in an antisocial direction; he is out of step with society and his rebelliousness against authority is out of hand—all of this is symptomatic of his illness. With such a patient it is the psychiatrist's function to uphold and confirm the accepted values of society as they apply to the patient himself for his own well-being. Using his specialized techniques, the psychiatrist encourages the patient toward an ideal of constructive rather than destructive behavior. In order to do this he must be a direct influence, giving the patient someone to identify with. In effect he provides a model by which the patient can evaluate his own motivation and behavior. His role thus becomes similar to that of the parent who sets an example for the child to follow. Since we acquire mature standards in the same way that we acquire immature standards, that is, through identification with mature and immature persons, it is especially important for the psychiatrist who treats young patients to possess a deep sense of values. Through his identification with the doctor and his exposure to the values the doctor represents, the young patient has the opportunity to develop his own system of values.

The psychiatrist does not impose his personal values on *any* patient. Nevertheless he has to be very much aware of their relation to the patient's problems. During his illness the patient is confused about his own personal value system because of his internal emotional conflicts and because he is under unusual stress. Not infrequently he comes into treatment with fears, doubts, misgivings, and a lack of basic trust. He may feel that he will be pressed to accept the therapist's standards. The purpose of treatment however is to help the patient, among other things, to define his values. This must be done by the patient in the course of treatment. The psychiatrist does not expect the patient to develop a set of values which is identical in every detail with his own. Psychiatrist and patient, for instance, need not worship in the same faith for therapy to be effective. It is true in some instances that a patient may feel more secure and comfortable working with a psychiatrist who has a similar background to his own. This might foster a greater degree of trust since the doctor would then be less of a stranger. But even strangers can become acquainted and find the mutual respect and trust that are such important ingredients in the doctor-patient relationship. This is an intimate professional relationship that is privileged and confidential, a relationship in which the patient can unburden himself with the assurance that he will be understood and not criticized since both doctor and patient seek the same goal—the restoration of the patient's health. The successful outcome of therapy often hinges on the quality of the doctor-patient relationship.

Nathaniel Hawthorne, in *The Scarlet Letter,* describes the role of the physician:

> If the latter possess native sagacity, and a nameless something more, . . . if he have the power, which must be born with him, to bring his mind into such affinity with his patient's that this last shall unawares have spoken what he imagines himself only to have thought: if such revelations be acknowledged not so often by an uttered sympathy as by silence, an inarticulate breath, and here and there a word, to indicate that all is understood; if to these qualifications of a confidant be added the advantages afforded by his recognized character as a physician;—then, at some inevitable moment, will the soul of the sufferer be dissolved, and flow forth in a dark, but transparent stream, bringing all its mysteries into daylight.[1]

The physician who engages in psychotherapy strives to bring into daylight the underlying causes of emotional conflicts. The insight achieved in therapy helps the patient work through his misconceptions and misunderstandings so that his basic system of values become clear and can begin to

[1] Nathaniel Hawthorne, *The Scarlet Letter,* New York: Random House, Inc., Modern Library Edition, 1950, pp. 140–41.

operate again in a way that is normal for him. He learns to recognize his own values and to accept them or to modify them as he is relieved of tension, anxiety, and other symptoms. He develops a new ability to synthesize the conflicting forces within him, to become more mature and to assume responsibility for his own decisions. Therapy helps him to achieve harmony within himself, to achieve the feeling that what he does and thinks is consistent with a set of values that is an integral part of him, the basis of his personal identity. He can then act with freedom and with the assurance that his decisions are consonant with the demands of his own conscience. But he makes these decisions himself. His experiences in therapy place him in a better position to reaffirm his values or reassess them in the light of his new insights.

## SELF-KNOWLEDGE REMAINS

Whether in illness or in health, it is in the light of self-knowledge that the traditional values can be most meaningful and useful to the individual and to society. Regardless of outside events and changing circumstances, there are certain stable and universal values that can serve as an anchor.

Certainly through the centuries, the precepts set forth by the three traditional Western religious faiths have influenced men toward goodness. They have emphasized the uniqueness and value of the individual, and in so doing have provided a yardstick for measuring what has value for all individuals in society. Our government is founded on this principle and so are most of our social institutions. Even today we can still proclaim the desirability and rightness of the brotherhood of man and condemn the exploitation of others as people did centuries ago. According to the traditional Judeo-Christian code of ethics man has an obligation in society to do justice, to be generous, to show mercy, to be honest, to be truthful, to cultivate a humane spirit, to love his neighbor, to be accountable for his actions, and to be true to his conscience. What better can we ask as a code of behavior than is offered by these time-tested values?

But this ethical code can serve only as a general guide. We have to translate it to fit our own times, making use of our intelligence to interpret the wisdom of the ages. These enduring and basic tenets can have meaning for human beings in any civilization and in any religion because they are based on profound human experiences that remain the same as in any past era. When they are deeply rooted, these tenets can support us through change and crisis. Socially we cannot cut ourselves off from our own past. Our problem now is to understand these tenets fully and to accept them and apply them, for they truly represent an almost universal set of values. We shall strive in spite of temptations not to replace them with some of the conflicting values that have crept into our civilization.

There has to be a distinction between materialistic and psychological values, and we have to understand them both to avoid cynicism and pessimism, to avoid succumbing to hopeless nihilism. With firm belief in our own ability to adapt to a changing world, we can find the proper balance; we can distinguish between relative values and choose our course according to a scale of values that brings us the most enduring satisfaction. And the higher the values, the more enduring these satisfactions will be.

### INVOLVEMENT GIVES MEANING

Dr. Liston Pope, Dean of the Yale School of Divinity, has deplored the fact that we present a blurred image of our American ideals and values to the youth of today, and he regrets the confusion that attends our stand on most public issues. We continue to teach that hard work is a great virtue, but the work week grows ever shorter. We plead for the unity of the family and the sanctity of marriage, but more children than ever before are growing up in broken homes. We know that we ought to give liberally of our time and energy and money for the improvement of our communities and the world, but our altruistic and civic impulses are often restrained by personal caution and fear. Dr. Pope points out that although we know we ought to oppose evil in high places and in low, the evil is so vast that we are reluctant to become involved.

Involvement or personal commitment is missing from many lives, and it is involvement that gives meaning to human relationships. When murder can be committed on a city street and citizens can stand by and allow it to happen without any motivation to intervene, something is lacking in the sense of responsibility of human beings toward their fellows. In some way the basic principles of goodness, brotherhood, and mercy have been ignored, conscience has been compromised, and behavior has been rationalized. It seems that more and more people are withdrawing from the assumption of social responsibility, a withdrawal which takes the form of apathy.

There is no room for apathy in an intensely competitive and rapidly moving world. All individuals are involved in what is going on; they are part of it. They belong to the world as it is, and whatever its values, these individuals are the ones who decide on them and who transmit them to the next generation. And they transmit enduring standards by upholding them in every way they can within the limits of their personal influence. They can live by their own values and be guided by their own convictions instead of allowing themselves to be influenced by the values and convictions of others. Parents can concentrate their efforts on building character in their children and teaching honor, integrity, and morality by their own example of responsible and mature behavior. These attributes are enduring.

Some of the values that regulated the lives of the present generation of adults may be obsolete in the current world. Even so, today parents can help their children cope with changing trends by training them to adapt, to resist stress, and to compensate for change. Although it may not be possible to anticipate all their future problems, parents can teach children to handle whatever comes if they teach them to expect change and prepare them to live with it. Children have to grow with the world, and the best thing the adult generation has to give them is the freedom to grow within the limits appropriate to their culture.

To be sure, there will be conflicts between the values of the past and those of the present. But every conflict has two possible solutions, a constructive and a destructive one. Only a thorough understanding of the nature of the conflict will lead to the constructive solution. The present conflict pulls people between the past and the present; they try to cling to the traditions of the past, yet must live in the present and prepare themselves and their children for the future. To find a way out of the dilemma and resolve the conflict, the difficulties that plague mankind have to be faced squarely. Only so can confusion be dissipated, ideals be clarified, and the path be found to personal fulfillment.

Men are not alone in this struggle; they are part of a society of other men, all of whom have the capacity to influence others. If they attempt nothing, they gain nothing. But by giving their children a strong base in the traditions of the past, they offer them the opportunity to strive toward worthwhile ideals and goals. If they transmit to them significant truths based upon the experience of mankind and if they place their trust in the younger generation, surely we may all hope for a better world. Educated and supported by parents with clear and firm values, youth will find its own path to fulfillment.

# 5

# REATMENT—WHERE MEANING, VALUES, *and* RELIGION ARE CONCERNED

# 19

# Spiritual Therapy for the Peptic Ulcer Patient

*Richard K. Young and Albert L. Meiburg*

THE ASSOCIATION of a full and properly functioning stomach with a contented mind is a very ancient one. Voltaire said, "The fate of a nation has often depended upon the good or bad digestion of a prime minister." C. T. Copeland paraphrased a more familiar quotation when he said, "To eat is human; to digest divine."

Most of us remain relatively unaware of the prodigious

---

RICHARD K. YOUNG, Ph.D., and ALBERT L. MEIBURG, Ph.D., are chaplains at the North Carolina Baptist Hospital, Winston-Salem, North Carolina.

From *Spiritual Therapy,* Richard K. Young and Albert L. Meiburg, copyright © Richard K. Young and Albert L. Meiburg, Harper & Brothers, New York, 1960. Reprinted with permission of Harper & Row, Publishers, Inc.

The authors wish to acknowledge their gratitude to David Cayer, M.D., Professor of Internal Medicine, Bowman Gray School of Medicine and North Carolina Baptist Hospital, for contributing the introductory paragraphs of this chapter and reading the whole for medical accuracy.

activity of our digestive tract. However, it is common knowledge that students before examinations may develop nausea and diarrhea, that businessmen may have heartburn at the time of an important conference or in connection with financial reverses, that housewives may develop indigestion when there is trouble with the children, and that children who are not making happy adjustments with their playmates in the schoolyard may have attacks of vomiting at schooltime. This is well illustrated by our general speech—the individual who loses his temper and is forced to "swallow his anger" which he is then unable "to stomach," "stews in his own juice," for which he blames his digestion.

Laboratory observations proving the long-suspected association between emotional stress and profound physiologic changes in the stomach, as well as elsewhere in the body, make clear the objectives and management of such patients. They must be directed toward the care of the man rather than merely to his stomach.[1]

Until recent years the minister has offered pastoral care to the sick with very little understanding of the individual's personality background. One minister said, "Before I had clinical training in a hospital I simply visited the sick members of my church. They were all sick, so I treated them all alike!" Today the pastor is no more justified in approaching every sick person with the same prayer and consoling scripture than the doctor is in prescribing the same medicine for every patient.

Medical science is accumulating a body of knowledge that can deepen the minister's understanding of the human personality which will result in a more effective ministry to the individual. This chapter attempts to summarize what medical science has to say about personality factors related to peptic ulcer. Then, with a specific case, pastoral care of the ulcer patient can be demonstrated.

By definition, the peptic ulcer is a localized erosion beginning in the inner lining or mucous membrane of the duodenum or less often of the lower portion of the stomach. It forms a sort of crater, which can punch through or penetrate completely the stomach wall. The exact incidence of peptic ulcer is unknown. It is estimated on the basis of autopsy studies that approximately 10 per cent of all persons

[1] David Cayer, M.D., personal communication.

suffer at some time in their lives from an ulcer.[2] Men are affected four times as frequently as women. Almost 50 per cent of ulcer patients will have recurrence of ulcer symptoms within one year, and 75 per cent within two years.[3]

The outstanding symptom of an ulcer is what the patient often calls "hunger pains," occurring one to four hours after meals, waking the patient at night, and usually relieved by food or antacids. Stomach distress may be present for several years before an actual ulcer develops.

How and why does an ulcer develop? Early studies stressed body type, chemical imbalance, allergy, and focal infection, but these factors are receiving very little attention today. In contrast, the factors constantly discussed today are the muscular activity of the stomach and duodenum, decreased tissue resistance to enzymes, and emotional and physical stress.

The effect of emotional stress on the stomach is mediated through the autonomic nervous system which is not under conscious control. This system is the means whereby the internal organs are regulated and helped to accommodate to changing demands. In the case of the stomach, for example, the sight, smell, or thought of food may result in an output of five to fifteen times the normal amount of highly acid gastric juice. The hydrochloric acid present in gastric secretion has long been viewed as the causative agent in the production of peptic ulcer, but it is actually the end result of a chain of events.[4]

The process by which an ulcer develops has been described in a simplified fashion by Flanders Dunbar.[5] Some emotional disturbance kicks off a large number of nerve impulses which are transmitted to the stomach. This results in the overproduction of hydrochloric acid and disturbance of the even contraction and relaxation of the stomach muscles. The mucous membrane becomes fragile and oversensitive. Any slight break in the mucous-protected lining may be further irritated by the acid and in time an ulceration appears in the stomach wall.

[2] W. L. Palmer, "Peptic Ulcer," in Russell L. Cecil and Robert F. Loeb, *A Textbook of Medicine,* 8th ed., Philadelphia: W. B. Saunders Company, 1915, p. 700.

[3] David Cayer, M.D.

[4] *Ibid.*

[5] Flanders Dunbar, *Mind and Body: Psychosomatic Medicine,* New York: Random House, Inc., 1955, pp. 163–64.

What type of personality is the minister likely to meet in the ulcer patient? Of course, it is always a temptation to categorize people rather than take the time to explore the facts in an individual situation. The physician would be the last person to insist that his patients fit some stereotype even when it is statistically derived.

Yet authorities on the mind-body relationship tell us we are likely to meet a tense, hard-driving individual who feels a compulsion to succeed. As a rule this individual plays as hard as he works, so far as winning is concerned. If he plays golf, for example, and competition becomes keen, the ulcer patient will not profit from his recreation because of his strong desire to win.

Unconscious dependency needs are deeply buried under a successful exterior. The individual compensates for his unacceptable dependency needs by working hard and striving for success wherever he finds himself. Success is satisfying but heightens his frustration because he is rewarded with increasing responsibilities. Instead of finding relief, he is caught in a vicious cycle.

The story of Frank Thomas illustrates the operation of some of the emotional factors just described and will show how one individual developed a way of life which resulted in an ulcer.

Frank Thomas is a slender young engineer 32 years of age. He has been married for eight years and has three children. For three successive years he has been hospitalized for peptic ulcer. At the time of his latest admission he stated to the chaplain his realization that he had been under a good deal of tension. He said his state of mind was not good. As he put it, "I actually think sometimes that I'm mad at God!"

He is the third of four children born into the home of a minister. Both his parents are now living although his father has retired. Frank stated that he saw very little of his father while growing up. On one occasion he hid in the car in order to go with his father to the golf course. His father did let him carry his clubs on this occasion.

His mother was the dominant person in the home. His father had to get her approval before he could even buy a new book for his library. Frank saw her as a strict person. "There was no place for pleasure in her life and so none in mine." Many of the marks of achievement in his life, such as scholastic honors, were won largely out of a sense of duty to his mother who was very ambitious for him. His mother worried because he was thin and was always urging him to eat.

Not until he entered college did Frank have a date. His mother insisted that he go to a small college, and during this time he fell in with the wrong crowd and stayed away from church. Later, on a state college campus he started dating and going with a more wholesome group and soon found his way back to church.

At the state college he felt inferior to his roommate, who was an accomplished athlete. In graduate school he had little time for recreation, taking his vacations to get experience on the job.

The first occurrence of his ulcer came while he was in graduate school in a distant state, which was the first time he had been away from home for an extended period. Here he was attracted to a girl who later became his wife. He found her to be a person he could talk to and has depended heavily upon her. "She has really been a second mother to me."

His wife has recently told him that she felt when they were first married that he practically hated his father. The patient admits having some resentment, but denies that it was as strong as his wife implied. For a long while after leaving home he did not write to his parents regularly, but now he tries to send cards and letters frequently. Visits to his parents are still somewhat embarrassing to him because his mother is always trying to do too much for him.

Frank states that he is happily married except for one or two sources of tension. One friction point is over decisions concerning out-of-town business trips which he often schedules without consulting his wife. He fears that if he asks her she will not approve. Usually, however, she goes along with his judgment, but resents being left out of the decision.

Another area of friction involves social activities. He is so consumed by the demands of his business that he has little time for play. He feels that this is hard on his wife who is more outgoing and uninhibited. "She had a much happier childhood than I did, for she knew how to play. In fact ambition is what is killing me. Why can't I enjoy life like the other men in my department? They take time off and go fishing while I am working twelve hours a day trying to set an example."

After being with one firm for four years, Frank took an administrative position with another company which required moving out of his home state. He feels that his executive role compels him to control his life and his emotions to an uncomfortable degree. He has difficulty delegating responsibility: "I guess I'm just afraid to trust other people."

He has always been uncomfortable in the presence of men. This causes problems for him in his supervision of a section of engineers. For example, there is one young engineer in his department who probably knows more about the newer processes than he does. As he says, "I know that if I moved out, this fellow would be put in my place." In relation to his own immediate supervisor he feels the worst tension comes in trying to know when and when not to consult him. "Maybe this goes back to my relationship to my father. He tried to give me money when there were things I wanted, but he gave me very little companionship."

Prior to his latest admission Frank had reached a point of nervous exhaustion. He broke down and cried at small provocation and had a feeling of helplessness which he described as a "nobody-loves-me" feeling.

During his hospitalization Frank received medical treatment for his ulcer, and the chaplain in collaboration with his physician saw him on five different occasions.

The facts given above, though somewhat limited, do provide some understanding of Frank's personality background. In tracing these events we find an overambitious mother doling out approval to her son as he attempted to measure up to her standards. Consequently, as a child, his need for acceptance was never adequately met.

As a result of his mother's overprotection Frank developed strong underlying dependent feelings for which he compensated by earning status through academic success. He developed a reputation for conscientious academic work to the exclusion of cultivating social maturity through his college experience.

We see a person leaving home for graduate school in a distant state still feeling strongly the need of his mother's support. As a child his mother was concerned over his thinness and he could gain her approval by eating. Thus, in this stress situation his emotional needs produced a biological overreadiness for food, and his ulcer first appeared.

His wife met some of his dependent needs and for a time his ulcer subsided. He continued, however, to drive hard toward success, and was rewarded by the assignment of heavier responsibility. This resulted in a depletion of his reserves since he was already overextended, and his ulcer recurred.

Frank was not helped any by his father's weakness as a husband and parent. Lacking a strong masculine example, he has had trouble in maintaining satisfactory relationships with men, and this has intensified his problem to this day.

His earliest effort to achieve independence came during his first year at college when he stayed away from church and, as he said, "fell in with the wrong crowd." Making decisions without consulting his wife shows a continuation of this pattern. Likewise, the anxiety he experiences in relating to his superior and the ambitious young man under him aggravates his dependency needs.

The pastor needs to have in mind some general idea of what the doctor will be doing to help the ulcer patient in the immediate crisis. This will prevent him from working at cross-purposes with the physician.

The aims of medical treatment of the ulcer patient are threefold: (1) to relieve the symptoms, (2) to heal the ulcer, (3) to prevent recurrences. Usually the doctor will restrict his patient's activities and with diet, sedatives, antispasmodics, antacids, and reassurance he can ordinarily relieve the symptoms within two weeks. Conservative medical treatment is usually highly successful and in a majority of cases results in prompt relief and eventual healing of the ulcer.

However, permanent victory over the ulcer is a different matter. Unless the patient can come to an understanding of the sequence of events which produced his ulcer he is likely to return to the hospital. Recurrent ulcers with uncontrolled bleeding may lead the doctor to recommend surgery to remove a part of the stomach.

The pastor can see from the medical goals that in the beginning of the treatment process he should avoid an aggressive religious ministry that might agitate the individual.

The aim of the pastor in ministering to the ulcer patient might be along the following lines: (1) to give support insofar as possible to his dependent needs, (2) to assist him to come to as much understanding of his own personality as he is willing to undertake so that he can learn to live in equanimity with his physical limitations, (3) to help him mobilize his spiritual resources for a fresh interpretation of his way of life.

In order to give support to Frank, the chaplain's first step was to establish a pastoral relationship. As is often the case with the ulcer patient, Frank was an attractive, pleasing person who made an interesting conversationalist. It was not long, however, until the chaplain detected underneath the surface a reaching out for help.

If the minister is aware of the ulcer patient's need for emotional nurture he can be more sympathetic toward any attempt the patient may make to "hold on" to him orally, that is by talking. Sympathetic listening can be an emotional counterpart to the milk in the patient's diet.

Another way dependency needs may be expressed is through a constant seeking of advice, which is characteristic of the peptic ulcer patient. This can be tempting to the pastor or the doctor since requests for advice tend to enhance one's ego. Remember that in the overall process the aim is to help Frank to a better understanding of himself so that he can make his own decisions.

The ulcer patient is no different from the rest of us in that he seldom sees how his immediate frustrations are related to his early childhood experiences. In the beginning the only thing Frank was conscious of was that he had been working hard. But when the doctor discussed with him the relationship between emotional stress and the ulcer condition, he became more interested in exploring with the chaplain the reasons behind his driving nature. On further visits as the relationship deepened, Frank shared with the chaplain enough facts about his background to gain some insight into his life pattern.

One basic rule in pastoral counseling is that insight cannot be forced. Instead, the person must be allowed to proceed at his own speed in his effort to find a deeper understanding of himself. This rule is particularly important in the case of the peptic ulcer patient. The research of such men as Stewart Wolf shows why.

In the case of several ulcer patients Wolf arranged to maintain continuous recordings of the muscular contractions and the acid output of their stomachs. He did this by means of taking periodic samplings of gastric juice, and by placing a balloon in the stomach. Contractions in the stomach decreased the volume of air in the balloon and this was recorded on a moving chart. While recordings of these factors were being made, he involved the patients in a vigorous discussion of significant personal problems. The tracings of his instruments showed that by exposing his patients to emotionally loaded situations, he could induce overactivity of the stomach and typical ulcer pain.[6]

These findings have significance for the chaplain and pastor. Picture a minister, fresh with a new idea of the role of emotions in disease, on his first visit to a newly admitted ulcer patient. He wants to help the patient get to the root of his "problem" so he begins to use a direct question-and-answer method to explore various likely areas of conflict. The minister's probing could result in aggravating the ulcer at the very time the doctor is trying to get the patient to relax and allow the healing process of his body to repair the defect in his stomach.

In the case of a woman patient who confided that she had married her employer following his divorce, a student chaplain with a probing statement replied, "How did you feel about marrying a divorced man?"

Contrast this direct approach with the more relaxed, supportive effect when Frank suggested, "Maybe this goes back to my relationship with my father." The chaplain responded, "You might have a lead there worth exploring."

Generally speaking, in counseling, the minister should strive to stay just behind the growing edge of the individual, aiding him to come to as much understanding of his own personality as he is willing to undertake. Once the patient has come to verbalize an insight, then the pastor may lend reassurance and support to counteract the pain which always accompanies growth.

When one is struggling toward a philosophy of life his questions must necessarily move into moral and religious areas. Like far too many persons in our society, Frank has

[6] Stewart Wolf, "Summary of Evidence Relating Life Situation and Emotional Stress to Peptic Ulcer," *Annals of Internal Medicine,* 31:637–49, Oct., 1949.

been going through the motions of formal religion with little if any awareness of the relevance of his faith for his flesh-and-blood daily struggle. The minister has a direct opportunity to assist such an individual to relate specific Christian resources to his own inner needs.

Sullivan and Rehfelt have given us a stimulating interpretation of the personality patterns in gastrointestinal diseases. They begin by saying that there are three basic instinctual human drives: the drive for self-preservation (survival), the drive for self-perpetuation (propagation), and the drive for self-extension (domination). While necessary and worthy when indulged in moderation, the needs can if distorted result in sin and disease. The traditional cardinal sins, Pride, Lust, and Avarice, are religious labels for the distorted expression of these needs. Hence the overactivity of the need for survival issues in Pride, for propagation in Lust, and for domination in Avarice. Thus, the besetting sin of the peptic ulcer patient, say Sullivan and Rehfelt, is covetousness. His "needed virtue" is Faith; and the medical advice given him corresponds to the biblical injunction "Go into the desert and rest awhile."[7]

These spiritually discerning physicians are quite accurate in their diagnosis, and they recognize that religious language is often a much more effective medium of communication with the patient than psychological jargon. However, they are weak in applying spiritual therapy, which is the point at which collaboration between the minister and the physician becomes imperative. Frank Thomas needs to "take heed and beware of covetousness," but it is doubtful that simply telling him this will of itself get at the root of his difficulty.

One ulcer patient shared with his minister his own reaction to this suppressive type of treatment: "If you had given me a self-help religious book the first time you talked with me, I would not have returned. I had read a dozen books like that already."

Only after Frank Thomas has been given an opportunity to pour out or "ventilate" his resentment against his father's weakness and his mother's domination can he come to see

[7] Albert J. Sullivan and Frederick C. Rehfelt, "The Spirit and the Flesh," *Southern Medical Journal,* 43:736–43, Aug., 1950.

their control over his life. Only then can he see that his mother is not 500 miles away as his conscious mind tells him. She is still with him in his personality affecting his present-day relationships. In striving toward business success and other outward marks of achievement, Frank is still trying to please his mother and cannot enjoy real success when it comes. There is no essential difference in his buying a swimming pool now and making the honor roll in high school when he unconsciously does it as a compensation for his dependency needs. Once Frank comes to an awareness of this distortion in his life he can then accept the positive teachings of religion regarding the eternal values of life.

Jesus dealt with a variety of individuals during his ministry. Does he have a word for Frank's life situation? If we can conclude that this individual is confusing success with self, then his idea of success must be broadened. He must look at life as a whole and not through a keyhole of materialistic values.

Jesus seems to be speaking directly to the ulcer patient when he talked to the man who wanted him to divide his inheritance. He gave a warning that "a man's life consisteth not in the abundance of the things which he possesseth." In fact, the whole passage, Luke 12:13–31, is highly relevant. In the light of a discussion of this passage Frank said to the chaplain, "You know I have been so intent upon providing my family with worldly goods that I have miserably failed to give of myself to them."

Frank began to see how dependent he really was when he realized that his ulcer first occurred when he moved to a distant state. He said, "I suppose I had just as well admit that at heart I'm still a little boy. This is why just before I came into the hospital I had that 'nobody-loves-me' feeling."

"Do you remember saying when I first saw you that you thought you were 'mad at God'?" asked the chaplain.

"Yes," said Frank, "I see now that I was really mad at my whole frustrating life situation without any real knowledge of why." The chaplain then turned the discussion to what Paul meant in Philippians 4:6–7: "Be careful for nothing; but in every thing by prayer and supplication with thanksgiving *let your requests be made known unto God* And the peace of God, which passeth all understanding, shall keep your hearts and minds through Christ Jesus." The aim of the chaplain here was to help Frank focus his ultimate dependence upon God rather than deifying his mother, regardless of her good qualities.

In spite of the fact that Frank's stay in the hospital was relatively brief, the chaplain helped him to see some of the blockages that were hindering his emotional and spiritual growth.

The Christian fellowship of the church and an understanding pastor can sustain and facilitate the emotional and spiritual growth of the ulcer patient. Because these people are usually successful in the community, their work load in the church is as likely to complicate their lives as their work load in the business world. Ulcer patients are often found on building, finance, and church promotion committees. An extreme example occurred in one North Carolina church where out of twelve deacons seven had active ulcers at the same time! Likewise, in recent times, peptic ulcer has almost become an occupational disease of the ministry. The righteousness of the cause does not prevent a conscientious pastor from being overwhelmed by the problems of the congregation, church building programs, and like demands. This raises questions about the quality of religious experience in such a setting. The fellowship of the church cannot be a healing influence on the peptic ulcer patient if the demands it makes upon the individual tend to aggravate rather than prevent his illness.

The ulcer patient should be given a place in the organizational life of the church with a moderate amount of responsibility, preferably one where he will be exposed to a good deal of appreciation and support. When the pastor preaches along the theme of "Awake, my soul, stretch every nerve," he should qualify what he says lest the ulcer patient go overboard in his response. Otherwise, he might not feel that he is being fed "with the food that is needful for me" (Prov. 30:8, RSV).

A concluding word is in order with reference to Frank Thomas. It is not to be inferred that all ulcer patients are as ready to grow as he was on his third hospitalization. By this time he was getting desperate. Oftentimes when the doctor first makes reference to the fact that emotions may be playing a part in the person's illness, the first response of the patient may be to look upon this as a reflection and to resent any interference in his emotional life.

Frank is an ideal example of what an ulcer patient can accomplish if he is willing to face the pain of growth and open up and seek help. It can be reported here that two years have elapsed and he has not kept his "annual date" at the hospital.

In fact, he went home, outfitted his garage with woodworking tools, and now has a much-needed hobby in his life. When his church completed a new building recently Frank took real delight in handcrafting in his shop the bookracks for the pews. He is spending more time with his family and enjoys being superintendent of the young people's department of his Sunday School.

Tucked away within a setting of worldly pessimism in the book of Ecclesiastes is a verse which nevertheless contains a truth the peptic ulcer patient might do well to learn: "Go thy way, eat thy bread with joy, and drink thy wine with a merry heart; *For God now accepteth thy works* (9:7).

# 20

# Therapy of Pastoral Care

*Peder Olsen*

## PAVING THE WAY TO HEALING

THERE ARE some sick folk with such an irrational view of medical science and natural means of healing that they are prevented from being benefited by them. They motivate this view on religious grounds, maintaining that God both can and always will heal them without medical treatment. If we are to help such people we must meet them on the level where the real hindrance is lodged.

A patient was in need of being operated on for a serious ailment, but she refused to consent to an operation when the surgeon told her of her need. She said that an operation was unnecessary, for God could heal her through prayer. She maintained this opinion also in a talk with the hospital chaplain. She had better leave the hospital, she said, and get in touch with someone who could pray for her. The pastor

PEDER OLSEN is Dean of the Cathedral in Tönsberg, Norway. This chapter was written when he was Chaplain at Lovisenberg Deaconess Hospital, Oslo, Norway.

told her that she need not leave the hospital to get someone to pray for her, as he had often prayed for patients. Her answer was that she meant intercessory prayer for sick folk as prescribed in the Bible, particularly in James 5:14, where mention is made of anointing with oil in the name of the Lord. When the pastor then said that he practiced in keeping with the Bible, she expressed great surprise that a state church clergyman did that. But this brought about contact between patient and soul counselor, and established confidence on her part. And it opened the way into an open, effective soul care conversation. They discussed in a straightforward way what the Bible says about healing through prayer, and she was led into a truer and saner view, which in turn helped her to regard the natural means of healing as means in the service of God. She was prayed for and anointed with oil in the name of the Lord, through it gaining spiritual succor: rest and confidence.

When the surgeon called again and once more suggested an operation, she willingly acceded. The operation was successful, and she returned to her home well and happy. She looked upon her restoration as the work of God, but also on the surgeon and the operation as the means He had used.

Some patients develop a neurotic repression which prevents their getting into contact with physician and psychotherapist, while they, on the other hand, readily agree to see the chaplain. In such cases the first contact is established by him, leading on to such soul care as the circumstances will permit with subsequent contact with the doctor.

For illustrative purposes I mention a patient in his middle thirties, an intelligent man, very well educated; but upon admission to the hospital he was, practically speaking, in a psychotic condition, marked by religious delusions and ecstatic experiences. He refused absolutely to be examined by physicians, insisting that his first need was to be absolved by a soul counselor from the ban under which he felt himself placed. He held that he was absolutely forbidden by God to unbosom himself to anyone but a pastor.

The physicians having advised, as the first step, an interview with the hospital chaplain, this was arranged, resulting in the establishment of a promising contact. Several interviews followed, and the patient adjusted well to his hospital surroundings, but continued to refuse to see the doctors.

During the many and frequent talks with the chaplain

he had the opportunity of unburdening himself of his religious experiences and difficulties, and also of his sexual conflicts. He showed himself increasingly receptive to soul care counseling. And as he gradually gained tranquility of mind, the chaplain was able to show him that he had confused *pneuma* and *psyche* and had mixed up cause and effect; he had been unable to differentiate between sickly and normal reactions in his religious life. It was fairly easy then to help him acquire insight into the nature of illness. And at length he admitted that what he had interpreted as divine guidance and spiritual experiences really were impulses of repression and unsound ecstatic states of mind. He was also open to conviction when he, soberly and clearly, was shown that his religious ideas were delusions caused by erroneous interpretations of the Bible (particularly of sections of Heb. 6 and 10).

As his strongly emotionalistic experiences receded in his consciousness, he began to react normally both in his religious and psychic life. "In the hospital he was a satisfactory patient, and toward the end of his stay there his contact with the doctors, too, was good. On dismissal he showed no psychopathic indications, but was naturally a bit uncertain about his future."

This patient has now been working normally for several years; he feels entirely well and enjoys good contacts with his fellow men.

The necessity of administering soul care manifests itself also in many sex neuroses or in neuroses where sexual life at least plays a large role.

In a physician's course of treatment a shut-in situation may develop which makes further treatment impracticable. That may mean a stoppage in the healing process. The cause may be a decision to be taken before further progress can be made. The decision may relate to one or another of many problems, such as sterilization, *abortus provocatus* [criminal abortion], prevention [birth control], sexual adjustment, etc.

Based on medical indications the doctor may have given definite advise in a given case, but the patient may demur and raise objections, usually on ethical and religious grounds, as for instance: "Is it right to be sterilized? Is it not a sin to remove a fetus?" In many of these cases the patient is not helped by the doctor's declaration that under the circumstances it is not a sin; but the situation is quite a different one for the patient if the soul counselor can say: "This you may do with a clear conscience, both over against God and man; it is not a sin."

In circumstances of this kind some patients have greater confidence in the pastor than in the doctor. The reason may be the difference in the calling and professional competence of the two men, each being a specialist in his own field. The case in reverse would be: That the pastor under given circumstances would feel convinced that nothing was the matter with the patient and would say to him, "You are not sick." The patient would hardly believe him. But if the doctor would say the same to him, the situation would be a very different one for him, since he would know that the doctor could speak with professional authority.

But if the pastor would neglect giving the needed soul care to patients in doubt regarding what decisions to make under circumstances described above, it would likely have unfortunate consequences. In my experience as a counselor of souls I have dealt with people suffering from a harassing feeling of guilt because they had acted on medical advice contrary to their inmost, holiest convictions. Or they were at the time not spiritually and physically mature enough for making a decision which to them seemed coerced. An interview with a soul counselor at the right time is likely to clear away situations which otherwise might lodge in their soul life and produce spiritual and psychic complexes and repressions.

It is an essential part of effective cooperation between physician and pastor that they help each other in bringing about good results for the patient.

Some physicians may, perhaps, hesitate a bit about sending a patient to the pastor under the above-mentioned circumstances, as they may fear that the pastor's advice might lead to the patient's not getting the medical attention which they know is needed. This fear is groundless. For countless instances of soul care administered will show that where medical indications support the doctor's advice, there the cooperative action of the pastor will be beneficial both to physician and patient.

I want in this connection to mention the large group of people having marital conflicts. Many of these find it easier to open up to a pastor, a circumstance which may have several causes. Some prefer to consult the pastor who officiated at their wedding, perhaps because the personality of the pastor appealed to them and created confidence, or because the conflict itself has ethico-religious implications; then again many will find it more natural and easy to talk things over with a pastor than with a physician [*sic*].

We have above mentioned some instances of *traumata* lodged in the soul life. Whether the religious experiences are contributory *causes* to the psychic distress or *symptoms* of it is not always easy to determine. To investigate this is primarily not the task of the pastor but of the physician. But it is a part of the pastor's work to help in releasing tenseness and psychic distress. He can penetrate into the religious *trauma* and also show the way to release and salvation. In such situations I have often thought of the one log which during the floating of timber gets lodged, thus hindering the entire raft from moving on. It is then the business of the raftsman to find this log and to dislodge it, This, too, is the business of the soul counselor in the area of soul life.

### ETHICO-RELIGIOUS SUFFERING

Most clearly are seen the psychotherapeutic effects of soul care when the essential reason back of the psychic distress lies on the ethico-religious plane.

The suffering may have been induced by an unsatisfied religious [conflict], or by an unsolved ethical conflict because of unconfessed sins, [or] by an unsatisfied religious demand.

A man in his fifties was admitted as a patient in a hospital section for internal medicine, suffering with pains in his stomach and also in other organs; these [pains] had hindered him greatly in his work for several years. After an exhaustive examination the doctors had to state that they could find no organic basis for these pains. A psychiatric examination was not suggested, as no indications pointed in that direction; and the man was about to be dismissed from the hospital. But before that was done he had a somewhat lengthy conversation with the chaplain, with whom he had established a good social contact. They discussed among other things what might be the cause of his distress, especially as the doctors had found no organic disease nor anything essentially abnormal in his *psyche.* The chaplain then, shunting the talk over to spiritual matters, suggested that the reason might be found in that sphere. The man's first reaction was a bit negative, but the chaplain noted that his thoughts had evidently been arrested, for which reason the chaplain tried to be as passive as possible, awaiting further developments. And after a while the patient said that there was something that he wanted to tell.

Ten years earlier there had been a religious awakening in the community in which he then lived; many came under conviction of sin and were converted to faith in Christ. He, too, was among the awakened; the Spirit of God convinced him of the true way to salvation and a new life. But he lacked the courage to act on his conviction. "But now I realize that I did the wrong thing, and since then I have had a deep sense of guilt, which has constantly tormented me."

In the talk which followed he unburdened himself of his gnawing feeling of suppressed regret, and it was established that his bodily pains had begun at the time of his spiritual refusal and had continued since. He was led to realize that he had consciously repressed his spiritual need and had left it unsatisfied.

Wholly spontaneously and voluntarily he now asked for spiritual guidance, which the chaplain, as a matter of course, gladly gave him, resulting in a full surrender to God on the man's part.

A very noticeable change took place in the patient's physical condition, something which his doctors also noted. After discussing the case with the chaplain the doctors concluded that the primary reason for the man's pains must have been the condition which had come to light under the chaplain's talks with the patient.

Such experiences in the cooperative work between physicians and clergyman do not occur merely in hospitals but also elsewhere, e.g. out in country communities.

A woman out in the country, about 40 years old, had gone into a psychotic stage. As it proved impossible to get her to a hospital, the local doctor ordered watchers over her, since she was very restive. By nature she was quiet and reserved, keeping her troubles to herself. She had many children. Her husband had become dissipated and had ceased to provide for his family. Wanting to shield him from neighborhood criticism, she had taken on extra jobs in order to keep want from the home. By working night and day she had managed to keep things going without outside assistance. She was a wholly exceptional type of person, self-sacrificing, intelligent, and psychically well equipped. But at last the burden proved too heavy; she had a nervous collapse which turned into a psychosis, marked by depression and melancholia. Early in her sad condition the doctor got in touch with the rector of the parish, and together they conferred about what should be done. When her restiveness subsided somewhat the rector began to call on her, and had many interviews with her.

These disclosed that she had during many years felt a deep religious need; she was, in other words, spiritually awakened, but had never arrived at assurance of peace with God. In her depressed state all these things pressed on [her] for a solution. And the soul care given her not only gave her a chance for unloading her troubled mind but also brought her rest and peace through the forgiveness of sins in Christ Jesus.

In a surprisingly short time her psychosis disappeared. She became a happy, liberated, confessing Christian, harmonious and poised in spirit. She went back to her household duties, an even more devoted mother than before. She was also able to adjust herself to her straitened circumstances because of her husband's failure as a provider, now accepting without embarrassment the outside aid which she badly needed. It was especially touching that she voluntarily began to take part in the work of the parish, offering her services to the Sunday school.

The many years of normal life since her breakdown show that her religious experience was genuine and dynamic.

I also wish to cite an incident told by a Danish physician, Dr. Ruth Poort, in a lecture which she gave in 1957 on the topic "Forgiveness of Sins, Responsibility, and Guilt":

> I once had a patient, a woman of about 30, who had become apathetic and paralytic after the death of her child in an accident of which the mother indirectly was the cause. Shock treatment had not helped her. Neither had the many attempts to explain away the tragic accident which well-meaning neighbors, relatives, and friends had tried to comfort her with: "You were not to blame" or "You know it was

an accident," etc. But no such attempts availed; she remained apathetic, and desperately unhappy.

At last I said to her, "Don't you want to see a pastor about the matter? For you *were* to blame, you know; you were the cause of your child's death. But there is such a thing as forgiveness, God's forgiveness. Do you believe in God? Do you have connections with the Church?"

She said she didn't know—she had, of course, been baptized and confirmed, but she had not been in the habit of attending church. But, on second thought, she would like to see a pastor.

And she did. A week later she left for home, well. Her guilt had been taken seriously.

A German pastor has told the following incident from his work among mental sufferers:

A young farmer lay in bed in catatonic rigidity. His stupor seemed to be increasing. His limbs did not move at all, not even his eyelids. Nourishment could be given him only through a gastric tube. Standing by his bedside one had the feeling of looking at a dead person, his reactions were *nil.* I stooped over him and said slowly: "Fear not, for I have redeemed you; I have called you by name, you are mine." (Isaiah 43:1) The attending nurse only laughed. After a few weeks the stupor began leaving him; he moved, and began to speak. To me he said, "That Bible passage came to me as a lifeline thrown to one about to drown. On account of the pessimistic remarks which I had heard while I lay helpless, I thought that I should be buried alive. But then came the word of God that he would not forsake me."

### *Conscientious Scruples*

A domestic scene—fireworks of passion—often consumes more "nerve energy" in a few moments than does steady work engaged in for a long time. The greatest wear is perhaps occasioned by conflicts not "made up." The making of a definite decision, grief, the death of one dearly beloved, are, very likely, less exhausting than some weeks fraught with suspense and dread. Sorrow produces sickness less often than supposed, at least not to the extent which conflicts, fear, and indecision do. (*Mental Hygiene,* 1937, p. 20)

Conflicts not settled may be cleared up through open discussion with subsequent settlement, and through counseling. It usually falls to the lot of a pastor to take part in such discussions in the varying everyday situations; and a hospital chaplain likewise, not only with patients in the psychiatric division but also in the medicinal [*sic*] and surgical sections.

A patient who had earlier been operated on for a stomach ailment complained that his "old" symptoms were reoccurring [*sic*]. After an examination by the surgeon in question, who found nothing indicating the necessity for renewed surgery, he was transferred to the division for internal medicine, but also there no organic trouble could be found. During these examinations he was called on by the chaplain, with whom a good contact was established, and to whom he disclosed that during the entire time that the annoying symptoms had been felt he had suffered under compunctions of conscience because of an unconfessed sexual experience which he knew was a breach of ethical conduct. A feeling of guilt of which he could not rid himself was constantly troubling him; no operation, no medical treatment could remove it.

But after he confessed and made up with the parties concerned, and received God's forgiveness for his sin, the painful symptoms disappeared, and he became a new man. A few days later he was dismissed from the hospital as a cured case.

### *Unconfessed Sins*

We have earlier *mentioned* private confession; here we want to *emphasize* its importance for psychic health, although the psychotherapeutic effects of confession are so commonly recognized that there may be need only of mentioning it. It is a well-known matter how the Roman Catholic confessional and also confession as practiced by other churches have helped millions of people.

On that account it is not necessary to give instances from everyday experience here. Besides, confession's obligation of secrecy and its intimate nature make such telling difficult. (As a matter of course nothing can *ever* be told without express permission of the penitent.) But one instance *can* be given, as it is told in the Bible. It is the classic story of the fall and restitution of King David. After his fall he lived through a period of bodily weakness and psychic distress, of which the Bible tells the following, using his own words: "When I declared not my sin, my body wasted away through my groaning all day long. For day and night thy hand was heavy upon me; my strength was dried up as by the heat of summer." (Ps. 32:3–4)

We are also told the cause of his organic and spiritual

distress. David had fallen victim to a temptation to have sexual intercourse with a married woman, Bathsheba, who became pregnant as a result. And when David learned of her condition he brought about the death of her husband.

Thus David had many sins on his conscience: adultery, unfaithfulness, murder, dishonesty. For a long time he covered up his guilt; that is expressed in his "When I declared not my sin." The Bible narrative makes it plain that he repressed his feeling of guilt (known technically as *regression*), that there was no open and conscious admission in him of the evil that he had done.

The prophet Nathan was sent to him to give him the soul care he was so badly in need of. The Bible has the following graphic account of what he [Nathan] told the king:

> "There were two men in a certain city, the one rich and the other poor. The rich man had very many flocks and herds; but the poor man had nothing but one little ewe lamb, which he had bought. And he brought it up, and it grew up with him and with his children; it used to eat of his morsel, and drink from his cup, and lie in his bosom, and it was like a daughter to him. Now there came a traveler to the rich man, and he was unwilling to take one of his own flock or herd to prepare for the wayfarer who had come to him. . . ." Then David's anger was greatly kindled against the man; and he said to Nathan, "As the Lord lives, the man who has done this deserves to die; and he shall restore the lamb fourfold, because he did this thing, and because he had no pity." (2 Sam. 12:1–6)

When David heard this story, aggression arose in him, but he projected his anger against someone else: "David's anger was greatly kindled *against the man*. . . ." Its inmost cause was the self-condemnation which he repressed.

"Nathan said to David, 'You are the man. . . . Why have you despised the word of the Lord, to do what is evil in his sight?' " The sword of the Word pierced David's heart, striking the sore spot; he admitted his sin. His aggressive condemnation was no longer turned against others, but against himself. "David said to Nathan, 'I have sinned against the Lord.' And Nathan said to David, 'The Lord also has put away your sin; you shall not die.' "

David himself tells about his confession, his admission of his guilt, and of the forgiveness which he received, in Psalms 51 and 32:

> Have mercy on me, O God, according to thy steadfast love; according to thy abundant mercy blot out my transgressions. Wash me thoroughly from my iniquity, and cleanse me from my sin! For I know my transgressions, and my sin is ever before me. Against thee, thee only, have I sinned, and done that which is evil in thy sight, so that thou art justified in thy sentence and blameless in thy judgment. (Ps. 51:1–4)

> Blessed is he whose transgression is forgiven, whose sin is covered. Blessed is the man to whom the Lord imputes no iniquity, and in whose spirit there is no deceit. When I declared not my sin, my body wasted away through my groaning all day long. For day and night thy hand was heavy upon me; my strength was dried up as by the heat of summer. I acknowledged my sin to thee, and I did not hide my iniquity: I said, "I will confess my transgressions to the Lord"; then thou didst forgive the guilt of my sin. (Ps. 32:1–5)

Deciding to go to confession is not easy for anyone, for inertia as well as conscious opposition within a person plays a part. Pride, self-defense, and fear of men mobilize both reluctance and dislike for exposing one's inner self. And even if we suspect that which we most desire to keep secret is the very thing we ought to confess, yet we often keep silent.

It is useless to force oneself to go to confession. Private confession is, indeed, a private matter; but as such it ought to appeal to our sense of responsibility. For, in the last analysis, we ourselves determine whether we are to obtain the needed help in confession. But that should not prevent us from assisting others by offering them an opportunity to be helped through this means.

In the matter of the opportune time for confession the individual's spiritual and psychic preparedness will, of course, play a part. A boil is opened when ripe for incision.

Often it may take considerable time before confession is made. We have known persons who have been patients in a hospital several times before they have themselves recognized and then disclosed the real cause of their ailment. And more than once we have been approached for soul care counsel only after the patient's dismissal from the hospital, which *then* led to private confession. For a deep regression of sin and guilt creates a deep resistance. Many patients seem to prefer long periods of expensive and often painful treatments to confessing their sin, and they always ask for something that may remove their annoying symptoms, e.g., medication or shock treatments.

But the feeling of guilt which is conditioned on unconfessed sin cannot be removed in that way. Such procedure may be likened to attempts at healing cancer by inducing hypnosis, or removing an abscess by means of a hypodermic injection of morphine. Our guilt over against God can be blotted out only through the declaration of the forgiveness of sins in the name of Jesus Christ.

In confession we meet problems from all walks and conditions of life. Very frequently they relate to sexual life, to love relationships, or to marital conditions. The difficulties may concern untruthfulness, unconciliatory attitude, bitterness, hatred, feeling of guilt because of masturbation, homosexuality, *abortus provocatus* [criminal abortion], prevention of conception, sterilization, etc.

The object of the confessor must not be to rationalize, explain away, or excuse the guilt confessed by the penitent. Nor should he treat as a trifle matters which the one making confession is convinced are sinful. His task is to listen attentively and sympathetically, and his most important commission is to absolve, i.e., to declare the forgiveness of sins.

Even a so-called peccadillo may be enough to fetter the conscience and to rob one of boldness and joy, as well as to drain one's psychic energy. I have seen some instances of what is often considered a trifle (for instance, masturbation) [that], if unconfessed, may rob a person of assurance of salvation for years. Many have said during confession, "This is the first time in my life that I have talked of these things to somebody else." After confession they have become, as it were, new men. The pressure of fear had been released; they were relieved of their burden, and became happy, secure, satisfied, and free men and women.

### *Healing in Answer to Prayer*

This important and timely question (often in English termed faith healing) we have not space in this presentation to discuss fully; but in this connection I want to call attention to the mighty forces of healing with which the prayer of faith connects us, something of which both the Bible and experience testify. Viewing the matter from the point of view of the help here made possible for sufferers, the Church should recognize the great responsibility resting on it in this connection. We have often neglected and failed sick folk by not making use of the tremendous possibilities given us through healing by means of prayer. Many suffering people would have received help if we had utilized the fountains of power laid down in prayer.

Often I have had the pleasure of noting a positive interest in this matter among physicians. I do not readily forget an experience I had along this line some years ago.

A patient at one of our larger hospitals had her ailment diagnosed as an inoperable tumor of the brain, and she was about to be dismissed, as nothing could be done for her at the hospital. But before dismissal she expressed the desire that she be prayed for in accordance with James 5:14. I was sent for, and upon my arrival she told me that she had communicated with her doctor about her desire, as she did not want to have it done without his knowledge. The doctor said that he had no objections to make; on the contrary, he had often wondered, he said, that such procedure was so rarely followed. "If you Christians," he said, "believe in the power of prayer, why do you not practice it more often than you do? I don't understand why." This expression by a physician has often been recalled by me and has been a challenge to me.

The story of the woman has a continuation. Several years afterward, while I was on a lecture tour, a lady who knew the former patient approached me after I was through speaking one evening, and she said that the patient not only was still living but also had apparently been feeling fine since being prayed for.

### *Strength To Bear Suffering*

There are many who do not get rid of their sickness and suffering but must endure them the rest of their lives. No one gets by the problem of suffering. It is well known that continued suffering may tempt one to become discouraged, more or less resigned, and bitter. In this situation soul care may be a real help to bring about release, new courage, hope, joy, peace—in brief, to act as a liberating power. Paul did not find it an easy experience with his "thorn in the flesh" (whether this was an organic disease or some other suffering). For this thing he besought the Lord thrice that it might depart from him. His prayer was answered in this wise that he was to keep his infirmity, but, too, that he was to experience the grace of God as a new power in the midst of it. Thus Paul was helped to accept his weakness, not in a spirit of depression and drab resignation but in faith and renewed hope. From that time forth his weakness ceased to be a hindrance in his spiritual life and in his service, and it was transformed into a channel through which the power of God flowed into his life. "My grace is sufficient for you, for my power is made perfect in weakness." He accepted his suffering, thus gaining boldness to say: "I will all the more gladly boast of my weaknesses, that the power of Christ may rest upon me." (2 Cor. 12:9)

There are sick folk who have not in themselves the power to get into contact with the healing and saving forces. There *we* must bring them to the Master (Matt. 9:2), as the suffering often limits the individual's personal sense of responsibility. There are sick and suffering persons who can be held responsible neither for what they do nor for what they omit doing. But that fact does not relieve *us* of responsibility on their behalf; on the contrary, it increases it. We have the responsibility for their getting the help needed, physically, spiritually. It is indeed the mission of soul care to bring this about. "Bear one another's burdens, and so fulfill the law of Christ." (Gal. 6:2)

# 21

# Integrity Therapy

*John W. Drakeford*

EDITOR'S NOTE: Since the last two chapters of Part 5 deal with a particular method of treatment, a concise outline of the approach is presented in this chapter. Integrity Therapy as a method has been developed by O. Hobart Mowrer over the past ten years or so. His two paperback books popularized both his theory and his method (*The Crisis in Psychiatry and Religion,* 1961, and *The New Group Therapy,* 1964, both published by D. Van Nostrand Co., Inc., Princeton, N.J.). Because of the theoretical ramifications and practical steps involved, there was a demand for a shorter form similar to the succinct "Twelve Steps" of Alcoholics Anonymous.

Professor John Drakeford was a suitable person to frame this outline since he spent a sabbatical year with Professor Mowrer in the Psychology Department at the University of Illinois as part of a five-year research program which began in 1961. Integrity Therapy had already been practiced for several years before this outline took shape. For simplicity's sake it is presented here in its original form without elaboration.

D. B.

JOHN W. DRAKEFORD, Ph.D., is Professor of Psychology and Counseling, Southwestern Baptist Theological Seminary, Fort Worth, Texas.

## BASIC PRINCIPLES

1. Integrity Therapy rejects all deterministic theories which make man a victim of heredity or environment. Every individual is responsible for his own life and exercises his right by making his own decisions.
2. Each individual has a conscience, or value system. When he violates his conscience, he becomes guilty, a condition which is not sickness but a result of his wrongdoing and irresponsibility.
3. A common reaction to personal wrongdoing is to cover up and deny its existence. In this secrecy, guilt gives rise to symptoms which may be so severe as to upset life's balance.
4. As secrecy causes man trouble and separates him from his fellows, so openness with "significant others" is the road back to normality.
5. Openness takes place with increasing numbers of "significant others" and progresses in ever widening circles as the individual learns to live authentically with his fellows.
6. By itself, however, openness is not enough. The guilty individual is under an obligation to make restitution or penance appropriate to the acknowledged failure in his life.
7. The only way to become a whole person is not only to remain open and make restitution but also to feel a responsibility to carry the "Good News" to others.

## CONSCIENCE

1. Man is an "evaluating animal" and characteristically has a conscience or value system.
2. Conscience may be defined as "the internalized voice" of society.
3. Although, ideally, conscience speaks as a "still, small voice," it can be ignored and apparently silenced.
4. Symptoms have been called "the amplified and distorted voice of conscience." They are the muted protests of conscience, after it has been "silenced," as it speaks through our body, emotions, sensations, and behavior.
5. Integrity Therapy rejects all ideas of an oversevere conscience. Conscience, even when it is "angry" with us, is our friend, not an enemy.

### CONFESSION

1. Because it is easy but self-defeating to put on a front and not acknowledge who one is, it is necessary to drop all pretences. This is best done by confession.

2. While confession may be initially made to just one person, it should then move out in ever widening circles of personal transparency and sincerity.

3. Confession is not made indiscriminately but to "significant others"—or to persons who may in this way be helped.

4. Complaining or blaming others for our troubles is not confession.

5. We have no right to "confess" other people's shortcomings but should concentrate on our own.

6. Boasting about our virtues is not confession—which should focus on our weaknesses rather than our strengths.

7. Confession is an indication that we are willing to come under the judgment of our fellows.

### MUTUAL RESPONSIBILITY

1. While there is value in a troubled person seeking help in Integrity Therapy, a way is provided for the therapist to take the initiative.

2. As early as possible in the interview, the therapist "opens his life" to the troubled person.

3. Only after his own gesture of trust does the therapist look for a deeply honest response from the subject.

4. The developing situation is not a one-way relationship of counselor to counselee, or counselee to counselor, but a shared dialogue between the two.

### GROUP RELATIONSHIPS

1. A man's attitude of secrecy about his conduct not only affects him personally but also beclouds his relationships with his fellows.

2. Individual responsibility and the sharing of experiences should be in balance: neither complete dependence nor complete independence.

3. Respect for society's rules is the basis of healthy liv-

ing, and the damaging result of lack of consideration is seen in the sociopath and delinquent.

4. The therapeutic group is a microcosm, "a little world" within which the deviant personality is both rebuked and supported along the pathway to maturity.

## ACTION

1. While some therapies focus on the intellectual and others on the emotional aspects of life, Integrity Therapy is concerned with purposeful activity and effort.

2. Confession may bring temporary relief from symptoms, but it is only a first step which should lead on to changed behavior.

3. A work of penance or restitution must be undertaken if the effects of wrongdoing and guilt are to be counteracted.

4. Although it is sometimes easier to straighten things out with God than it is with man, willingness to do something about our relationship with man is frequently an evidence of a right relationship with God.

5. Do not wait to take redemptive action until you "feel like it." Good feeling comes *after* good action. Effort comes *before* comfort.

6. An experience of benefit from Integrity Therapy brings with it a responsibility to carry the message to others.

## WHAT THE BIBLE SAYS

1. *Failure.* "If we say we have no sin, we deceive ourselves." (I John 1:8)

2. *Accountability.* "Every one of us shall give an account of himself." (Romans 14:12)

3. *Conscience.* "The law written in their hearts, their conscience." (Romans 2:15)

4. *Covering up.* "When I kept silence my bones waxed old." (Psalm 32:3)

5. *Confession.* "He that covereth his sins shall not prosper: but whoso confesseth and forsaketh them shall have mercy." (Proverbs 28:13)

6. *The group.* "Confess your faults one to another." (James 5:16)

7. *Restitution.* "If I have taken anything from any man by false accusation, I restore unto him fourfold." (Luke 19:8)

8. *Telling others.* "Go home to thy friends and tell them how great things the Lord hath done for thee." (Mark 5:19)

22

# The Neurosis, "Confession," and Recovery of a Protestant Minister

*O. Hobart Mowrer*

THERE IS a widespread and tragic anomaly in Protestant Christendom: the minister who from the pulpit proclaims, week after week, the doctrine of Christ's redeeming death upon the Cross and God's free and unconditional pardon of sinners but who, himself, is wracked with unresolved personal guilt. Is it any wonder that when others consult such a minister concerning their own distress of soul, he often *refers* them either to a secular healer or "directly" to God? If the minister is to help other people deal with their guilt, he ought first to deal with his own guilt in an open and creative manner. To paraphrase the words of the First Letter of

O. HOBART MOWRER, Ph.D., is Research Professor of Psychology, University of Illinois, Urbana, Illinois.

John: "For he who is not open with his brother whom he has seen cannot be open with God, whom he has not seen." The young minister who wrote the following paper discovered that the "grace of God" was not a substitute for authentic relationship with one's fellowmen; rather, when he tried to use the "grace of God" as a substitute for confession and restitution on the "horizontal," human level, it became for him the "judgment of God."

In both the Old and New Testaments there is repeated admonition to "uncover" our sins to one another. During the early history of the Church, both confession and penance were carried out in an essentially public manner. Even in post-Reformation theological circles there is ample precedent, as Belgum[1] has recently demonstrated, for mutual confession for the relief of conscience. Yet Protestantism, in practice, has stressed the *vertical* rather than the horizontal dimension as a means of grace. One would think that the Church would be a place where people could confront one another openly and honestly, since the Church historically has made no pretense about man's condition and his need for redemption. But all too often the Church is today a place where people hide behind Biblicism and dogma and theology and liturgy. Does the Church really want to be taken seriously when it speaks of itself as a "company of sinners"? The Church has the resources to offer a healing corrective to the increasing breakdown of authentic community in our automated society. But it cannot be truly redemptive as long as it uses the doctrine of grace as a substitute for genuine encounter among its members, and between its members and the rest of society.

In the illuminating account which follows, we see this paradoxical situation reach crisis proportions in one young clergyman's life. We also see it successfully resolved in a way which will perhaps please neither the professional theologian *nor* the psychologist or psychiatrist, but which, I believe, is "an ever-present help" to all mankind. This man finds that powerfully redemptive resources were within his reach all the time but that his theological "sophistication" had blinded him to them. I have known many similar instances, but this is the first one in which the individual has

[1] David Belgum, *Guilt: Where Religion and Psychology Meet,* Englewood Cliffs, N.J.: Prentice-Hall, Inc., 1963.

recorded his experiences, graphically and candidly, and been willing to have his account reproduced.

At what point does a person begin to suspect that there is something wrong with him? I rather imagine he knows it all the time and that is why he works so hard to deny it or to prove it isn't so. I believe that the neurotic person is over-sensitive to the approval of others; and even when he denies this—that is, when he says "I don't care what people think about me," it is usually because his ego has been deflated in a recent experience. So the point at which one begins to suspect there is something wrong with him is the point at which he is no longer able to play the game of getting the approval from others which he cannot give himself because of a tormented conscience.

About a year after my graduation from theological seminary, I had an experience which indicated that the game was near the finish. I had just been through a very busy week, and after taking a church visitor from India to a nearby town so he could continue his speaking engagements, I returned home to discover that my wife had made an appointment for me to counsel with a couple who were about to be married. The woman was already a member of our church, but the man wanted to join the church as a part of his preparation for marriage. I felt very ill-at-ease with them in my study; and as I began to read the membership vows to the young man, I grew breathless, flushed, and terribly embarrassed. "What will they think?" I asked myself, and I knew that I had to get myself out of this situation in a way that would save ego. "I feel sick," I said; and with deep sympathy for the over-worked pastor, they left my office. I went to our bedroom and asked my wife to call the doctor. He gave me some tranquilizers along with a lecture on the need for relaxing, and I took it all in stride promising that I would pace myself more evenly in the future. My feelings were ambiguous: I felt a sense of pride at being able to "come out of it" so quickly; but that awful tormented feeling that the problem wasn't really solved, but only tranquilized, just wouldn't go away. Soon after this happened I did write my superintendent and tell him that I had been having some emotional troubles and asked if we could get together. We did, and without mentioning my experience with the young couple, I admitted I was afraid of leading groups and wondered if there was something wrong with me. He told me that the reason I was afraid of groups was because I was afraid of revealing my inadequacies, and he suggested both humility and prayer. How much better his counsel would have been if he had helped me to deal with my anger and guilt!

The point of no-return came about two years later. A young and attractive married woman in my congregation had become more and more dependent on my relationship with her as a pastor. During the months preceding this experience, she had come to our parsonage on frequent occasions to check on incidental things, and she had called me over to her house on other occasions to give her counsel. I had sexual fantasies about her, and would sometimes envision certain possibilities as I masturbated. On this particular occasion she called me over to her home to soothe her troubled conscience because she was being criticized by some of the church school teachers for her antagonistic attitude toward the work they were doing. I tried to play both ends against the middle, letting her feel that the anger she had released against some of the members of the church was justified, but trying at the same time to keep her from simply ripping things apart. Well, this didn't help her, and it gave me an awful feeling of helplessness. As I started to leave she looked terribly downcast and I was drawn to her sexually. I put my arm around her and said, "We love you"; and I tried to kiss her. She drew away from me in fright. I told her, "I'm sorry I did that"; and she replied, "That's all right," I left her house feeling as if the world had caved in.

I lived the next month in dread, for I carried this little secret all by myself. The question that tormented me was: "Has she told anybody?" I made every effort to avoid her, although she continued to be active in the church. About a month after the experience, this woman's husband came to my study and asked me if I had made a pass at his wife. I said I had not, although I admitted I had put my arm around her shoulders. I wanted to talk with him at greater length about the experience, but he would have none of it and stamped out of the door with a feeling of righteous indignation. My wife asked me about my visitor, for she suspected something was wrong, and I told her part of the story without revealing my deep sense of wrong and guilt. Whatever chances I had had for redemption up to this point I had muffed every time, and the game was drawing nearer and nearer the finish.

Within the coming weeks I could no longer conceal what I had done; the body has a way of registering what the voice will not reveal. The first anxiety attack came as I introduced myself to a new minister in town: the same breathlessness and flushed feeling as I had had two years before—but this time I knew only too well why pills and relaxation would not solve my problem. Here I stood, trying to talk with this minister as members of my church filed out the door, and wondering if they were looking at me—if they knew—if possibly I could hide awhile longer. I went home and felt sick, terribly sick through and through, as if I wanted to vomit some awful pain which was in the pit of my very existence.

The next anxiety attack came when I was reading Scripture before a group of fellow ministers. My heart began to beat very fast, I couldn't get my breath, and I had to stop for periods of time before I could go on. Reading the Holy Scripture in front of my brethren was more than my temple of God could endure. I felt sure, when I finally finished, that some minister would look at me and say, "What is wrong? Can we help you?" But no one said a thing. Instead, the group went on talking about "theology" in general and St. Paul's theme of "joy through suffering" in particular. I had asked for help, at least the uncontrollable part of me which would not let me rest from my guilt had, but no one responded.

Continuing anxiety attacks forced me to close even the few doors that had been left open for expression and relationship. I quit attending meetings of various community organizations. I cut the organizational life of our church down to a skeleton so that I did not have to attend more than one or two meetings a week, and I got out of these when I could. I had my wife make telephone calls for me and when I had to talk on the telephone, the receiver shook in my hand. Greeting someone at the door was like a nightmare. I never knew when I would have another attack, and I had to make sure that every chance for an attack was circumvented whenever possible.

But at the same time that I was closing these doors between me and the outer world, I was also searching for help. This is the most difficult part of my experience to describe. The more I closed off the outer world, the more I had to order the little world I had left; so I would spend enormous amounts of time each day getting my desk in order, making sure no one had tampered with my papers or notes, looking under the desk to make sure I had not dropped something, and checking in the wastepaper baskets to be certain I had not accidentally thrown away the wrong thing. Sometimes I would go through this procedure several times. Then, when everything was checked and found to be in order, I would pace up and down the floor of my study smoking cigarettes. I still preached on Sunday; but since I could no longer write a sermon, I had either to use old sermons or borrow from a book. This was sheer torture for me since I have usually been a fairly creative person. The Christian symbols became meaningless to me during this time. I began to go into a depression which was far more serious than I permitted myself to believe at the time. At the deepest point of this depression I still held on to my faith in one aspect: that is, I knew that God was working in me for good. But I did not know if the good within me was going to win. I did know that the constructive and destructive forces of life were waging a terrible battle.

During this period I tried to find "help," although I was not willing to tell anyone straight-out what I had done. First I went to a superior in my denomination and told him I was afraid of people. He told me that he was also somewhat afraid of people, and that part of the reason for my fear was my great sensitivity. He wasn't of much assistance. I went to another minister and told him that I had been accused of making a pass at a woman. He told me that this kind of accusation is one of the dangers of the ministry, and that he had been kicked out of a church after being accused of adultery. Neither was he very helpful, and I wonder to this day who needed confession more—he or I? One morning after I had reached the point of near-naked despair, I told my wife I *had* to find help; and after kissing her goodby, I started on a 150-mile trip to visit a minister who had done considerable work in the field of pastoral counseling. Fortunately this busy pastor had time for me and agreed to counsel me on a regular basis. He was kind and accepting, but two days after my session with him I experienced my most severe anxiety attack.

The anxiety attack came upon me while I was reading a prayer at the beginning of a funeral service. As I started to read the prayer I thought to myself: "What would happen if I had an attack here and now?" No sooner had the thought crossed my mind than I began to tighten up, my heart began to beat at what seemed a frightful pace, and I had to force my breath much as one might try to force open a door which is locked from the other side. How I ever managed to get through that prayer I don't know, but I finally added the amen and wondered whether to run or throw myself in the arms of someone or become non-existent. The manager of the funeral home came into the room where I was and asked if the public-address system was turned on. I looked at the casket which was within two yards of the lectern, and decided I had to go through with this thing for the sake of the family even if I had another attack. "What was wrong?" they asked me afterward. I replied that I felt sick, and indeed I did. When I went home that afternoon, I knew that the game was up. I spent a day and a half in bed, and then I made a trip to confer with a seminary professor and friend. I wanted him to put me in contact with a psychiatrist, which he could easily have done; but instead he simply told me, in a kind and gentle way, that the church had finally caught on to me. How right he was, but how much more help he could have been if he had not added: "Of course, your personal integrity is without question."

So the only source of help I had at this point was the minister in a church 150 miles away. I continued to make weekly trips to counsel with him. I told him about my problem of masturbation, which had started in early adolescence and continued, with lessening frequency, throughout my married life. I told him most of the truth about the experience with the woman in my parish, although I never got to the point of accepting responsibility for my relationship with her. I began to tell him about my dreams, and his dream interpretation was most helpful. I remember one dream which seemed to represent movement toward more responsible behavior:

> *There was a gathering of the congregation in the basement of the church. All of the people were drinking malts, sodas, etc., and enjoying themselves. But the dishes were piling up, and nobody took time to wash them. We were running out of dishes, and I knew somebody had to dig in and start washing them. I finally took the initiative and told some others that I would start the project if they would help me. Soon I was fast at work, elbows in the water, washing the dirty dishes.*

The "dirty dishes" pile up when we travel the road of self-indulgence without any sense of responsibility for others. I was moving toward something better in my life, but I had not yet taken a decisive step toward personal responsibility. I could not yet understand, or didn't want to understand, that I was really an angry person instead of much abused, as I preferred to think.

After five sessions with this minister, I made a trip to New York and committed another act of injustice against myself and society. Once before I had gone into one of those night-club spots where for $1.00 you can buy a glass of beer and watch the girls take it off, and for $10.00 you can buy a woman a drink and take some of it off yourself. Once again I told myself that I needed to be more human and allow myself a little pleasure. After some 40 minutes of watching and feeling, I left the place, thankful that I still had my coat and pocketbook—and wondering, as I had wondered so often during the preceding months, where I had left my self-respect and why I didn't feel soothed. After this happened I had one more session with the minister; and then, while he was on a vacation, I saw a member of the professional staff at a mental-health clinic. I shall refer to this man hereafter as Mr. Jones.

Mr. Jones talked about things which seemed strange to me: my responsibility toward people in my parish, *my* anger and *my* guilt. He used my dreams to show me how I felt guilty about the things I had done and how I really desired warm relationship with people, with God, and with life. His interpretation of the following dream helped me to realize that God, as the source of warmth and goodness, will indeed accept us if we try to do well.

> *My brother and I were engaged in a contest. We were to wash the walls of a room as quickly and efficiently as possible, and the judge would decide which one of us did the better job. We both began, but as I worked I realized that there was a large group of people gathered around my brother cheering him on while I was all alone. I wondered if it were worthwhile, if I should even try to win the contest, but I decided I would go ahead and do my best. When the time was up the judge turned to my brother and said, "You had a lot of people cheering for you, but that isn't the most important thing. The most important thing is the kind of job you do, and therefore I pronounce this man [he turned to me] the winner."*

Another dream helped me to realize that I did feel guilty about my relationship with my father.

> *Father had given a man some help, and the man was telling others what a fine man my father was. I was walking in the business area of my hometown with my father, and people were talking about what a grand person he was. I noticed that I had not shaven, and I stopped in at a drug store to take care of this detail. Then I also noticed that I had forgotten to brush my teeth and comb my hair. On our way over to another drug store, a man stopped to tell us what a fine person Father was. After I came out of the drug store alone, the same man stopped me and told me what a son-of-a-bitch my father was.*

In the first dream about my brother, I was able to realize that God is just; he does reward us in relation to what we do, even if it is for the cleansing of our own sin, and he does not compare us unjustly with our brother. This is the whole story of Cain and Abel, isn't it? "If you do well, will you not be accepted? And if you do not do well, sin is crouching at the door; its desire is for you, but you master it" (Genesis 4:7). The dream betrays the fact that I have had trouble with my brother, who is indeed surrounded by the approval of the crowd. But at long last I do not have to live my life in reaction to him. My brother has his reward; whether that reward of outward approval is sufficient for his life only time can tell. I can no longer hate him for what he is doing, not even for the acts of wrong he has committed against me. The judge of life has been just to me; and in that justice and approval I have found the courage to reach out to my brother and correct the estranged relationship we have had with each other during the past few years. The second dream reveals the ambiguous attitude I have toward my father: I feel guilty in the presence of his warmth and integrity, but I also hate him—partly because I cannot measure up and partly because of his own pretentiousness. Father is a very aggressive and authoritarian type of person, but he also has a real concern for other people and is highly respected by his community. I was an unwanted child; in fact, my maternal grandmother tried to get my mother to have an abortion when she was pregnant with me. My parents already had one boy, and that was all they wanted or felt they could afford. So my mother felt guilty about me, and this guilt caused a cleavage between her and my father. My mother would get angry and ask my father to punish me, but before he could lay a hand on me she would become afraid and withdraw her request. Every time this happened I became more dependent on Mother and more afraid of Father, and in the process Father became more aggressive in his attitude toward me.

The crucial point in my relationship with Mr. Jones came the week he handed me a paper by O. H. Mowrer entitled "You *Are* Your Secrets." Mr. Jones had been disgusted with me on several occasions because he knew I wasn't coming through with the "real stuff." He had made various statements which were calculated to open me up: i.e., "We aren't getting anywhere. . . . You can handle this yourself now. . . . Maybe next week should be our last session." We had only one session left on the day he handed me this paper, since my minister friend was returning from his vacation and would again take over. After reading Dr. Mowrer's paper, and realizing that it was a beautiful analysis of my own situation, I became tormented toward the truth. In our last session I came through with what was really bothering me.

What was it? A whole lifetime of kidding myself, a whole lifetime of fakery and hypocrisy, a whole lifetime of self-indulgence and sin. My brother and I had engaged in mutual masturbation during three years of my adolescence. I continued with this form of self-indulgence by myself during the years preceding marriage, and took it up again shortly after marriage. During my seminary years I added the extra guilt of reading pornographic literature and buying nude pictures, all in the name of soothing my anxiety. I would isolate myself in my room, and after sufficient visual stimulation and fantasy would masturbate. Then I would take a shower and ask God to forgive me, promising Him that I would never do it again. Sick all over, from head to toe, with a terribly numb feeling except for the shaking which would not go away—that is how I felt, but still I did it again. And that is how I would describe my period of depression: a terribly numb feeling except for the shaking which would not go away. So you see the anxiety attacks were really the power of God's love which would not *permit* me to continue leading a life of destruction.

All of this came out in my last session with Mr. Jones. To be sure, there were still plenty of excuses offered: i.e., I had been abused as a boy, my brother had been given preference, etc. But the truth was out, someone knew my secret, and now I could begin to live, at least in part, an authentic life. As soon as I read Dr. Mowrer's paper I began to share some of my personal history with my wife, and as I did this I began to feel a surge of warmth and love and goodness. That week I took the children out to a lake where we met an older friend. The children wanted to return to town in the other man's car, and I gave them permission. I remember watching them walk with him by the side of the lake as they journeyed toward his car. The last rays of the day's sun cast their light of love upon this man and my children running by his side. A great flood of love and warmth came over me and I wanted to cry. The feelings I had denied so long, the feelings about Father and children and people and life and God, had begun to emerge; and the love which had been shut in for so long wanted to cry, for it was not accustomed to the light.

The following September we (Mr. Jones and I) gathered together a small group of ministers who were interested in looking at their own lives; and we still meet regularly to share our experiences and help move each other toward the truth. I am glad to have had the help of this group at such a crucial time in life; and as I have shared my experiences with them, the feelings of love and warmth within me have been able to find expression in more wholesome and productive ways. One of the most important insights I have gained from the group is the great extent to which I love my brother, who on various occasions has hurt me so deeply. After expressing great anger and hostility against one of the members of the group, who represented my brother to me, I began to feel that I could not really live without my brother. That was a painful thing to recognize, since he seemed to be doing so well without me. But then I realized that surely he needs me as much as I need him, that the approval of his brother is probably more important than the approval of the crowd which surrounds him. I realized that part of my anger was due to the fact that I had not really decided against the kind of relationship we had had with each other as teen-age boys, and that I was partly angry because he would not satisfy me in my distorted need for self-indulgence. Once I was able to accept the fact, at least consciously, that I no longer wanted this kind of relationship and that I didn't need to fear his aggression against me as long as I was sure of myself, I was also able to accept the fact that I wanted reconciliation with him. With great love and patience I wrote to him, and his reply was evidence that he also felt an emptiness and that the great success which he now enjoys is not at all sufficient for him.

The relationship between my wife and me grows deeper every day. I wish I could tell you in more detail what has happened to us during the past year, but just let me say that my wife and I have been recipients of a responsibility which to most people seems overwhelming. There are no hours left in our day for self-indulgence of any kind. People say to me, "I don't see how your wife always manages to look so happy and attractive." We know the secret, for we have found strength in complete openness with one another. Do we also get strength from our religion? Indeed we do, for it is our obedience to Christ which enables us to accept each other as sinners, to find reconciliation in front of the cross which judges every man, and to be open to that love which is more than we are.

You see, we are in reality one human family. Sometimes life is pretty hard on us, and sometimes we are torn by forces we do not understand. But along the road of life there are areas in which we can choose to be responsible or irresponsible, where we can choose sin or integrity. No child of God is hurt nearly as much by the forces which pound his life—physical abuse or insensitive parents or rape or social rejection—as he is by the wrong choices he makes. The amazing thing isn't so much what has been done to us to hurt our feelings or hinder our growth as it is what we can do for others when we are willing to take the yoke of responsibility upon our own shoulders. When this happens and we become open to feelings we have denied in our self-centeredness, the whole world becomes open to us. We cannot always make restitution to those we have hurt, but restitution is always possible, for the world is full of brothers and sisters who need us as much as we need them.

*There is only one man in the world,*
*and his name is all men.*

*There is only one woman in the world,*
*and her name is all women.*

*There is only one child in the world,*
*and the child's name is all children.*

The foregoing account speaks eloquently for itself and needs little by way of interpretation. Here I wish merely to underscore certain considerations which are implied or exemplified but not, perhaps, made fully explicit.

1. One is struck again and again in this statement by the

extent to which the author—let us call him the Reverend Mr. Clark—sought and failed to find resources within his own profession. He had long preached and prayed in the conventional manner, and he had counseled with several fellow clergymen; but his isolation and despair only grew. Here we have, so to say, an "inside look" at a cross-section of America's ministers. Insecurity, doubt, and ineffectiveness, in the domain of the sick soul, prevail; and sensing this inner weakness, religious laymen have turned increasingly to secular healers, as have many ministers and seminary professors themselves, only to find, again, impotence behind a facade of pretention. *This* is the "crisis" alluded to in *The Crisis in Psychiatry and Religion.*[2] Fortunately, as the foregoing account indicates, there *is* a balm in Gilead, one which can be found in a formally religious or in a secular context. But it is *not* something that can be "dispensed," either from the pulpit or by a "doctor"; it has to be actively sought and laid hold of by the suffering, alienated person himself.

2. Mr. Clark is not, of course, the first minister who has used the rationalization that he needed to "relax" and be a little more "human" or that certain forms of illicit pleasure would be therapeutic in the sense of "soothing" his anxiety. In fact, it has become a sort of vogue, on the part of some ministers, to belittle what they call "moralism." I know a minister for whom this took the form of feeling that it would be good for him to smoke and drink a little, on the sly, just so he would not get to thinking of himself as "too good." It has been my observation, which is well borne out in the foregoing account, that when we lay our souls bare to other human beings, it usually turns out that we are quite "human" enough and have no need to deliberately add to our existing record of deviant actions.

3. Mr. Clark speaks of his "anger and guilt." I am certain that he experienced a great deal of both of these emotions, but what needs to be emphasized is that the guilt was probably far more basic than the anger. Naturally we are irritated, annoyed, angered when, as a result of persistent irresponsibility, conscience begins to "make life miserable" for us. And since it is so hard to "get back" at conscience,

[2] O. H. Mowrer, *The Crisis in Psychiatry and Religion,* Princeton, N.J.: D. Van Nostrand Co., Inc., 1961.

there is a powerful tendency to "project" our anger in quite diverse ways. But I have yet to see a man's or woman's neurotic wrath fail to melt away and turn into a far gentler sadness and remorse when there is an honest and contrite acknowledgment of wrongdoing. It is typical that Mr. Clark also recovered the capacity to love and be joyous when he dealt, courageously and radically, with his guilt.

4. In some quarters it may be held that Mr. Clark has not found salvation at all but has, in point of fact, invited his own more serious damnation by committing the "sin of pride"—that is, the sin of thinking that he himself has been able to do something about his condition. The prevalent notion that we are unable to help ourselves is surely a kind of modern heresy. It is true that we cannot find salvation *alone,* for it is available only in renewed communion and fellowship; but *we* alone can take the necessary steps to move from isolation and duplicity into openness. Jesus said: "If ye have *done* it unto one of the least of these, my brethren, ye have done it unto me." He also rebuked those who said, "Lord, Lord," but did not keep his commandments. And other New Testament writers urge us to be *doers,* rather than mere *hearers,* of the Word. The abuse that is today often heaped upon what is known as religious "activism" is surely more a latter-day creation than anything that is indigenous to either Judaism or Christianity.

5. The word "confession," as it appears in the title of this chapter, is put in quotation marks to indicate that Mr. Clark's recovery did not hinge upon "confession" in the usual sense of the term. He did not go to any one person, furtively admit his sins, and then ask for forgiveness or absolution. Instead, he began to "confess" in the sense of talking honestly with his wife and a few close friends and has since gradually extended his sphere of openness. Also he has been able to embark upon a program of restitution and renewed responsibility. Surely one of the weaknesses, from a psychological standpoint, of both *private* confession, in a religious context, and *private* psychiatric treatment is that they do not alleviate our fears of being "found out" or "known" *by others.* And until one has "worked through" and resolved his guilt in the face of all mankind, he is not fully healed and whole. (I do not mean to say, of course, that the

erstwhile sinner has to "tell everyone." *Everyone* is not all that interested in him! But he should, for his own peace of mind and redemption, carry his openness to the point that he does not *care* who knows what about him. And if, by sharing the story of his life with a stranger, he can *help* that person, he should be able and willing to do so.

6. Finally, a word about the rapidity with which Mr. Clark recovered, once he saw and seized the opportunities which had been before him all the time. I do not have an exact record of dates, but it is evident that the period of most active movement and change occupied only a few weeks, perhaps only days. The notion that "psychotherapy" necessarily takes a long time—months or even years—has been widely disseminated, and it is hard for many laymen (and professionals, too!) to conceive of personal "transformations" occurring relatively suddenly. If a person insists upon a *private* restoration, it will indeed take a long time, a *very* long time. In fact, it is doubtful that recovery without loss of "privacy" is *ever* possible. But if one is willing to be more radical, if one is willing to risk his very life, his old, unsatisfactory life, and to receive in return a new and more abundant life, then "miracles" can still occur. The pity is that so few people today have the "faith" that makes such miraculous healing possible.

**ADDENDUM**

While this chapter was still in typescript, I presented it at a meeting of the "ladies auxiliary" of a large and fashionable Protestant church. I had been invited to speak on the general topic of personal responsibility and mental health and decided that this paper would be more graphic and interesting than a more formal and abstract discussion. An unusually large group put in an appearance, and there was evidently good attention and interest throughout the presentation. However, afterwards I noticed a somewhat ominous "hush" over the group; and as I presently walked to my parked automobile, I found little clusters of women busily talking at various points on the church grounds and near their cars. There was such a group near by own automobile; and as I approached, one of the members of this group said: "We were just discussing what you said. I hope most of the group weren't too stunned by the first few pages of your paper to hear the rest of it." "Stunned?" I said. "Yes," came the reply. "Most of those women probably had never heard masturbation discussed in public the way you discussed it. They *were* stunned!"

We talked on for a few minutes and then went our respective ways. I dare say a good deal of self-righteous indignation *was* expressed in those little conversational groups that day; but it would be much more interesting to know what the *inner* thoughts and feelings of those women were. Masturbation indeed! Most of them were the mothers of growing children, some even grandmothers, and virtually all of them have had to deal with childish sex play of one kind or another. Many have had adolescent sons or daughters and have shared or *should* have shared in the conflicts of this period. Unresolved masturbatory tendencies were probably also a persisting reality for some of their husbands. And if the law of averages held, it is likely that a good 50 per cent of these women had themselves at some time engaged in autoerotic behavior.

It has been my observation that people who take exception to honest self-revelation on the part of others are bothered, not by the *evil* thus exposed (most of us know a good deal about *that* already) but by the new-found *honesty and courage* which make the revelation possible. In other words, they are not nearly so much "shocked" or "stunned" by the truth itself as by the unusual degree of truthfulness thus exhibited. If the churches wish to avoid the common charge of false piety and hypocrisy, their members need to take stock of their behavior in this area. I recall, for example, the much greater objectivity on the part of a group of doctors' wives whom I addressed a few years ago or, more recently, a group of women deans and counselors; and I would even rank the average PTA group or women's club relatively high in this regard. But when women, perhaps the very *same* women, get into a formal religious context, they evidently feel called upon to assume the appearance of a purity and innocence which borders on the ridiculous. In various forms of "group therapy" the country over, mixed groups of people are finding emotional health which they have not been able to find in churches.[3] Here candor is practiced, so to say, *in person,* directly, without even the element of anonymity involved in the foregoing account.

But perhaps, on second thought, it was not the discussion of masturbation, or homosexuality, or any of the other individual sins which our "case history" reveals that so "stunned" these women. There is, in the situation, something about which they—and we Protestants in general—have every right to be shocked and scandalized. If the opening sentence of this chapter has any substantial degree of validity, we should all drop to our knees, in dismay and repentance. I suppose it *may* come to some as a surprise to learn that there is good reason to doubt one of the most emphasized tenets of Protestant theology: namely, the doctrine of justification by faith *alone!* And when one sees the futility and perversity of this doctrine exemplified in the very lives of those who proclaim it most loudly and often, it is—or surely should be—a distressing experience. Perhaps this is why other women's groups, to which I have made comparable presentations, were more objective and undisturbed: *they* were not so committed to and dependent upon the Protestant doctrine of "grace." I would like to think that at least some of the women to whom this paper was addressed did not rest content with a superficially pious attitude of rejection and allowed themselves instead to absorb its fullest and deepest implications.

Dietrich Bonhoeffer refers to the Atonement, as it is commonly interpreted in many of our churches today, as the doctrine of "*cheap* grace." And in *Life Together,* he further chastizes and challenges our churches thus:

> "Confess your faults one to another" (Jas. 5:16). He who is alone with his sin is utterly alone. It may be that Christians, notwithstanding corporate worship, common prayer, and all their fellowship in service, may still be left to their loneliness. The final breakthrough to fellowship does not occur, because, though they have fellowship with one another as believers and as devout people, they do not have fellowship as the undevout, and sinners. The pious fellowship permits no one

[3] M. P. Jackson, *Their Brother's Keeper—a Directory of Therapeutic Self-Help Groups, Intentional Communities, and Lay Training Centers,* mimeographed: Department of Psychology, University of Illinois, and Berkeley Baptist Divinity School, Berkeley 4, Calif., 1962.

to be a sinner. So everybody must conceal his sin from himself and the fellowship. We dare not be sinners. Many Christians are unthinkably horrified when a real sinner is suddenly discovered among the righteous. So we remain alone with our sin, living in lies and hypocrisy. The fact is that we *are* sinners![4]

In confession the breakthrough to community takes place. Sin demands to have a man by himself. It withdraws him from the community. The more isolated a person is, the more destructive will be the power of sin over him, and the more deeply he becomes involved in it, the more disastrous is his isolation. Sin wants to remain unknown. It shuns the light. In the darkness of the unexpressed it poisons the whole being of a person. This can happen even in the midst of a pious community. In confession the light of the Gospel breaks into the darkness and seclusion of the heart. The sin must be brought into the light. The unexpressed must be openly spoken and acknowledged. All that is secret and hidden is made manifest. It is a hard struggle until the sin is openly admitted. But God breaks gates of brass and bars of iron (Ps. 107:16).[5]

The individual who, to use a currently popular psychiatric term, has never been emotionally "decompensated"—that is, in a severe anxiety state or depression—may have some difficulty understanding why there is any need for confession or a "breakthrough to community." He has his little secrets, and since they have never caused him any serious trouble, he intends to *keep* them. Therefore, he may think that anyone who advocates or practices personal openness is something of an idiot. But let someone else or, indeed, such a person himself become "decompensated" or "unbalanced," in the sense that his unresolved load of guilt comes to *exceed* his capacity for self-affirmation and approval, *then* what is to be done? The common temptation, of course, at this point is to dismiss the problem as one of "illness" and refer the person thus afflicted to a "good psychiatrist." But psychiatry, as we now know full well, does not "have the answer" either. Therefore, what Dietrich Bonhoeffer, "the Reverend Mr. Clark," and others are beginning to say is that we must once again recognize radical openness with the "significant others" in one's life, not only as the most effective means of "treatment" but also as the best form of *prevention,* as a *way of life.* Instead of being told that, as long as we are

[4] D. Bonhoeffer, *Life Together,* New York: Harper and Brothers, 1954, p. 110.

[5] *Ibid,* p. 112.

"normal" or "well," confession to our fellowmen is not necessary, we thus should be led to see the virtue of this kind of openness in general. Here I believe is a powerful new "psychiatry" and the basis for a revitalized and wonderfully effective professional and lay ministry as well.

# 23

## Some Practical Values of Mowrer's Insights for Pastoral Counseling

*Allen Whitman*

"WHEN I RECOMMEND a parishioner to a psychiatrist," one priest remarked to his fellow clergy, "I never stop praying for that person and I always keep in contact." At the time I overheard this statement I was impressed by the pastoral concern of this priest as a shepherd of his flock. However, accepting the validity of Mowrer's[1] insights, the Christian pastor's attitude toward his own role would go considerably farther. For uppermost in the pastor's mind should be the

---

ALLEN WHITMAN, B.D., S.T.M., is Rector of Saint George's Episcopal Church, Minneapolis, Minnesota.

[1] O. Hobart Mowrer, *The Crisis in Psychiatry and Religion,* Princeton, N.J.: D. Van Nostrand Co., Inc., 1961. See also his *The New Group Therapy* issued by the same publisher in 1964.

distinct possibility that his parishioner might be emotionally ill because of repressed guilt, shame, or ego deficiences that might be helped if that person could squarely face them with Christian people with whom he dared to be honest and who would support him in a new life. If this were the pastor's conception of his possible role with at least his own people, it would follow that he would not merely keep in contact with the disturbed person but feel a genuine desire—yes obligation—to make himself available to the professional therapist in the case and to members of the sick person's family, in order that either he or certain members of his parish might play a part at an appropriate time to help restore the individual to wholeness—to emotional, vocational, and spiritual health.

Mowrer suggests that the Christian church, through its clergy and people, recover a certain confidence and mission toward the emotionally ill—especially to those in its own midst. This should be immediately qualified in the sense that pastors or other leaders should not look upon themselves as anything more than members of a potential team—as partners in a group seeking to aid in an effort that may take various forms. For example, the pastor as he encounters a parishioner with emotional difficulties would be wise to learn the realities of that person's physical condition either by recommending that the person see his family doctor or by requesting permission to speak with the physician if the person has recently been checked. The majority of physicians are quite willing to talk with a clergyman after securing permission to do so from their patient.

Then too, the pastor may often wish to have a psychiatrist or psychologist render a professional opinion as to whether the pastor or someone else should work with a parishioner during a given period of time. Such a procedure not only protects a clergyman or church leader from any undue criticism if a parishioner does not respond to his ministry but most importantly establishes a relationship between the therapist and the pastor. By so doing the therapist now has additional resources in understanding and helping the individual. The pastor or church leader generally has three significant contributions he can make to any team ministry. In the first place as a concerned outsider he can often spot an emotional problem which the family might wish to ignore or be unable to handle. In this connection the pastor can often encourage the family or parishioner to do something about the situation. Such was true in the following incidents which happened in my parish.

Mrs. O was having hallucinations in which she felt that she was in direct contact with God. These were so glorious that she did no housework and would sit in a kind of trancelike state around the house. She absolutely refused to see her physician, and her husband in desperation brought her in to see me. Only me, as a man of God, would she believe. In short order I was able to assure her that hospitalization was a good idea and supported her husband's decision to do so immediately.

In another case, Mrs. E came to see me in a deep depression. We talked for an hour but at the end she seemed no better. As soon as she left, I called her husband at his place of work and suggested that he get her to a psychiatrist whom she had seen some years before.

Secondly, the pastor or church leader has a first-hand knowledge of the resources within his own congregation which might be beneficial somewhere in the therapeutic process. It may be another home wherein the person temporarily might live. It might be someone within the parish who could be helpful in giving special training to teach a special skill.

Finally the pastor has some indication of a sick person's attitude toward God, his fellow man, and himself—some conception of the various personal and religious resources that exist for or within that individual. It has been my experience as a pastor that physicians and therapists pragmatically desire nothing more than that their patient recover, and that they welcome aid from any quarter so long as it is not "interference." While it is unlikely that a physician or psychiatrist will ever contact a church leader unless a patient has been referred to him by the pastor or unless the patient requests it, still the pastor is well within his bounds to make overtures to doctors where he is humbly making himself available and offering his services.

Miss W was a 19-year-old college girl who attempted suicide. Fortunately she bungled her attempt and was discovered unconscious in her hotel room and turned over to city authorities. She was released to her parents after they had secured a psychiatrist and made arrangements for her hospitalization.

Since I had worked with her parents for over four years, had presented Miss W for confirmation, and had been involved in their turmoil over her disappearance, I telephoned the psychiatrist and made myself available to him. As a result, I received his blanket permission to visit Miss W.

Neither the psychiatrist nor I was able to find any specific acts about which Miss W felt extremely guilty although she had been taking some narcotics and was extremely remorseful for causing her parents so much anguish. I encouraged her to be honest with her physician and her parents.

She assured me she had made her confession to God and went through a silent confession, received absolution and Holy Communion.

Several times I shared my insights about her with the psychiatrist.

When he released her from the hospital, he in turn telephoned me and suggested ways in which she could be encouraged to live and deal constructively with her parents, since this was where the problem appeared to be.

During the time of her hospitalization, Miss W and I became far better related than ever before. As a result, she has come to see me on several occasions when she has had some slight recurrence of depression.

There are certain church situations where a closer tie can exist among parish, pastor, and therapist. I am referring to the situation where a counselor is hired as an official member of the church staff, or where a therapist occupies an office on the church premises, or where there is a close connection between pastor and physician such that referrals and mutual exchange of information take place more easily. The obvious advantages of such an arrangement are that it encourages pastors to make quicker referrals and to get professional diagnosis more readily. Also this arrangement tacitly puts the weight of the church itself behind such treatment so that parishioners are more inclined to seek out such counsel and advice.

There is an Episcopal Church in Monrovia, California, where a doctor of psychology has been added as a half-time member of their staff with office in the parish house. The psychologist not only works with groups within the parish but is available for consultation and diagnosis. In addition, two Jungian analysts in the area are regularly called upon for expert consultations. The question is always to whom should an individual go—to the pastor, to a group working with the psychologist, to an analyst, or perhaps should the individual be hospitalized and turned over to a physician? Clearly in the therapy of any one person all of these possibilities might be utilized.

Wherever such a staff situation exists within a Christian church there is no question in the minds of the congregation or of the community of the attitude, commitment, and mission of the church to the emotionally ill. In fact an internal arrangement with a therapist on the paid staff of the local church is more feasible and workable than the church custodial care centers Mowrer has suggested.[2] Not only is it more easily administered but the therapist has the given resources within the Christian community itself to aid in the recovery of its patient.

Dr. Mowrer, of course, has rather discouraged "professionalism" in the treatment of guilty people and has pointed out the possibilities in groups of laymen who can be supportive through their willingness to discuss their own past and how they themselves changed, and who are able to give personal time and energy in helping others recover a moral life. This poses a question of whether a Christian pastor would be willing to use such resource people within his parish and whether the laity would be willing to serve in such capacity. Since any organization takes on many of the characteristics and attitudes of its leader, apparently much hinges here on the pastor as well as on key church leaders. At this juncture certain problems are raised.

Is the pastor willing to be honest and open enough about himself to encourage this in others by his own candor and witness?

Is the church leadership willing to have their pastor break an image of sanctity and rectitude, which they perhaps expect, to enable him to do this?

How far and under what conditions should pastors or church leaders go in admitting their past sins and efforts at recovery?

[2] *Ibid.*

As a principle in leadership in any area it would seem that no pastor or church leader should expect from others what he is not willing to do himself under certain conditions. This would mean that no pastor can expect that a program of mutual help in personal guilt can be initiated in a parish unless he himself is willing to be involved from the pulpit, in teaching situations, in personal conversation, and in counseling. It would seem wiser to speak of one's own past sins, guilt, and dishonesty either in counseling or in a small group where one speaks to a given situation and within a structured context. There would be less difficulty here of one being misunderstood—less tendency for sensationalism or masochism. On the other hand, in preaching and teaching it is vital that the pastor, through illustrations in his own life, indicate that he too is human and subject like his people to error and sin. Too often members of a congregation either will disassociate the preacher from one like themselves or inwardly wonder if he is not a hypocrite. If one had to analyze why many people within Christian congregations are unable to come to a pastor when they are in need because of personal guilt, the recalled statements might reflect their perception of him:

"I know what he'll say before I go to see him." (That is to say he will not understand what I have done and will misjudge me.)

"He has such a different impression of me now that I can't bear to tell him." (That is to say he thinks I'm a moral person and I'm ashamed to disillusion him.)

"Oh, he's so busy that I wouldn't want to bother him." (That is to say I'm not very important in the parish and he does not really wish to know me or know me as I really am.)

Needless to say this kind of image can be broken down only from the pastor's preaching, teaching, and subsequent pastoral calling or other contacts.

I remember once as a pastor participating in a group where I told that I had had a certain kind of problem. I cannot now remember exactly what it was. A woman near me said almost under her breath, "Why, I never realized *you* would ever have such difficulty. I thought it was only me."

Once I told the story in a sermon how in the army ASTP program I had tried to cheat a former roommate out of a mirror that we had agreed in advance to flip a coin for. The boy had been a reasonably close friend but had been so hurt by my action that our relationship never again was restored. Several people later remarked that I had had courage to tell that story about myself in such a public manner. But as a result these same people became even closer to me for I was to them far more a fellow sinner and one who might be trusted with a knowledge of their sins or shortcomings.

How often is a pastor willing to admit failure, sin, guilt, or shame? And yet he is not likely to have any redemptive groups within his parish, in Mowrer's sense of the term, until he is willing to allow some sort of self-exposure along this line.

In the same vein the Christian church might again explore the possibilities of testimonials by certain lay people of their fall from grace, so to speak, and of their return. The testimonials of laymen have been a key to many a fundamentalistic, revivalistic church and even to Christian Scientists.

Recently a former member of the Mafia talked to members of our parish about his early life, his conversion or recovery, and his current work among boys who had been like him. His craving for "big money" and what it did to him struck deeply in the lives of many people who heard him, even though they would never have participated in an underworld organization themselves. They could sense he was speaking as one of them.

The Bible itself offers the pastor rich preaching material in which the whole subject of guilt can be used as part of the drama of the people of God. Judas in his remorse kills himself in self-punishment for what he has done to his Lord (Matthew 27:3–6). Had he been alive to face the resurrected Christ as did Peter, guilt-stricken by his denial, the drama of Easter might have been rewritten. Paul participates in the stoning of Stephen (Acts 7:54–60), fanatically persecutes the early church (Acts 9:1, 2), encounters the risen Christ on the Damascus road (Acts 9:4, 5), is overcome with blindness which leaves him only when ministered to by Ananias who represents the Christian church. How vividly the dynamics of guilt, forgiveness, and reparation are shown in the whole life and missionary zeal of the Apostle Paul!

But the theme is in no way exhausted with Paul. There is the woman taken in adultery (John 8:1–11, Luke 7:47), the case of the paralytic whose sins are forgiven him (Matthew 9:2–8, Mark 2:3–12, Luke 5:12–16), the dynamics of reconciliation advocated in the Sermon on the Mount (Matthew 5:25–28), and the admonition of James that Christians should confess their sins one to another (James 5:16).

Mowrer himself has suggested the plight of Nebuchadnezzar (Daniel 4:19–36) as a clinical study in the effects of guilt. The struggle of David with his conscience during the sickness of his child by Bathsheba (II Samuel 11:7–23) would be another case in point. Often overlooked is the strange change that occurred in the life of King Saul which manifested itself in moody depressions and violent actions. The biblical author of the life of Saul gives the strange account of how Saul went against the word of the Lord from Samuel, that he should not take spoil from the Amalekites (I Samuel 15:4–31). And the writer goes on to recount how when he pleads for pardon but is refused by Samuel (I Samuel 15:24–28), Saul asks one favor. "I have sinned," he told the Seer of Israel, "yet honor me now before the elders of my people and before Israel." (I Samuel 15:30) And this Samuel did. Thus Saul kept the tortuous secret from the rest of his people that Samuel had told him his kingdom would be torn from him. Does not the Bible itself imply then that Saul became ill, depressed, and violent because he could not acknowledge and confess his sins before his people nor find any assurance of forgiveness from the holy man, Samuel, who was the man of God within the land?

Preparation for Holy Communion offers another area in which Mowrer's insights might support preaching from the Sacred Scriptures. St. Paul admonishes the Corinthians that "Whoever . . . eats the bread or drinks the cup of the Lord in an unworthy manner will be guilty of profaning the body and blood of the Lord. Let a man examine himself, and so eat of the bread and drink of the cup." (I Corinthians 11:27, 28) He then adds a significant warning, "For any one who eats and drinks without discerning the body eats and drinks judgment upon himself. That is why many of you are weak and ill; and some have died." (I Corinthians 11:29, 30)

Most exegetes conclude that Paul is not merely speaking about the drunkenness and clannishness that accompanied many of the communion celebrations in the church of

Corinth but is addressing himself to other sins which the Corinthian Christians may have committed—thus profaning both their covenantal relationship with Christ and their participation in the sacrament. The judgment of God upon them, causing their sickness and ill health, would in Mowrer's terms be the unconscious effect of their guilt taking its toll on their very lives.

The Roman Catholic Church has always said that a communicant in mortal sin must make confession, receive absolution, and do a form of penance before presenting himself at the altar. Protestantism as a whole in recent years has not taken such a strict stand. Paul's concern for self-examination, lest judgment befall through unworthy reception of the sacrament, might prove a healthy tonic to many congregations.

Hence Holy Scriptures lend themselves to the very kind of emphasis that Mowrer suggests should characterize the whole pastoral ministry within the Church, and can be used to set the stage for the personal ministry of the people of God toward one another that his insights would imply.

From his biblical preaching on guilt and his own openness, it would be within the pastor's province to ask certain laymen to personally talk about their pasts and subsequent changes to another individual in a somewhat similar situation. Any disclosures would have to be up to the layman and not the pastor or there would be an appalling break of confidence. But in every parish are known alcoholics, criminals, adulterers, married couples who have come through certain tense years, persons who have been depressed—sick with one disease or another, persons with certain skills that might help another through an embarrassing situation. Let me illustrate this:

On several occasions I have discovered people in economic difficulty of a kind that they hesitated going directly to a bank or financial institution. In these situations I have suggested that they sit down in their homes with a skilled accountant, corporation treasurer, or banker and go through the gory details with a fellow churchman and face what to them is a shameful situation.

We have a man in our parish on our vestry and teaching our church school who was convicted of embezzlement some years ago. In several situations where boys have been caught stealing he has approached them on his own, told his story and what living an honest Christian life has meant to him.

Mowrer's "New Group Therapy" would carry mutual help within a parish even farther, especially with those who have developed emotional problems such as depression, hysterical anxiety, etc. He would indicate perhaps a more continuing group on the order of Alcoholics Anonymous where not only one's past but one's tendency to be dishonest or hide oneself could be brought out and where one's difficulties with personal integrity could be aired.

A close approach to such a group in my own parish has been established through four-week sessions on "What does it mean to be a Christian housewife?" or "What does it mean to be a Christian at work?" These have involved groups of eight to twelve women or men for two-hour periods. I recall one woman at a beginning meeting saying after a long pause in the conversation, "You know, I shouldn't even be here. My home is a mess." This led to a discussion of a woman's feelings for her home and her attitude towards her husband and children, which are tied up in it. Another woman brought out the fact that at a coffee party in the neighborhood she had been afraid to disagree with one who had verbalized marked racial prejudice with regard to housing.

The men discussed everything from quality control to government tax laws in business. With regard to quality control I learned that there are certain variables in products and that certain buyers will accept lesser quality than others. "Is it honest to send them the poorer products?" it was asked. At the end of this discussion one man turned to me and said, "Well, it's lucky you don't have this kind of problem." I replied, "What do you mean? I have this question every time I present a person for confirmation."

The pastor's initiative appears essential if these kinds of groups or personal encounters are to take place. Thus if liars are to speak to former liars, or adulterers with past adulterers, it will be up to the pastor to see that the right people get together. To do this, obviously he must believe these meetings will be worthwhile. Mowrer of course has offered clinical evidence that such groups should be every pastor's concern. The following case in my own parish suggests what can transpire: Mrs. Y is a married woman. About six months ago she read Dr. Mowrer's book, *The New Group Therapy*. Three months later she asked to see me. She told me about her sister's daughter who had gotten into difficulty with several boys. There had been one abortion. When told that the daughter still had not changed, Mrs. Y asked to see her niece and sister together. She then shared with them her own life of infidelity which had ended two years before. She spoke to them of her guilt, her shame, and her newly found life in the Church. This was the first time Mrs. Y had shared her guilt with anyone. I asked her if her husband knew. She told me she had not yet dared to tell him. Within a few days she did. He in turn told her about his infidelities. Both she and her husband tell me their marriage has never been better. Both availed themselves of the sacrament of absolution. It is too early to gauge the long-term effect upon the niece.

The man who has attempted to take Mowrer the most seriously and to apply Mowrer's insights to the pastoral practice of the Christian church has been Dr. David Belgum in his little, provocative book, *Guilt: Where Religion and Psychology Meet*. In it he notes the fact that almost all Christian churches from Orthodox and Roman Catholic to those of the "Radical Reformation" have historically dealt with guilt in their midst in concrete ways.[3] Whether through the private confessional, administering the sacramental rite of penance, or in the midweek evening prayer meeting the Christian churches have attempted to deal with many of the very kinds of problems of which Mowrer speaks. However, it is indicative that Belgum entitles his chapter[4] on the subject, "What Was Available in the Churches," since the tendency in recent years has been to replace personal confession with a general liturgical confession in the service of worship, or to relegate it entirely to an optional element in pastoral counseling—with the exception, of course, of the Roman Catholic and Orthodox churches. Thus initially within Protestant churches there was a common practice, in one form or another, of personal confession, absolution, and amendment of life. For acknowledged sinners this has largely been neglected in the present day.

[3] David Belgum, *Guilt: Where Religion and Psychology Meet*, Englewood Cliffs, N.J.: Prentice-Hall, Inc., 1963, pp. 95–117.
[4] *Ibid.*, pp. 60–94.

Mowrer notes in his discussion that the goal of the Christian Office of the Keys or Penance is not forgiveness but restored fellowship in the Church, with God, with one's neighbor, and with oneself. That is to say that classical Christianity has conceived therapy for sin as involving one's relationship to God, one's neighbor, the Christian community, and finally toward one's self. Restoration thus involves far more than psychological insight into the dynamics of one's behavior—it involves reconciliation at various levels to significant others including the Church and God. Classically this restoration has involved three factors: (1) contrition—sorrow and repentance for what one has done, (2) confession—absolution or forgiveness, and (3) amendment of life. Belgum suggests that Mowrer's approach to therapy fits in rather well with the classic, Christian scheme except that confession or honest self-disclosure should be extended to significant persons in one's life and amendment of life must be far more than several "Hail Marys" or "Our Fathers." Belgum offers to Christian clergy the idea of what he calls a "functional confession." At the innermost level this means one must first renounce sins, admit pride or hardness of heart which prevents one from realizing one's predicament, and finally, admit hypocrisy which he calls a "non-functional attempt to deal with guilt and social alienation caused by his sins."[5] The validation of this action he suggests comes only when one is actually restored to one's intimates, to the Church, to one's God-given vocation, to one's personal integrity, and to God.

> A major concern must be not to short-circuit or short-cut any of the steps or essential elements in the treatment of the guilty person, for an easing up or cutting corners drastically weakens the Church's effectiveness.[6]

Interestingly, Belgum offers his most thoughtful ideas with regard to the last step—amendment of life. He suggests that just as in Alcoholics Anonymous, a guilty person needs to help another guilty person to overcome a similar sin.

> The man who has been rescued from the painful predicament and torture of his personal guilt will know that he has found a solution that

[5] *Ibid.*, p. 119.
[6] *Ibid.*, p. 123.

is worth sharing with others. He will be like a salesman who believes in his product, not like the one who is simply peddling goods and trying to put something over on the public. A man who has been rescued and now lives in freedom, openness, and eagerness to serve others . . . has a wholesome motivation for entering the ministry or any other vocation.

The training of pastors will have to take a new direction . . . Roman Catholic moral and pastoral theology will have to take the satisfaction aspect of Penance more seriously. Three "Hail Marys" and two "Our Fathers" or the "Stations of the Cross" may be excellent devotional experiences and may deepen worship but may not be adequate as amendment of life related to specific sins of which the penitent is being healed.

Lutherans will have to think more clearly and preach more biblically about truly good works, the fruit of rescued life. The discipline of Wesley's method and the judgment of the early Anabaptists need to be restudied and applied to contemporary church life.[7]

The following case history may serve to indicate how this might be done following Belgum's and Mowrer's theories but applying them within the framework of a church tradition—in this case the Episcopal Church.

Mrs. Z was a former parishioner who lived well outside the bounds of our parish. Her husband contacted me to request that I visit her in the hospital where she was being treated for a severe depression. He informed me that she had been depressed for well over a year and that for six months she had been visiting a psychiatrist.

I called upon Mrs. Z who appeared disheveled and lethargic. She told me that her psychiatrist had suggested that her husband was too demanding and perfectionistic in what he expected her to do around the home. Medically, she told me, there was a possibility that she might be in an early menopause since this had been her mother's experience.

Mrs. Z and I conversed for about forty minutes. We prayed together and the next day I returned to administer Holy Communion.

Shortly after this last call Mr. Z again telephoned. The psychiatrist had decided to release Mrs. Z temporarily. My visits, he declared, had done Mrs. Z a world of good. However, about three months later Mr. Z contacted me to say his wife was still depressed and wanted to see me personally.

This time Mrs. Z came directly to my office. After some

[7] *Ibid.*, pp. 129, 130.

preliminary conversation, I asked her a direct question. "Mrs. Z, is there anything you are hiding from me or that you are ashamed of?" After a long pause Mrs. Z began to tell me about an extensive affair that she had carried on with a neighbor some two years before. The affair had been terminated. "He isn't half the man my husband is," she said. I inquired if her husband knew. "Absolutely not!" was the reply. Had she talked this over with her psychiatrist? Yes, but not recently.

As is usual in such cases, the duplicity was quite involved. The neighbor's wife had accused her to her face, but she had been so convincing in her denial the neighbor's wife had later apologized. During all the period of her infidelity, Mrs. Z regularly attended worship services in her church and received Holy Communion. As time went on, nevertheless, this had become more and more difficult for her.

At this point I explained the power of guilt to cause depression. We discussed the possibility of telling her husband but she adamantly refused. "He would have another heart attack," she said.

I shared with her some difficulties of mine in being open and told her about a past sin which I had confessed to a significant person (in this case the Bishop). We then made an appointment to meet in the church several days later for the sacrament of Absolution (Penance) and Holy Communion from the reserved sacrament. She made her confession as planned, received absolution and Holy Communion.

The next day her husband telephoned me. His wife had broken down and told him everything. She was very upset and he wanted me to see them both immediately.

When we met, Mr. Z expressed how really relieved in a sense he was to learn the real cause of his wife's depression. Mrs. Z, however, expressed her fear that he would do something rash to the neighbor or become really angry with her. Again I shared with them my own experience with guilt and my own attempts to lead a more honest and open life. I also raised the question of being honest with the neighbor's wife and Mrs. Z's mother who had come to many false conclusions regarding her illness.

Both of them felt that Mrs. Z could be open with her mother, but agreed that the neighbor's wife was having enough problems with her husband without their rehash of another old affair.

Mr. Z admitted that during the period of his wife's unfaithfulness, he had been so preoccupied with a new job that he had really permitted the situation to exist. We prayed together and they left.

So far—some five months later—this has been an astounding success story. A new relationship has developed between Mr. Z and his wife—a relationship built upon mutual honesty. At first Mrs. Z continued a patter of small lies, but now even that deception is gone. The depression has left and Mrs. Z is living a normal life.

It is apparent here that Mrs. Z was suffering from what Belgum and Mowrer term "the amplified and distorted voice of conscience." It is also apparent that as a priest of the Church I was able to go further, through the sacrament of Absolution (Penance), than a psychiatrist would have been able to do. For, as Belgum notes, all Christian theology of guilt depicts sins against one's neighbor, husband, or self as sins against God as well.

# Index

## T



## U



## V



## W



## Z